JIM GILBERT'S NATURE NOTEBOOK

Jim Gilbert's Nature Notebook

A daily guide to many
biological and physical events
in nature in the Upper Midwest,
using the Minnesota
Landscape Arboretum
as the vantage point

TEXT AND PHOTOGRAPHS
by James R. Gilbert

LINE DRAWINGS
by Carole A. Kinion

ANDERSEN HORTICULTURAL LIBRARY
MINNESOTA LANDSCAPE ARBORETUM
1983

Library of Congress Catalog Card Number: 83-73135
ISBN: 0–935476–14–8

Dedication

To Elmer L. Andersen who said, "I especially admire scholarship in the sense of a person who focuses on a particular subject and utterly dissects it."

To my mother and father who encouraged and supported their son in his quest to become a naturalist and first drew his attention to the wonders of God's creation.

To Sandra, Andrew, Christian and John Gilbert for their patience and love.

CONTENTS

JANUARY

FEBRUARY

MARCH

APRIL

MAY

JUNE

JULY

AUGUST

SEPTEMBER

OCTOBER

NOVEMBER

DECEMBER

FOREWORD

This world of ours is made of whole cloth — and each of us is a mere thread of it. Not only are *we* a mere thread, so it is with all natural things. The beat of a dragonfly's wing, the hop of a grasshopper, the opening of a precious bloom of some wildflower — all and each to its own somehow or another affect this world of ours. They are as much a part of the whole as we are.

Each thing, however, plays its own part in relation to everything else, and does it in its own time and at its own place. The periodic comings and goings of all of these things make up a fascinating science called phenology — and that's what this notebook by Jim Gilbert is all about.

As a naturalist, school teacher, researcher, and lover of people, places, and things, Jim has been an acute observer of the natural Minnesota scene for many years. He has been instrumental in harnessing the combined observations of a network of interested people in our region, has taught thousands of youngsters how to observe and therefore appreciate life to a greater extent, and through his classroom, field tours, writings, radio information, TV data, and general intermixing with the general public, has given countless people the tools to know better those things which surround us every day — with all of their mysteries, in all of their beauty.

It's one thing to hear a robin singing or notice lilacs in bloom. It's quite something else again to be sensitive to not only robins and lilacs, but everything else — on a daily basis — year after year — methodically collecting the data, compiling the trends, investigating the oddities, and making the information available to the general public in an interesting and informative way.

Jim Gilbert has done this, taking the mass of data he has collected over the past years and rearranging the information by months on a daily basis in his nature notebook so the interactions and sequences of life about us in the greater Minnesota area become more meaningful, more understandable, more challenging.

Each day for you can be exciting, more suspenseful, more fun, more satisfying when you learn to observe, know what to expect — yet be constantly amazed at the constants and the changes that end up being the current year.

Phenology is a science full of surprises that enrich each day. *Jim Gilbert's Nature Notebook* will help you prepare for those delightful moments when anticipation is rewarded. Because you saw and experienced, you somehow feel closer to that everyday life around you. It's a whole new dimension of living.

RICHARD G. GRAY, SR.

Freshwater Foundation
Navarre, Minnesota
August 4, 1982

PREFACE

Each moment of the year
has its own beauty,
a picture which was
never seen before
and which shall
never be seen again.

RALPH WALDO EMERSON

This year in Carver County we observed the first active chipmunk of the season on February 23, the first American robins and male red-winged blackbirds returned March 14, and grasses were turning green in ditches and on south-facing slopes April 13. By May 24 a farmer had cut the first crop of alfalfa hay, and the first garden raspberries were ripe on June 23. These happenings are examples of phenological observations.

Phenology, the study of the chronology of natural events, is the subject of this book. It is the science that studies the timing of natural events from year to year and from place to place and their relationship to season, weather and climate.

All living things, the players in our theater of seasons, react to temperature, moisture and other weather elements of the script differently each year, making an individual year different from the preceding one in its own unique play or production. Taking into consideration the variability of a year or month weatherwise, I have chosen to pick certain events from particular days over several years of time, and for this reason a daily entry from 1978 may be followed by one from 1974. The reader can thus begin to trace the order at which solar energy flowed to and through some of the living organisms in past days, and these same entries should be helpful in comparing the progress of events in coming years.

The theme of my learning has been that as knowledge conquers certain fears, so does it lead us to an appreciation of beauty. The selfish destroy beauty around them, the lazy become overwhelmed by detail, but the truly educated usually find happiness in beauty and detail.

ACKNOWLEDGEMENTS

In an afternoon of mind searching I came up with a written list of more than one hundred persons who have been my formal education science teachers or interested people who have shared their seasonal nature observations with me, thus making this book possible. To mention each separately, with thanks equal to their contribution, would take a chapter of pages.

I am thankful for all who have helped me along the way to becoming a professional naturalist and phenologist. Besides those who have personally taught me to read, observe and understand, there are the centuries of painstaking study by botanists, ornithologists, entomologists and other specialists, plus the work of the generalists of outdoor studies, the naturalists.

I am especially grateful to members of the staffs of the Eastman, Lowry, Richardson, Dodge, Wood Lake, River Bend and Quarry Hill Nature Centers, the Environmental Learning Center at Isabella, the Minnesota Zoological Garden and the University of Minnesota Landscape Arboretum for sharing with me their observations of our natural world.

My sincere thanks to Charles L. Hamrun who introduced me to the world of insects while I was a student at Gustavus Adolphus College; Dick Gray who has encouraged me in my study of Minnesota phenology; Al Zander for many enjoyable hours spent visiting about birds; Kathy Heidel and Orwin A. Rustad for making me a better observer; Carole A. Kinion, nature artist, for her line drawings; Taimi Anderson for the maps; June M. Rogier, librarian at the Andersen Horticultural Library at the Arboretum, for cheerfully answering hundreds of my reference questions, providing an atmosphere conducive to study and research and for helping to assemble a selected reference list; Elmer L. Andersen for his help and suggestions; the Elmer L. and Eleanor J. Andersen Foundation for its financial support and Elaine Frost for her editorial skills used in the revisions of the manuscript to bring it to completion.

JAMES R. GILBERT

Waconia, Minnesota
August 17, 1982

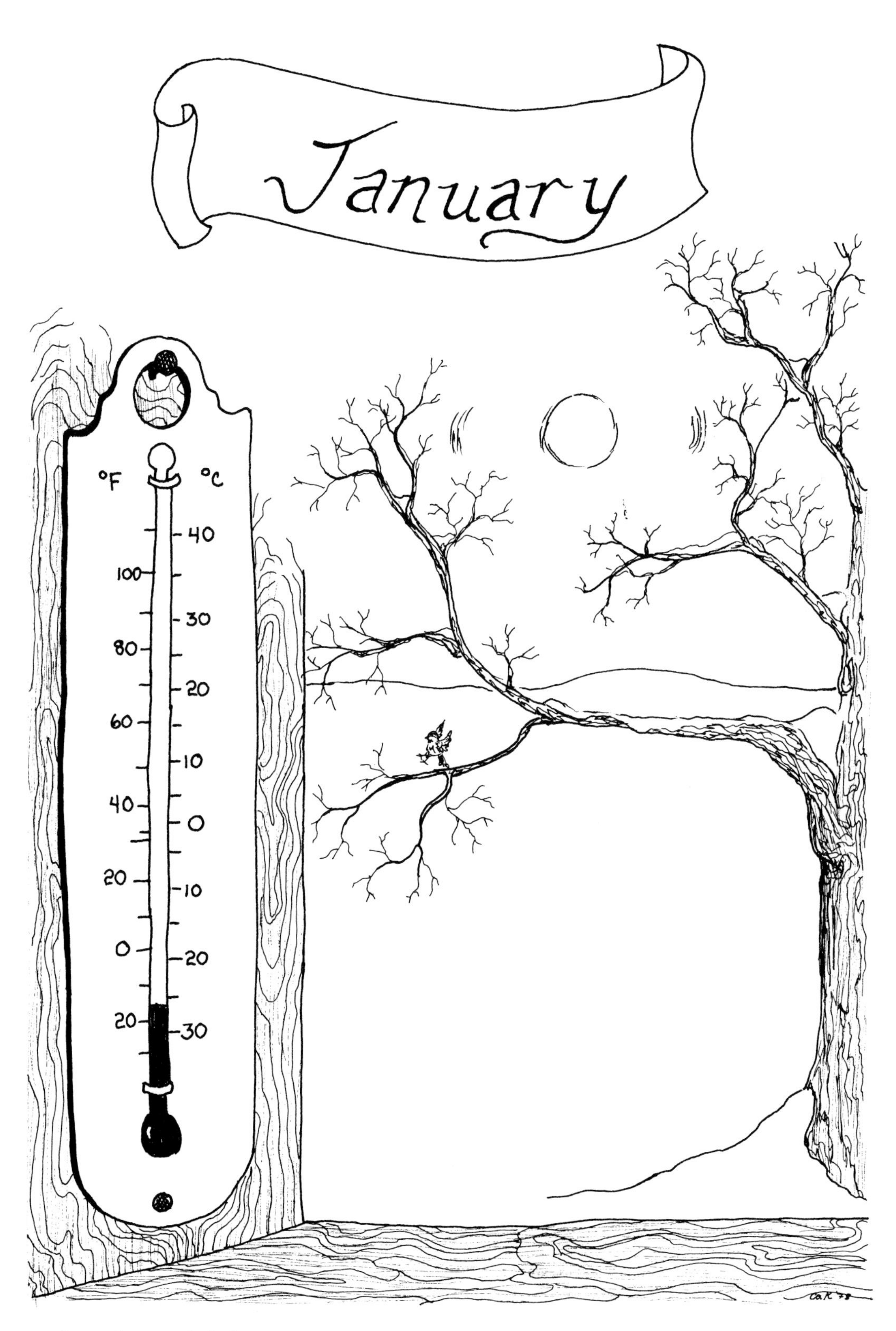

−15°, Sundogs & Chickadee

January 1, 1978 New Year's Day

Happy New Year! It's a beautiful day in this winter wonderland as we dig out from yesterday's snowstorm. The seven inches that fell and were blown around by the wind last evening and this morning have given us a fresh white New Year's Day.

The first bird species I saw in the new year was a pine grosbeak. In fact, twenty of these Northern visitors were feeding on the seeds from a large Norway spruce. About forty miles east of the Arboretum, near Afton, Minnesota, eighteen people spent the day searching the area for birds, observing fifty-seven species (8,434 individuals) for the annual Audubon Christmas Bird Count. They saw evening grosbeaks, pine grosbeaks, common redpolls, pine siskins, red crossbills and golden-crowned kinglets. My wife Sandra and I skied the Arboretum's cross country trails in the late afternoon. We were surrounded by quiet beauty. Ring-necked pheasants, tree sparrows, mice, squirrels and a fox had left their tracks in the snow along with those of skiers on this clear, cold day, with a wind chill of minus 20°F. The clusters of red sumac fruit and the new snow on red cedar branches enhanced the picturesque trails through the forest.

We traveled easily over the trail. It was in perfect shape and we were never cold. There was much to see — the old red barn through sparkling snow on black forest branches, the white-breasted nuthatches checking tree bark for food morsels, the dark red twigs of the red-osier dogwood. Our enjoyable ski tour was about to end when we noticed brilliant sundogs in the clear sky. Sundogs are bright, rainbow-like spots on each side of the sun, and, as we watched, they set with the sun at 4:42 p.m.

January 2, 1978 Early Sounds of Spring

It's a sunny day with a few cirrus clouds and a strong northwest wind that's blowing the snow into interesting patterns. The temperature is rising into the teens on the Fahrenheit scale for what may be the day's high. It's a typical January day, certainly not springlike, and yet there are sounds of spring in the air.

The clear "fee-bee" whistling of a black-capped chickadee, the "whi, whi, whi, whi . . ." song of the white-breasted nuthatch, a hairy woodpecker hammering on a sounding board and the pumphandle song of the blue jay all conjure up memories for me, a birder, of springs past. Yes, the days are getting longer but only by a total of about five minutes since winter began on December 21. I often wonder if the birds really are responding to the minute increase of daylight. Anyhow, we can't hold back the seasons, and winter is already sliding into spring.

January 3, 1978 Arboretum Hike

I was fortunate to be out early enough to enjoy a brilliant sunrise, complete with sundogs and cirrus clouds. The sun made the white frost that covers every twig and brown oak leaf glisten brightly. During the ten years that I have led hikes in the Arboretum, many people have asked me to tell them the best time to visit here. Today I would have to say that this day was one of the best times, despite the minus 8°F temperature and six inches of snow cover. Just think, no mosquitoes either!

Today I hiked to the old-fashioned rose garden and back to the Snyder Building. I stopped under the big white oaks to listen to the still-attached, dry, brown leaves rustling in the wind and to enjoy the trees' dark shadows on the new snow. A blue jay called from over Green Heron Pond. I saw squirrel tracks, tunnels and other diggings in the snow and wondered how they find acorns under a snow blanket, but small piles of shells show that they are usually successful. Several people have hiked the trails since New Year's Day and left their tracks. The wind from the south was strong and cold, and yet the sun's rays felt warm on my face. As I reached the top of the hill and saw the rose canes sticking up above the snow, I realized that there's an advantage to growing many of these old-fashioned roses as they need no special care to live through a Minnesota winter.

Just before heading back, I stopped to observe two Amur choke cherry (*Prunus maackii*) trees that stand next to the old roses. Their bronze bark, which peels off in thin strips like birch bark, is beautiful. It's a tree species worth planting to add interest to the winter landscape.

January 4, 1978 Pine Grosbeak Invasion

An enthusiastic Arboretum volunteer reported seeing about twenty pine grosbeaks in the crabapple collection. I don't know if it was always the same flock of birds, but he reported about that same number each time he hiked to the crabapple trees. I'm not sure which varieties they liked best as they feasted on the fruit, but, with over 300 trees representing over 100 crabapple varieties, they had quite a menu.

Pine grosbeaks have been seen often in the area this year and usually feed on the cones, berries and crabapples. We consider this an "invasion" year for these robin-sized winter finches as they are unusually numerous. We had another invasion year in 1972.

The pine grosbeaks are about nine inches long and are easily recognized. They are plump and stocky, with short, stubby black bills, two white wing bars and a slightly forked tail. The mature males are rosy-colored, but the females and young males are gray, tinged with brassy-yellow. They are lethargic birds, very deliberate in their movements. In Newfoundland the pine grosbeak is called "the mope," an appropriate name for a bird that spends so much time sitting still or moving about very slowly. When they are here in the winter, they are surprisingly tame or unafraid, allowing us to approach closer than any of our other common birds do.

Pine Grosbeak

The grosbeak makes its summer home in the coniferous forests of Canada, northern New England and in the extreme northern parts of a few other states. It breeds as far north as the limit of trees in northern Canada, but south of the Canadian border it is rare or extremely local. Pine grosbeaks are not migratory in the usual sense, but rather they show up here and there, apparently motivated by shortages of food in their normal areas. They do not make regular latitudinal movements in spring and fall but usually remain on or near their breeding grounds throughout the year. They move southward only when their food supply becomes scarce and they are forced to look for it elsewhere.

Pine grosbeaks' winter food is usually the buds of the maple, elm, birch, apple, mountain ash, willow and other native trees, and the seeds of birch, pine, fir and spruce. Their first choices seem to be crabapples, mountain ash fruit, pine seeds and maple buds. Birders observing a grosbeak eating the ripe fruit of serviceberries and highbush cranberries have noted that it would pick one fruit at a time, manipulate the fruit in its beak, and then extract the seeds as the outer skin and pulp fall to the ground. In the summer they may eat grasshoppers, ants, spiders and caterpillars, but, in general, their diet is made up mainly of plant materials.

January 5, 1976 Deer at the Bird Feeders

A partly cloudy sky helped create a colorful sunrise today. Early this morning and throughout the day, the bird feeders in Carver Park Reserve were extremely active. Tree sparrows, juncos, house sparrows, downy woodpeckers, hairy woodpeckers, a red-bellied woodpecker, American goldfinches, white-breasted nuthatches, black-capped chickadees and blue jays could be seen in a few moments of observation. Gray squirrels and red squirrels also came for their handouts. Once in a while a mink or weasel will eat from one of the suet feeders, but none came today. In late afternoon, as the birds were devouring a few more tidbits before disappearing into the cold night, five white-tailed deer walked into the feeding station and immediately started eating the cracked corn and sunflower seeds that remained. These beauties generally come about this same time of the day throughout the winter, and sometimes we see fifteen or more at the feeders. They could eat us out of "house and home," but we only let them clean up after the birds.

The deer do not depend upon us for their food needs. Our bird feeding station is more of a place to stop by for a quick snack. The white-tailed deer are primarily browsing animals. They will eat fungi, acorns, grass and herbs in season, but this is the time of the year they nibble on twigs of sugar maple, basswood, staghorn sumac, red-osier dogwood and red cedar. I come upon them sometimes as I hike the trails of Carver Park. I enjoyed seeing the winter sky with its clouds, the crescent moon and colorful setting sun, and then the thrill of deer just a few hundred feet from me! Soon I saw their large white flags wagging back and forth as they vanished into the now-dark forest.

January 6, 1978 Red Twig Dogwood

Today the mercury rose to 31°F. Foggy conditions in the morning and evening were interrupted by traces of rain and snow at mid-day. The red-osier dogwoods in the Arboretum with their glowing red stems and branches looked warm and bright against the snow.

The red-osier dogwood (*Cornus sericea*) is common throughout our state. Although its native haunts are moist thickets, swamps, lake shores and other wet places, it thrives quite well in drier soils under cultivation. It grows from three to nine feet tall and received its common name for its habitually osier-like or willow-like bright red branches. Spreading by means of underground shoots, a single plant quickly becomes a thicket and makes a good shrub to plant for preventing the erosion of stream banks.

The first small white flowers on flat-topped clusters appear during the latter part of May, and then small white fruits, which are unpalatable to humans but eaten by many bird species, can be seen. The bark loses much of its brilliant color when the leaves and flowers appear but regains it again in autumn.

January 7, 1976 Woodpeckers' Delight

The high temperature today in Minneapolis was minus 9°F, tying the 1912 record for the coldest high. With a strong northwest wind and a resulting wind chill of around minus 40°F for most of the day, it was hardly surprising that many birds visited the feeding station. The woodpeckers stayed close to the suet feeders. I counted nine downy woodpeckers at one time on two suet feeder trees, and many times during the day I noticed that several didn't move from there for minutes. Other woodpecker species at the suet feeders included the hairy, red-bellied and pileated. The red-bellied seems to be the most omnivorous of our woodpeckers, little at the feeding station escaping the eye of this inquisitive bird. Often we see a red-bellied picking up pieces of cracked corn on the ground, flying to one of the suet feeders and finally ending up eating sunflower seeds on a tray feeder.

Beef suet is a favorite of all insect-eating birds. Chickadees, nuthatches, brown creepers and blue jays are extremely fond of it, and it is practically the only food that will attract woodpeckers consistently. If you are interested in attracting woodpeckers to your yard, pick up some beef suet at the store. Sheep suet is inferior as a bird food, but other fats, including lard, roast drippings and bacon drippings, can be used, either as substitutes for suet or as added ingredients. As long as these fats are free of rich seasoning or excessive amounts of salt, they appear to be perfectly safe for bird feeding.

Suet can be placed in mesh bags such as those used to hold oranges or onions and then hung from nails or tied to branches, high enough so neighborhood dogs can't reach it. Pieces can also be fitted into suet holders on posts or tree trunks, but if hardware cloth is used, the wire should be coated with suet so birds don't freeze their tongues or eyeballs to the metal. Another warning: Once you start feeding the birds in fall or winter, don't quit. Since the birds learn to depend upon you, continue feeding until insects and fruits become available again in spring and summer. If you feel like it, feed them all year, of course.

January 8, 1976 Sundogs

On this very cold day, minus 22°F at 8 a.m. in Waconia, we saw spectacular sundogs in the clear sky from sunrise to sunset. At midday when the sundogs were the most brilliant, I observed one halo around the sun plus part of a second.

Sundogs are bright-colored spots of light that are occasionally seen on the ring of a solar halo, especially during very cold weather. I often see sundogs in December and January but have even seen them in June. These bright spots are caused by sunlight shining through the ice crystals in the air. The ice crystals, either high in the sky in the form of cirrostratus clouds or near the surface in the form of light ice fog, can produce vivid displays in the sky.

January 9, 1977 Bitter Cold Day

Under a gibbous moon in a clear sky, a great horned owl called repeatedly during the night. On the shore of Lake Waconia our thermometer showed a low of minus 41°F while Minneapolis, with a minus 32° this morning, tied its record low for this date. Just outside of Rice Lake, Wisconsin, someone recorded an unofficial low of minus 60°. Duluth had a minus 35° and Culver a minus 55°, only four degrees short of the all-time record for the state. January is the month with the coldest average temperatures on record, with cold air from the Canadian northwest responsible for the low temperatures and high air pressure.

I don't know how cold it got in the Arboretum where the azaleas are planted, but the Northern Lights azaleas, developed by the late Albert G. Johnson, have flower buds that are purported to withstand winter temperatures of minus 45°F without injury. The Northern Lights Hybrids, which will be available through Minnesota nurseries starting in the spring of 1979, are the only winter hardy azaleas that can be counted on to produce full bloom every year in the Upper Midwest. Today's temperatures will be a true test.

May 14, 1977: I'm happy to report the Northern Lights azalea shrubs are covered with pink-colored flowers with a pleasing spicy fragrance as I write this.

January 10, 1975 Snow Fleas

8:30 a.m. I just took a quick hike into the fog and drizzle in 35° weather. Mosses at the bases of trees were lush green and photosynthesizing, and even this early there were snow fleas on top of the forest edge snow. They were especially numerous at the base of a big basswood tree.

A snow flea, a member of the springtail order, is a minute, dark-colored insect that can propel itself through the air with a forked structure under its abdomen. Although only three millimeters long, it can jump two or three inches. I usually notice many snowfleas on the edge of forests near wetlands when the temperature is above 27°F. There they may be as thick as 500 to the square foot on level surfaces. When they accumulate in hollows and depressions such as deer footprints from which they cannot easily escape, they sometimes become a solid mass that could be dipped out with a spoon.

10:00 a.m. The snow has started. Big wet flakes are coming down. Squirrels and birds are active at the feeders.

10:00 p.m. The barometer is still dropping. It is already at a new record low of 28.6, and we have a strong northwest wind. I just saw lightning! The snow continues to fall through surface air that is at the freezing mark.

January 11, 1975 Snowbound

We are in the midst of what will probably be called the "Blizzard of the Century." Eight inches of snow have fallen since yesterday morning, and more is still falling. Visibility is near zero. The temperature is below zero, a northwest wind is gusting to sixty miles per hour, and we are snowbound. It's survival of the fittest for the plants and animals as we see tree sparrows, black-capped chickadees and white-breasted nuthatches having a difficult time flying to and from the feeders.

January 12, 1975 Digging Out

The wind has subsided, and our visibility has increased to about two miles this morning. Now we can see the ten-foot drifts, the dirty surface snow from wind-carried Dakota soil and the stranded cars. Our neighbors are helping each other dig out, but travel is impossible in most parts of the state, and many people have no heat or electricity in their homes. This storm is considered to be worse than the Armistice Day storm of November 11, 1940.

The birds are very active at our feeding station, and I know they are depending on the suet and seeds for their lives. Countless birds must have perished in the storm as several area birders have reported that certain bird species have not appeared at their feeding stations. At ours we have seen only about six tree sparrows coming regularly, and I'm sure we had more than thirty before the storm.

In the Arboretum many of the forest ironwood trees are bent over and form inverted U's. The bent ones are usually under four inches in diameter and still have last year's leaves. Junipers and pines are also bent and contorted, showing the effect of wet snow and strong winds, but the new snow does add an extra dimension to the beauty of the landscape.

January 13, 1978 Common Redpolls

Common redpolls are starting to appear at area feeders. This species of finch is usually just a regular winter visitant throughout Minnesota, but I would say that we are in an invasion year as so many people have reported seeing them at feeding stations.

The common redpoll goes from its breeding ground at the edge of the Canadian tundra to the northern part of the United States for the winter. This species also breeds in the Scandinavian countries and in

Poland, Russia and Alaska. The birds are usually seen in flocks of from five to fifty birds. Like their relatives the American goldfinches and pine siskins, they often feed on seeds from grasses and trees. In size, shape and actions, also, common redpolls resemble the goldfinches and siskins. Redpolls are little gray-brown birds with black chins and bright red caps, with the males having a pinkish-red breast. They favor alder and birch groves as both trees have large quantities of seeds that remain during the winter.

The farther north you go, the more often you can expect to see their isolated flocks as they prefer to stay as close to the tundra edge as weather and food permit. I like seeing these visitors from the North here.

January 14, 1978 First Active Raccoon

After the first of the year, we naturalists are constantly on the look-out for raccoon tracks in the snow so that when we see them we can record that event as one of the first signs of spring. Since the high temperature was only 21°F, I would assume that the active raccoon whose tracks I saw was a male, driven by hormonal changes in its body to seek a female that would accept him in her winter quarters.

The raccoon is a medium-size mammal with a black mask and rings on its tail. The average weight of an adult is about twelve to sixteen pounds; it is unusual to find one that weighs more than twenty pounds. Its normal life span is from ten to twelve years. The raccoon's home range is about a square mile if its food requirements can be met in that area. Raccoons are classified as carnivores along with dogs, cats, wolves, foxes and weasels, but, actually, they are omnivores. Besides fish, frogs, crayfish and insects, they relish grain and berries and over the years have also found tasty meals in picnic area trash barrels. They have well-developed salivary glands, and much of their food is eaten unwashed.

In Minnesota raccoons den up for the winter. Natural dens are hollow trees, logs and caves, but they also live in abandoned houses, farms and barns. They build up fat reserves in the fall that enable them to stay holed up in their dens during deep snow or very cold weather, but those living in the southern states remain active all winter and are constantly hunting for food because they have not stored up body fat.

The raccoon is not a true hibernator although it dens up and remains inactive for several weeks. Its body metabolism does not decrease nor its temperature drop like a hibernating animal such as the woodchuck.

Temperature is the controlling factor in a raccoon's denning up, with the dividing line between remaining active and inactive about 27°F. As long as most days remain above this, the raccoon will roam the landscape, but when it drops below this point, it retires until the weather moderates. Also, if there is deep snow or strong wind, a raccoon will stay in its den even though the temperature rises above freezing.

As winter continues, the raccoon becomes acclimated to the cold and will move about at lower temperatures, and by the time the breeding season arrives in January or February, the male moves in almost zero weather. He may travel several miles in a night searching for a mate.

January 15, 1978 White Frost

Beautiful white frost covers every twig, spruce needle and dried meadow grass on this overcast, slightly below-zero morning. This was preceded by a night of clear skies and moist still air.

Years ago I learned in a weather class that the ideal conditions for the formation of dew or white frost, which is deposited on solid surfaces, are a clear sky, little or no wind, a fairly moist atmosphere and relatively long nights. It is well-known that both dew and frost are much more likely to occur on nights that are clear and calm than on those when the sky is overcast and a wind is blowing.

Cloudless skies or skies with only a few high clouds permit a rapid loss of heat from the earth's surface by radiation. The adjacent air layer in turn becomes chilled, and if the temperature of the lower few inches of surface air is reduced below the dew point, which is the temperature at which the air is saturated with water vapor, condensation takes place. This may be in the form of dew if the dew point is above 32°F or white frost if the dew point is below 32°F. Both collect on cold objects close to the earth.

January 16, 1978 Blue Jays

Fifteen minutes after sunrise about twenty-five blue jays came to our feeding station. They were a welcome sight on this cold, sunny morning of minus 16°F.

Although many people tell me they don't like blue jays, I don't share this feeling. Their alarm calls are often helpful in saving the lives of other creatures, and they are also among the most active, amusing, beautiful and clever of our native birds. The large number of

Blue Jay on Pine

birds that share the same area with them indicates that any nest robbing they might do can only be seen as another natural control of numbers. I feel they are no more dominant than other birds of the same size and make no effort to keep other birds away. If anything, I would say that their activities often cause passing birds to inspect an area, discover food that has been put out and become regular visitors too.

January 17, 1978 Spring Catalogs

With the jet stream still south of us, it's not going to warm up much in the next few days. International Falls had a low of minus 33°F this morning. Some other lows reported were minus 20°F at Waconia, minus 30°F at Lake George and minus 36°F at Embarrass. Sunset today is 5 p.m. CST, which is certainly an improvement over 4:33 in December. Even on this cold day we are made aware that one season has a way of sliding into another. When Gurney's 1978 spring catalog appeared in our mail box, it made me realize that as our planet is racing through space around the sun toward the point of the vernal equinox, we can't slow its pace, and already plants, animals and people are preparing for spring.

Both the Burpee seed catalog and the Farmer Seed and Nursery Company catalog arrived earlier this month in the Andersen Horticultural Library, and the librarian also mentioned that some spring catalogs arrived even before winter officially began in December.

Librarian June Rogier started collecting seed and nursery catalogs for the Arboretum seven years ago, and the project has been expanded. Catalogs are ordered, processed, housed and records maintained, and now the number of catalogs is 410.

The acquisition of nursery and seed catalogs is the first phase of the project. The second phase is a search through the catalogs for the plant materials that are grown on the Arboretum grounds. Much of this phase is being done by volunteers who have found about 1,300 plants, and the list keeps growing. You can see how people prepare for the coming season.

January 18, 1976 A Monarch in Mexico

Professor Fred Urquhart, the renowned entomologist who has been investigating the migrations of the monarch butterfly for more than twenty-five years, made a startling discovery. Dr. Urquhart who is from the Zoology Department, University of Toronto, picked up a monarch butterfly in an overwintering colony in the volcanic mountains of Mexico, and his later discovery that the monarch had been tagged September 6, 1975, on the University of Minnesota Landscape Arboretum prairie was amazing to him.

From Professor Urquhart's letter —

. . . "I found it (ps 397) on January 18, 1976, in the overwintering colony in the volcanic mountains of Mexico (a straight line distance of about 1,750 miles) at an altitude of approximately 8,500 feet, temperature about 34° Fahrenheit.

"The way I found it was quite remarkable. A branch of a pine tree had been so loaded down with the weight of the butterflies that it had broken and thousands of butterflies were in an inactive condition on the ground. The photographer from *National Geographic* had asked me to sit down on the ground so that I would be surrounded by the butterflies. As I was sitting there, I reached into a pile of butterflies and was amazed when I picked up the tagged specimen, which, of course, the photographer snapped immediately. I have had a lot of exciting experiences during the many years of this work, but I can safely say that this was the most exciting one I have ever experienced, thanks to the hard work of you and your students. This was the only tagged specimen that was recaptured in our three week stay in Mexico . . . Your students might be interested to learn that in all of my experience this is the first tagged butterfly that I have recaptured that I have not tagged myself. The butterfly was in excellent condition."

Before finishing this story, however, we must go back to September 6, 1975. The morning began with a temperature of 47°F, but since the sky was quite clear, the air over the prairie was above 55°F by 9 a.m. Below 55°F monarchs have difficulty flying, and they can't fly at all below 50°F. When the temperature jumped up above the 55°F mark, the 200 or so monarchs on the ten-acre prairie began visiting laitris, goldenrod and sunflower blossoms. Jim Street and Dean Boen, two of my students, who attended Hopkins North Junior High School, went out to the Arboretum prairie that morning with me to tag monarch butterflies. The three of us tagged close to 100 monarchs. We applied small pressure adhesive tags, one-fourth by one-half inch, to the right front wings of the butterflies. One that was numbered ps 397 was picked up later by Dr. Urquhart and subsequently became famous.

Every butterfly we identify receives its own number and a tag that says, "Send to Zoology, University Toronto, Canada." For each one tagged, we record its species or correct common name, number assigned, location found and time tagged. We also include notes on its condition and, if it was feeding, the kind of flower. At the end of the monarch migrating season, which is about mid-October in Minnesota, we send our data sheets to Professor Urquhart at the University of Toronto.

January 19, 1978 Longer Days

The spring song of the white-breasted nuthatches, the "fee-bee" whistle of the black-capped chickadees and the drumming of woodpeckers are sounds heard more often now as the days lengthen. All of these birds are regular visitors at our feeding station, so we can often enjoy their spring songs at close range.

January 20, 1977 Snow Flurries in the Bahamas

For the first time on record, snow flurries fell in the Bahamas, the temperature dipped to 23°F in Daytona Beach and 31°F in Miami, Florida, and here in our area we had a high of 25°F under sunny skies. Blue jays, white-breasted nuthatches and black-capped chickadees were singing their spring songs today.

Many scientists believe that periodic changes in the earth's orbit around the sun are the cause of ice ages. A moderate cooling trend has already begun, according to some observers. If we project the rela-

JANUARY

January averages out as the coldest of all the months of the year.

If the snow is deep, and with proper clothing, a snowshoe trek can be an unforgettable treat.
(1–4)

1

2

3

4

5

6

7

8

Evergreens, such as northern white cedar **(5)** and black spruce **(6)**, add living color to our winter landscape. A snow covered evergreen is one of the most beautiful sights of nature. Jim Gilbert walking among snow covered spruces in Itasca State Park. (7) Snow on the boughs of a Norway pine; Minnesota's state tree. **(8)**

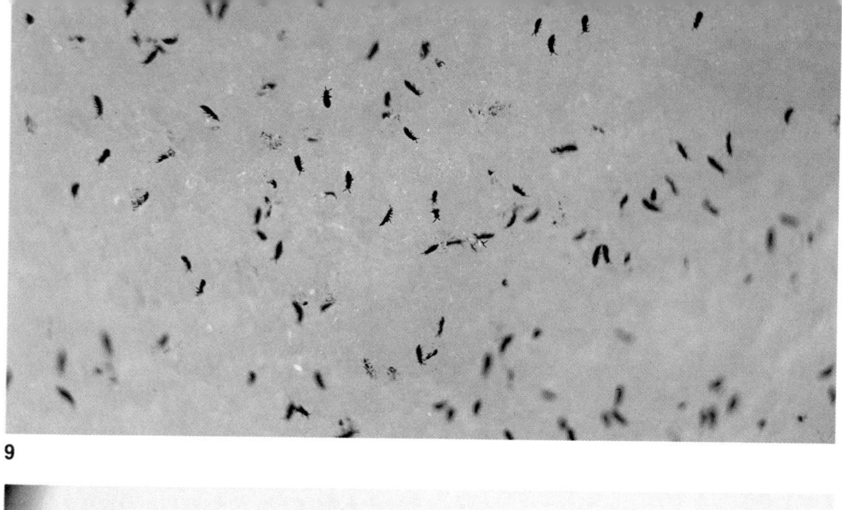

9

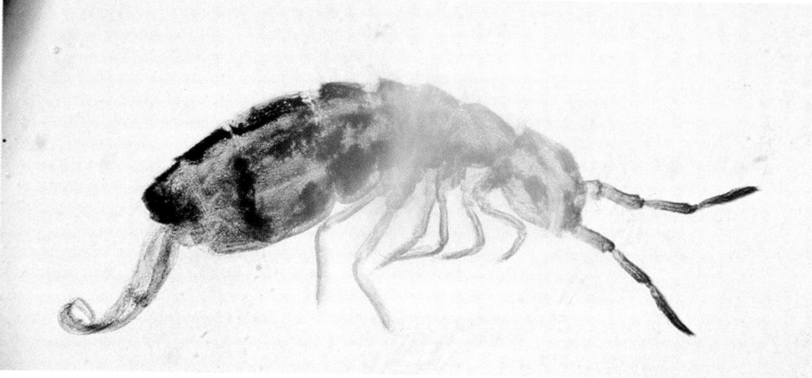

10

11

12

When the air temperature is above 27°F, look for snow fleas. They can be seen jumping and crawling on the surface of the snow in some forests which border on wetlands. Snow fleas look like pepper or specks of coal. **(9)** Snow flea magnified twenty times. **(10)** Though only about 3 millimeters in length, a spring-like tail can propel these small insects 2 or 3 inches.

If you feed birds, you may attract the handsome blue jays **(11)** or colorful evening grosbeaks. **(12)**

13

14

15

16

A bird feeding station will also attract several mammal species. Red squirrels **(13)** and gray squirrels **(14)** are fond of sunflower seeds, short-tailed weasels **(15)** like small chunks of suet, and the white-tailed deer will clean up any seeds. **(16)**

FEBRUARY

February is the most pleasant month of the winter. The first half of the month usually remains cold and cloudy but warmth and sunshine appear in mid-February and continue throughout the month.

Usually the first active chipmunks appear in February. **(17)** Red-osier dogwoods glow in the landscape. **(18)** Because the sun is higher, melting occurs on sunny south slopes even when the air is below 32°F. **(19)** Dragon's-teeth form on south and west facing roadside snowbanks. **(20)**

21

Nature's art in February: Ice storms can coat grasses and anything else on our landscape. **(21)** Rime frost is composed of layers of ice crystals deposited on outdoor objects in supercooled fog or mist. This fleeting beauty melts quickly in the sun. **(22)** Rime frost on a pine **(23)** and on Korean barberry. **(24)**

22

23

24

25

26

27

28

A hike in the forest to look for evidence of animals can be very rewarding. An owl print in the snow **(25)**, an old northern oriole nest swaying from an elm **(26)**, squirrel tracks **(27)** and a deer trail **(28)** are animal signs easily observed.

29

30

Building a quinzhee (snow shelter) is a fun activity **(29)** but sleeping out in one on a cold February night is a real adventure. **(30)** A hike in Itasca State Park to the Mississippi River Headwaters, during the winter solitude, is a fantastic experience. **(31 & 32)**

31

32

tionship between the orbits and the climate in the future, this cooling trend should continue for about 20,000 years, and during that time it is thought that nature will have built substantial ice on the northern hemisphere continents.

January 21, 1978 Cold and Clear

Bemidji was the cold spot in the nation today with a minus 28°F, Boston, Massachusetts, has twenty-six inches of snow on the ground, but in the Twin Cities area we have only five inches of snow cover. We don't seem to be living in a snowbelt. Instead, we have white frost covering every twig and brown grass leaf in the Arboretum on this cold clear day, making the winter landscape a veritable fairyland.

January 22, 1978 Spring is Coming

The dates on which cardinals have been first heard in this area:

January 17, 1974
January 21, 1975
February 8, 1976
February 1, 1977

Today I heard my first cardinal whistling "what-cheer, cheer, cheer," which is a sure sign of spring as cardinals sing in response to the lengthening days. The male cardinal, a bit smaller than an American robin, is a predominantly red bird with a crest. Females are yellowish-brown with tinges of red and are recognizable by their crests and red grosbeak bills. The singing of the male cardinals becomes more frequent by the middle of February, and from then until nesting both the males and females can often be heard whistling. This is closely connected with the establishment of the breeding territory.

Cardinals are now permanent residents in the central and southern regions of Minnesota, and in the last 100 years the species has extended its range significantly. In the late 1800s it was only a visitant, entering the state occasionally along the Mississippi River, but by the mid-1930s it was established as a resident in the Twin Cities area. In the last ten years there have been a few nests recorded north of Mille Lacs Lake and a number of birds sighted in the summer as far northwest as Red Lake and as far northeast as Duluth.

January 23, 1975 Antler-Shedding Time

White-tailed deer are numerous in the Arboretum area. Most people are thrilled at the sight of a deer; however, because it is a browsing animal, it can harm garden and farm crops, orchards, nurseries and forest plantations. Some people consider deer to be a nuisance for this reason. Of course, all people can't be pleased all of the time, and I think that if the present deer population stays about the same, the value of their presence far outweighs the damage they do. The white-tailed deer is the largest wild animal we have in this area. Daybreak and just before nightfall are its chief periods of activity so if you keep this in mind when you drive some of the side roads, you may catch a glimpse of one.

Today a white-tailed buck shed a single, large, four-point antler while nibbling on some corn at a feeding station in Carver Park Reserve. It is more common for antlers to fall off one at a time rather than both together, and bucks are often seen with a single antler. Antlers are grown and shed annually and are usually dropped after the breeding season, from the middle of December until February. If the antlers were grown to be used in defense against predators, they would not fall off in the winter when deep snow puts the deer in the greatest danger. The breeding or rutting season starts about the last week of October when the bucks, previously indifferent to the does, begin to court them. As the rutting season reaches its peak during the last two weeks of November and continues into December, bucks often engage in severe fights using both their antlers and hoofs, for possession of the doe. The bucks in the finest condition and having the largest racks are usually the first to drop their antlers. On rare occasions a doe has been observed with antlers, but hers are usually small and greatly modified.

Many people are not aware that bucks shed their antlers because they have never found the shed antlers, which are difficult to see as they become covered with leaves and snow. During this time wild mice and other animals gnaw them because of their high calcium and phosphorus content, and by summer most of the antlers have been consumed, their minerals a part of another animal's body.

A buck is without its antlers until April or May. At this time new growth begins and continues for about fifteen weeks. While the antlers are growing, they are supplied with blood vessels and have a thick skin covering with velvet-like hair. The antlers gradually harden into bone about five months after growth begins. The blood circulation then stops, and the dried skin is rubbed away against trees or shrubs.

A buck does not grow antlers during his first year, but in the second year he will probably develop spikes. These are usually straight, smooth, unbranched antlers that measure about four or five inches, and he is known at this stage as a "spike buck." A buck feeding under ideal conditions may skip the spike stage and develop branched antlers immediately. Many people try to tell the age of a buck by his antlers, but this cannot be done because antler development is not an indication of age but of nutrition and the amount of food consumed.

January 24, 1976 Flying Canada Geese

We had a January thaw today with a high temperature of 39°F. The air was filled with spring songs from black-capped chickadees, white-breasted nuthatches, blue jays and woodpeckers. Canada geese from the wintering flock in Carver Park Reserve were flying about, too. It's always a thrill to hear their honking and to see these large brownish-gray birds with long, outstretched black necks and white cheek patches. Although their flights look heavy and labored, they are really strong and swift. For such heavy birds they are very agile. When flying about their feeding grounds or on other short flights, they fly in compact or irregular bunches. The ones I observed today are among about 260 giant Canada geese wintering in Carver Park where the Hennepin County Park Reserve District is providing food and open water for them.

The Twin Cities metro area is one of several urban areas in the United States where large flocks of honkers nest and rear their young. They also nest in Colorado, Connecticut, Delaware, Massachusetts, New Jersey and New York where a few cities still have marsh areas. They flew over Twin Cities' area marshes before the first European settlers came but later disappeared, probably due to over-hunting. Starting in 1955, they were introduced to the metro area from a variety of captive and semi-domestic flocks, with most birds obtained from game breeders in Minnesota, Wisconsin, Indiana and Oklahoma. At the present time the Twin Cities is home to about 1,800 birds, and twelve major breeding flocks are distributed throughout the seven-county metropolitan area. The flocks were established by holding wing-clipped birds until they nested and then allowing the young to fly free. When Canada geese have raised a family in an area, the pair and their offspring return there every year.

Studies by University of Minnesota researchers continue on the ecology of Canada geese nesting in the Twin Cities area. They are not barnyard birds that someone has raised; they are free-flying, migrating, wild birds. By putting collars and bands on them, it has been found that some Twin Cities area geese travel to southern Illinois and southern Missouri for the winter. It is when traveling long distances that they fly high in the well-known V-shaped flocks, which experience has taught them is the easiest and most convenient for rapid flight. Migrating geese from here return from their wintering grounds in February and early March and join those that have wintered in the Twin Cities area. Most nests are started during the last of March and the first part of April.

The Twin Cities metro area is fortunate to have many marshes remaining, since without them there would be no Canada geese. The geese have brought a bit of nature to a large population center. Most urban Americans have to travel far to catch a glimpse of them, but Twin Cities' residents can often step outside their front doors and look up in the sky to see the geese flying. They are enhancing the quality of our metropolitan environment, and wherever and whenever these elegant, graceful, and wary waterfowl with their distinctive calls are observed, people's instant reactions are pleasure and enjoyment.

January 25, 1978 Tree Sparrows

Sparrows are small birds with brown bodies, streaked backs and short, conical beaks. They feed mainly on seeds in shrubby open areas except during nesting time. In summer the large number of sparrow species with similar coloring is discouraging to most beginning birders trying to identify them, but in winter most of these species fly south, allowing us to more easily identify the few that remain.

One of these, the tree sparrow, summers in northern Canada, and so the only chance we have of seeing it is in winter when it migrates to northern United States, including Minnesota where there are many in the southern half of the state. A tree sparrow is easily recognized by the dark spot in the middle of its clear gray breast and by its rusty cap. As the birds gather in winter flocks with juncos to feed, their primary food is grass seeds, and at our feeding station they are very fond of millet seeds.

I hold a federal bird-bander's license that permits trapping and examination of song birds. Actually, I have a sub-permit under Kathy Heidel who is the master permitee. Kathy and I both band at the Lowry Nature Center in Carver Park Reserve. We both work as teaching naturalists, quite often banding birds as part of our program for Nature Center visitors. Even though our banding is devoted to educational purposes, we each have a research project to work on also: Kathy is watching the movement and distribution of chickadees and nuthatches in Carver Park, and I'm interested in tree sparrows and their return to the winter range. We have banded several hundred tree sparrows and have recaptured many of them numerous times. About thirty tree sparrows, which we banded, returned to our feeding station and were recaptured after having been gone for more than six months. Since they were gone from late spring to early fall, we assumed they were nesting in northern Canada.

Last fall the first tree sparrows arrived at our feeding station on October 12. They are commonly seen at the feeders during the winter months, and the last ones usually leave by the end of April. Today I recaptured a bird that I had banded February 25, 1977. It is interesting to think about the attachment exhibited by this bird for its same wintering site. How did this summer bird of northern Canada find its way back to our feeding station? Will it return next year and the following year? Bird banding has shown us that some tree sparrows return here for three years or more, but we still don't know how they repeatedly find us.

January 26, 1978 White-breasted Nuthatches

One of the resident bird species that you can attract to a feeding station in almost any area of Minnesota is the white-breasted nuthatch. Even on this minus 10°F morning they are calling their spring songs and are active at our feeders. This five-inch long, short-tailed, short-legged, tree-climbing bird can be identified by its white face and the solid black cap of the male and gray cap on the female. Usually seen in pairs even throughout the winter, they are apparently mated for life.

The nuthatches are the only winter birds that regularly descend a tree trunk, head foremost. A characteristic pose, which is unique among birds, is the nuthatch standing head downward on the trunk of the tree with its neck extended backward and the bill pointing straight out. Other trunk climbers such as the brown creeper and the woodpeckers generally rely on sitting back on their tail feathers for support and usually face upward, but this bird holds on with its feet and wanders up and down tree trunks any way it pleases. This may give it some slight advantage in finding insects that creepers and woodpeckers miss, coming down tail-first.

The forest is the nuthatches' home and here they nest and roost in tree cavities and spend their days searching the trunks and branches for beetles, ants, caterpillars and insect eggs. Besides these foods, nuthatches feed on seeds of many kinds and can even crack acorns. At our feeding station we have found they are especially fond of sunflower seeds and beef suet.

Kathy Heidel, who has been banding white-breasted nuthatches here for eight years, has found that most nuthatches appear to be

White-breasted Nuthatch

permanent residents with fairly small feeding territories. Both of us have recaptured a male several times that she originally banded in 1971. He has continued to live in the Nature Center area since then and must be at least eight years old now. Frank and Marie Commons banded a white-breasted nuthatch April 28, 1923, on Tanager Hill, located on the north shore of the Lower Lake in Smiths Bay of Lake Minnetonka. This bird made countless trips to their bird feeding area and was recaptured thirty-six times over a period of five years.

January 27, 1978 Why You Are Cold

A beautiful sunrise through cirrus clouds greeted us on this extremely cold morning, as black-capped chickadees whistled "fee-bee" and a white-breasted nuthatch sang its spring song. Our backyard thermometer read minus 14°F, but the weatherman reported a wind chill of minus 50°F. After hearing that bit of news on WCCO Radio, I put on several layers of clothing before heading out to fill the bird-feeders.

Arctic explorers, military doctors and weather bureau researchers developed the wind chill index, which indicates the cooling effect of various combinations of winds and temperatures on the exposed flesh of people. The basic principle is quite simple: wind carries heat away from one's skin faster than the same air would if it were still. In still air, when air particles touch our skin they become warmed and so are more energetic and move away. If the air against the skin is already in motion, the heat lost to each air molecule is as great, and many more molecules come in contact with the skin. In general, the stronger the wind, the lower the temperature seems, and the effects of cold are more harmful.

The wind chill index is a figure that reflects how low the equivalent temperature would be under specific wind-temperature conditions. For instance, if the actual air temperature is minus 15°F, a fifteen mile-an-hour wind will produce a wind chill equivalent to 51°F below zero.

Wind Chill Table

Temp. (F)	10°	5°	0°	−5°	−10°	−15°	−20°	−25°
Wind MPH	wind chill index — the equivalent temperature (equivalent in cooling power on exposed flesh under calm conditions)							
calm	10	5	0	−5	−10	−15	−20	−25
5	7	1	−6	−11	−15	−20	−26	−31
10	−9	−15	−22	−27	−31	−38	−45	−52
15	−18	−25	−33	−40	−45	−51	−60	−65
20	−24	−32	−40	−46	−52	−60	−68	−76

January 28, 1978 Cirrus Clouds

It's been another bitter cold day, but those who ventured outside or looked out their windows this morning were rewarded by the sight of beautiful cirrus clouds. They are our highest clouds and are frequently blown about into feathery strands called "mares' tails."

Cirrus, a Latin word meaning lock, curl, or tendril, is the name of clouds that occur only at high altitudes of about 25,000 to 30,000 feet. Here the temperatures are so low that water droplets, the building blocks of clouds, are frozen into ice crystals. These are then dispersed by strong winds to give the clouds a fibrous, windswept appearance. Wisps hanging from the clouds are falling drops of rain that evaporate before reaching the ground.

Cirrostratus clouds form at the same altitudes as cirrus. They are thin sheets that look like fine veils or torn, wind-blown patches of gauze and are also made of ice crystals. Sunlight or moonlight occasionally passes through the ice crystals of cirrus or cirrostratus clouds and is refracted by them, making the sun or moon appear to be ringed by a halo that varies from red on the inside to white on the outside. Cirrus clouds and halos often announce an approaching storm.

January 29, 1976 Appearance by the Horned Larks

This morning I saw four horned larks along a county road. In January and February we look for horned larks along country gravel roads and in open meadows, another sign that spring is on the way. As you drive on a rural gravel road, you may see small flocks of these little grayish-brown birds fly up as your car goes by. They are smaller than an American robin but bigger than a house sparrow and have a dark brown tail with white outer feathers as a distinguishing mark and small tufts of black feathers on either side of the head like horns.

Horned Lark

A few horned larks remain in our area through the winter, left behind by the bulk of the flock to fare as best they can. They are joined again, as spring approaches, by the returning birds that have wintered farther south and now appear with the warmer sun and milder days of late January and February. This species is one of the first to nest, but, unfortunately, many nests with eggs or young in them are destroyed by March and early April snowstorms.

January 30, 1978 Black-capped Chickadees

Today while trapping and banding birds at Carver Park Reserve, I recaptured twenty-seven that had been banded at this station earlier. Nineteen of the birds were black-capped chickadees, and one had been banded here on February 25, 1972. On another day this winter we recaptured a black-capped chickadee that had been previously banded March 17, 1970.

Although there is evidence that a few of the species may wander farther south in winter, the black-capped chickadee is a common year-round resident throughout Minnesota. The birds appear in small flocks in the winter and often in the company of nuthatches. The chickadees, hunting eggs, work on the twigs and ends of the branches while the nuthatches, looking for insects that are tucked away in winter quarters, usually work over the bark of the trunk and larger branches. About three-tenths of the food of the chickadee is plant matter such as wild fruits and seeds. The other seven-tenths is animal matter including caterpillars and eggs of gypsy and coddling moths, bark beetles, plant-lice and other insects. Spiders, too, are considered a delicacy.

The chickadee works throughout the year to subdue the insect enemies of the farm and garden and to help keep the balance of nature in woodland areas. This fascinating little ball of feathers, constantly overflowing with cheerful song, can be easily attracted to most bird-feeding stations that have suet and seeds. If you carefully observe the birds in your yard, you will find that chickadees like the food at feeders, but they spend most of their day prospecting for animal matter in the twigs of trees. A chickadee first looks a twig over from above and then hangs, head down, and inspects it from below. It is a thorough worker and doesn't intend to overlook anything.

Chickadees retire about sunset. They may sleep in old woodpecker holes, in old nesting cavities they have constructed in a rotten stump or in dense conifer branches and dense thickets. Since there is a definite tendency for groups to roost in the same area each night, it is possible to station oneself at a known roosting place and observe them returning to it. As the flocks break up and pairs form in the spring, the winter roosts are abandoned.

January 31, 1978 The First Active Striped Skunk

This morning the first skunk tracks of the year were spotted in Carver Park Reserve where a skunk and a raccoon had left their meandering tracks behind in the snow.

Skunks are carnivores, members of the weasel family. The striped skunk is a furry, glossy black animal, the size of a house cat, with two distinct white stripes. It is active mainly at night and at dusk and may not retire until sunrise. It roams in early and later winter but during mid-winter is more or less dormant, although true hibernation does not occur. Skunks may bed together in groups of about eight to twelve in underground dens, but there is seldom more than one male. Occasionally males may be seen in winter and may sometimes take a sleeping den alone. Adults become less sluggish by the last of February, and by the end of March both adults and last year's young move around more often. In autumn a skunk may wander a few miles to find a suitable wintering place, but ordinarily its home range is within a one-half-mile radius.

Skunks prefer areas of mixed woodlands and fields, their winter food consisting of fruit, nuts, seeds, mice, shrews, carrion and garbage, which they often find. In the summer more than half their food is insects, grasshoppers, crickets, beetles, caterpillars, cutworms, bees and wasps.

The skunk's interesting method of defense has given the animal an undeservedly bad reputation since it will spray only as a last resort. First it will try to gallop away, and if that fails, it will turn to face you while stomping its front feet. If this does not make you retreat, the skunk will turn and spray its scent. This can be sprayed up to about fifteen feet, usually in an arc so as to be sure to hit its target.

The chemical responsible for skunk scent is butylmercaptan, a sulphur-alcohol compound that, like all volatile sulphur compounds, is malodorous. Skunk fluid has been said to have a lasting harmful effect if sprayed into the eyes, but this is not true. One's eyes will smart and burn for a few moments, sometimes for nearly an hour and even blind a person temporarily, but the pain is soon gone and there is no lasting effect.

Grey & Red Squirrels

February 1, 1975 Snowshoeing in Itasca State Park

This is one of the unusual winters when we have had several weeks of good snowshoeing in the Twin Cities area. One needs at least one and one-half feet of snow cover to have good snowshoeing, and it seems as if we can expect such conditions about every four years. This is a very popular activity at the Lowry Nature Center.

The snowshoe, almost 6,000 years old, is holding its own in our complex technological age. There is something in its simplicity and its closeness to nature that speaks directly to an increasing number of people who attempt to live with nature, not to subdue it. Archeologists have not been able to date the origin of either snowshoes or skis, but the best evidence suggests that the first device to serve as a foot-extender for easier travel over the snow originated about 4,000 B.C. in Central Asia. The snowshoe-ski is one of the oldest inventions of man and ranks in importance with the wheel. Without the snowshoe, aboriginal peoples would not have been able to expand over and then to occupy some parts of the northern hemisphere.

Most snowshoes today are used for recreation as it's a good way to relax one's mind and body and to enjoy the winter landscape. It helps firm muscles that don't often get enough of a workout in a somewhat sedentary world, but it is not too demanding as it is a sport of moderation in energy expenditure. The snowshoes help us stay close to the surface of the snow by spreading our weight over a greater area, and only slightly more effort is needed to get around on snowshoes than to walk on dry ground, if one isn't using the snowshoes for racing or climbing steep hills.

My father, brother David and I recently drove to Itasca State Park to enjoy its winter splendor and to snowshoe. Because of the wind protection offered by the vast forests, the snow comes straight down and forms thick layers, and it was two feet deep on picnic tables and bird house roofs when we arrived.

We needed our snowshoes to travel anywhere in the deep snow off the plowed roads as we went toward the Mississippi River Headwaters, where the water was open and crystal clear and where we had a good drink. The air temperature was about 10°F on this sunny, calm day as we traveled beneath large Norway pines, through spruce groves and tamarack swamps, past handsome lichens on paper birches and over beautiful Lake Itasca. We saw weasel, mouse, snowshoe hare, deer and red squirrel tracks, a black-capped chickadee whistled "fee-bee," and blue jays called from a distance — this was a memorable day!

February 2, 1978 Groundhog Day

7:32 a.m., the sun is rising, and the sky is clear except for a few cirrus clouds. I just checked the thermometer, which read minus 23°F. This is Groundhog Day, the day on which it is said that if the groundhog, or woodchuck, comes out of hibernation and sees his shadow, we will have six more weeks of winter.

Contrary to this old tradition, Minnesota groundhogs or woodchucks do not emerge from their sleep promptly at sunrise on the second day of February to watch for their shadows on the snow or earth. They are still hibernating at this time, and we usually see the first one about mid-March. This morning the sun is out, and I don't see any woodchuck tracks in the snow, but, on the other hand, I just saw my own shadow, so I predict we will have another six weeks of winter weather.

Many people are interested in this bit of folklore brought to our country from Europe centuries ago. I have read that in England and in Germany it is the badger that is supposed to forecast an early or late spring, depending upon whether or not he appears outside his den on Candlemas Day, February 2.

The woodchuck is the largest member of the squirrel family, and an adult may be twenty-one to twenty-five inches long and weigh from five to ten pounds. Its home range is about one-fourth to one-half mile in diameter. It is primarily a diurnal animal that spends most of the daylight hours during the growing season eating green vegetation and storing up fat so that it can spend the long winter in hibernation. In our area woodchucks often hibernate before the first killing frost, the last one being observed here on October 16, 1977. These heavy-bodied, short-legged, brown furry animals dig a complicated burrow system twenty-five to forty feet long, about four feet below ground level. Usually there is a front and back entrance, and occasionally there are side entrances to the burrow. Summer burrows are dug in open meadows, preferably near or in a clover field, but winter burrows are dug in a woodland or hedgerow, possibly because they offer more protection there and have a more even temperature.

Wood chucks breed when they are one year old. Mating takes place in March and April, and two to six (usually four) young are born in April or May. Each pink, naked baby is less than four inches long when it is born and weighs about an ounce, but four weeks later, even before their eyes are open, young woodchucks are well-furred. At about five weeks they leave the underground den and play about its entrance.

February 2, 1981

Now is the time we expect black bear cubs to be born. Young are born in January or early February in the Superior National Forest while their mother is still in her winter sleep, according to Dr. Lynn Rogers who has been studying black bears for fourteen years. At birth the young, usually two or three, are six to eight inches long and weigh seven to twelve ounces, about 1/500 of the weight of the mother. It has been suggested that because the mother bear must often nurse her cubs three or four months with no food for herself, the young have to be small.

February 3, 1977 Pileated Woodpecker

A large woodpecker spent part of the afternoon calling loudly from the maple-basswood forest behind the Lowry Nature Center. The call was more of a cackle, resembling a flicker's call but louder and richer in quality. Throughout the greater part of the year this woodpecker is a relatively silent bird, but during the nesting season, drumming and calling are frequently heard. Sometimes we hear a sharp note or two when these large woodpeckers approach our suet feeders in winter, but today's chattering sounds were different. This must be another sign that winter is moving toward spring.

The large red-crested woodpecker goes by the name pileated woodpecker, which means crested. The species is a permanent resident throughout the forested part of Minnesota and heavily timbered valleys and lakeshores of the prairie areas. It lives almost wholly within the canopy of the trees and so easily eludes observation. The pileated woodpecker feeds on insects that infest standing and fallen trees and supplements this diet with wild berries and acorns. Ants are its main food.

It is in the pursuit of ants that the woodpecker cuts large furrows about four to eight inches wide, deep into the trunks of living or dead standing trees. The cuts may be from a few inches to more than a foot long, are often aligned in vertical rows and run together in furrows several feet in length. It may be difficult to spot a pileated woodpecker, but it's easy to see where it has worked in a forest. Examining its excavations in tree trunks, it is apparent that the birds penetrate the passageways of the great carpenter ants. Since ants and beetles make up the bulk of their food, the presence of pileated woodpeckers is beneficial as they work to pursue the ants and help to conserve the timber.

Today we also heard the calling of our resident Canada geese as we watched these heavy, powerful birds in their flights. Added to this was the whistling of cardinals and black-capped chickadees and the sight of raccoon tracks in the snow. A naturalist could easily come down with symptoms of spring fever.

February 4, 1978 Flocks of Cedar Waxwings

If you have a Red Splendor crabapple tree with fruits still on it or some other tree or shrub that retains its fruit throughout the winter, you have probably seen cedar waxwings as they stopped by to feed during their wanderings. On my winter hikes I usually hear the waxwings first, before I see them. Their vocal powers are limited to a faint high-pitched, vibrant lisp as though they were saying "zeee, zeee, zeee . . . " or "three, three, three . . . " in a kind of whispered

Cedar Waxwing

monotone. We usually see them in flocks of twenty to seventy as they feed in the crabapple or cork tree collections.

It's hard to predict when to look for cedar waxwings as their appearance is uncertain. In winter there can be many cedar waxwings anywhere in the state, and, although they are common in southern Minnesota, their presence in any area is irregular. People who live where fruits from the red cedar, highbush cranberry, cultivars and species of crabapples and mountain ash are available are very likely to encounter flocks of the easy going, friendly, sociable birds several times during the winter and early spring. It's a treat to see these crested brown birds, halfway between a sparrow and a robin in size, with sleek, silky plumage, a black mask, and a broad yellow band at the tip of their tails. Some individual cedar waxwings have extended scarlet shafts on their secondary wing feathers that give the appearance of having been dipped in sealing wax, and it is from this peculiarity that the bird gets its name.

February 5, 1977 Short-Eared Owl

This afternoon I watched a short-eared owl hunting over a snow-covered meadow, its irregular flopping flight resembling a common nighthawk's or large moth's meanderings. A few days ago naturalist Kathy Heidel had told me about this day-flying owl, and if she hadn't alerted me, I probably would have thought it was a marsh or a rough-legged hawk, at the distance from which I was observing it. Eventually the crow-size owl came to rest on a nearby power pole, so I could see its pale buffy-brown color and stripes.

Short-eared owls are inhabitants of marshes and low fields where they nest on the ground in spring. They feed mainly on mice but will eat insects and ground squirrels in the summer. They are more commonly seen in the southern half of the state in winter but are most numerous in the northwestern and west central regions in summer.

February 6, 1978 Twentieth Anniversary of the Arboretum

On this important date in the history of the Arboretum, I took time to hike on a few of the 620 acres, which is the present Arboretum size. As I went out of the Leon C. Snyder Education and Research Building into the bright sunlight, it was 10°F with six inches of snow on the ground and an east wind blowing. It was difficult to believe that the first wildflowers would be blooming in the woodland garden in less than two months. The "chick-a-dee-dee-dee" calls of several black-capped chickadees, the loud "caw, caw" of a common crow and the rustling sound of still-attached oak leaves broke the quietness. Both red and gray squirrels and the common redpolls and tree sparrows had left tracks in the snow, reminding us that wild animals must actively look for food most of their waking hours.

As I walked, I thought of the beginning of the Arboretum, together with its successful development. The deed for the Arboretum site, which was then 160 acres, together with a check for $25,000 for development, was given to the University of Minnesota on February 6, 1958. The Minnesota State Horticultural Society had received assurance from the Board of Regents that the development and direction of the Arboretum would be a part of the ongoing research and education program in the Department of Horticultural Science. A ceremony to complete the transaction was held that day at a luncheon of the University Regents in Coffman Union. The deed and money were given to President J. L. Morrill by G. Victor Lowrie, president of the Minnesota State Horticultural Society.

Although the Arboretum officially began on this date, the idea for it had originated with a group in the Men's Garden Club of Minneapolis earlier. This group had started a test planting of unusual trees and shrubs in a member's yard, but they lacked adequate space for more plantings. The men then turned to the Minnesota State Horticultural Society and requested the Society to commission a committee to explore the possibility of acquiring land for the purpose of developing an arboretum for the state.

The group from the Society and from the Men's Garden Club of Minneapolis met on January 28, 1955, to discuss this request. Those present were Leon C. Snyder, temporary chairman, Archie H. Flack, Vincent K. Bailey, Richard Stadtherr, Walter Beneditz, Mrs. William Whiteford, Mrs. E. F. Koempel and Eldred M. Hunt. Under Cortis N. Rice Jr., president of the Minnesota State Horticultural Society, an Arboretum committee was appointed, and Archie Flack became chairman.

After many meetings had been held and possible sites considered, Dr. Herbert J. Berens offered to sell 160 acres. The land was near Excelsior and not far from the University of Minnesota Fruit Breeding farm, now called the Horticultural Research Center. With the native trees, shrubs and wildflowers that would add interest to the horticultural plantings, this was a good site. The hilltops commanded inspiring views of the countryside, and the various exposures, resulting from the rolling land, would provide varied habitats for many kinds of plants to be grown. An added feature was the availability of other adjoining land that could be purchased later to accommodate even more anticipated plantings.

In June, 1956, with $1,000 provided by Mrs. Bruce B. Dayton, an option to purchase was taken on the land. A goal was immediately set to raise $75,000 for the actual purchase of this property and for the initial development of the Arboretum. A finance committee was appointed, headed by G. Victor Lowrie. The Lake Minnetonka Garden Club raised the $35,000 needed to complete the land acquisition.

The Arboretum was founded to serve one of the coldest areas of the United States, for it was felt that progress made here would affect the future of ornamental horticulture in a large part of the nation. Looking back over the past twenty years, we can see that this has been done, and it is continuing every day with the help, the interest and the support of thousands of people.

February 7, 1978 Herald of Spring

From WCCO Radio comes word that the northeast is having the worst winter storm it has ever had. Providence, Rhode Island, has received twenty-six inches of snow and Boston, twenty-seven, and Cape Cod has winds of ninety-two miles per hour. Meanwhile, back in the Twin Cities area, we have beautiful white frost covering the landscape and only six inches of snow on the ground.

Local merchants set out attractive flower and vegetable seed packets today, a good sign of spring! People with visions of garden-ripe tomatoes and bright zinnia flowers in their heads are already gathering the packets and taking them to the checkout counters. As these packets are handled, looked at and thought about for weeks, I'm sure it helps some people make it through the winter.

More fascinating than the enticing packets, of course, are the seeds inside. Each one is a miniature plant, an embryo surrounded by food and a protective coating. The seeds are alive and will germinate when conditions are favorable. You may provide those favorable conditions by indoor seeding of cabbages or peppers about April 1, or you may wait and let nature provide those conditions after you seed other species directly in the garden.

February 8, 1974 The Singing Horned Larks

I not only saw my first horned larks of the year today, but I listened to them sing their sweet, tinkling, high-pitched, spring-like song, strangely out of place with light snow falling and a temperature of 10°F. I encountered this flock of fourteen horned larks as I drove on a seldom-used road near Cologne, Minnesota. One of the things I noticed as I stopped the car to watch their actions on the shoulder of the road was that they walk, not hop. I also noted that they do most of their singing while in flight.

The first returning larks appear in late January and early February, and once here they are not easily driven back but remain to brave the arctic winds and snowstorms. Their winter food consists of seeds such as foxtail and quack grasses, smartweeds, pigweeds, purslane, rag weeds and grain, the latter picked up in bare or manured fields. In early days they gleaned much of their food along the horse-traveled roads.

February 9, 1976 First Active Woollybear Caterpillar

Partly cloudy skies and 46°F were enough to bring out the first banded woollybear caterpiller, which was seen crossing County Road 11 near Victoria. Banded woollybears are the well-known fuzzy caterpillars that are brown in the center and black at each end of their bodies. They are often seen scurrying across the highways in the fall to their hiding places in which to hibernate. They overwinter as larvae (caterpillars) and form pupae (cocoons) in the spring. Adults emerging from the cocoons are called Isabella moths and are yellowish-brown with a wing expanse of about two inches. Woollybears feed on a variety of herbaceous plants, particularly the leaves of plantain, and when disturbed, they curl up and lie motionless as if dead.

February 10, 1977 A Warm Winter Day

It's great to have a break during the winter, and for some people this may be a trip to Miami or Honolulu. Today, however, everyone in our area was treated to a break as the Twin Cities had a record high temperature of 47°F. Big Lake had 53°F, and south of us in Des Moines, Iowa, the thermometer registered 63°F.

Here are a few of the things I saw on this mild, sunny winter day in the Arboretum area:

honey bees out on cleansing flights
snow fleas hopping on the snow
white-breasted nuthatches singing their spring songs
black-capped chickadees whistling "fee-bee"
uncovered mosses looking lush green

together with:

> first muddy county roads
> first convertible car top down
> first chipmunk out in Webster (about thirty miles southeast of the Arboretum)

Now is a good time to prune your apple trees. Winter or early spring pruning before growth starts is best for rapid healing of wounds. Cuts made in summer could invite disease. Pruning is done to limit the number of apples that a tree will produce, so the fruit will be a good size, and to open the tree so sunlight can ripen the fruit.

February 11, 1979 Dragon's Teeth

Today I noticed the first dragon's-teeth forming on the south- and west-facing roadside snowbanks. Although we have not yet had a winter thaw, the sun's rays are more direct and for longer periods of time, causing snow to melt.

We can see the snow melting along the roadsides, forming rows of icicles or teeth in the snowbanks. I have seen this phenomenon happen under the same circumstances at the same time in other years.

February 12, 1978 Ice Thickness

Fifteen inches of ice covers Lake Minnetonka, and about six inches of snow covers the ice and the ground. For comparison I checked conditions in Itasca State Park when I was up there and found the snow to be eighteen inches deep with Lake Itasca having an ice covering ranging from two to four feet, according to local fishermen. We hiked to the Mississippi River Headquarters at the north end of Lake Itasca where the clear stream was open, however.

February 13, 1979 American Kestrels

Driving home I observed two American kestrels, which are also called sparrow hawks, perched on power wires near St. Bonifacius but widely separated from one another by a mile of hilly countryside. American kestrels are birds of prey, primarily found in open country and on the edges of forests where they find most of their food on the ground. In summer these small birds feed mainly on grasshoppers and other insects, but during the winter in northern latitudes birds and small animals are their prey. With the greatly reduced winter food supply, it's not surprising that most of them migrate south and return in March and April.

The American kestrel, which is not much larger than a robin, is our smallest hawk. It is the only small hawk with a rufous-red tail and an attractive black-and-white face pattern that can be seen if you get close. It flies with great quickness, but perhaps its most remarkable aerial accomplishment is the ability to arrest its flight through the air by facing the wind and hovering in one spot. The body is tilted upward, and the bird hovers on rapidly beating wings as it scans the ground hunting for a mouse or in summer a grasshopper.

February 14, 1977 Deer in the Meadows

Most of the nine-inch snow cover we had a week ago has now melted, and area meadows are starting to look bare. It's dry, as we have had only .76 of an inch of precipitation, or rain equivalent, so far in 1977. We need more moisture for the soil and to fill our ponds and lakes. The white-tailed deer are taking advantage of the open meadow spots. Just minutes before sunset tonight, I counted eighteen deer searching a large meadow for green plant parts, which, I'm sure, are a nice change of diet from the usual browsed winter twigs.

February 15, 1974 Pine Siskins

Area birders are reporting that pine siskins are at their feeding stations, with flocks of 50 to 250 commonly seen. They often feed together with redpolls, American goldfinches or purple finches. Although siskins have been known to nest in southern Minnesota, we see them more commonly as winter visitants.

Pine siskins are four and one-half inches long with heavily streaked brown bodies and yellow feathers at the base of their tails and in their wings. In shape and actions they resemble American goldfinches. Their winter food includes seeds from herbaceous plants, birch and alder.

They are sometimes very tame and bold, landing on people's heads and shoulders, and they even tolerate being picked up as they eat from feeders. At feeding stations they have always liked millet and sunflower seeds and especially sunflower hearts, but since birders started putting out thistle seeds, pine siskins have become so attached to this food that they will go to thistle feeders in preference to others. Al Zander from the Glen Lake area of Minnetonka reports that the siskins are most at home on Droll Yankee feeders containing thistle or on thistle-bag feeders.

The seed that is commonly sold as thistle is really niger, a member of the thistle family imported from Africa. This has been a popular food for caged birds for a long time but is a fairly recent discovery for birdfeeders. It is valued for its special appeal to a select bird group that includes purple finches, redpolls, pine siskins and goldfinches. The price of thistle seeds is high, but yet it may end up being economical because the small black seeds cannot be rapidly consumed, do not spoil in wet weather and attract only a select clientele.

February 16, 1976 Lush Green Mosses

Under the snow the leaves of heal-all, common mullein, evening primrose, thistles, yarrow, hawkweed and many other plants are green all winter, and, when spring comes, they are prepared to start working immediately. These plants, as well as pines, spruces, hemlocks, cedars and yews, are true evergreens, which together with mosses, lichens and duckweeds add green to the winter landscape.

Rain and warm temperatures the last few days have melted some snow and exposed mats of mosses, and today, while hiking in the forest, I observed many lush green, densely packed moss mats. Some mosses continue to photosynthesize and grow much of the winter, but at times all mosses become desiccated to a point at which metabolism ceases and dormancy begins. The plants are still greenish when dormant, and, when water is again available, mosses absorb it rapidly and begin to function normally, in a short time becoming a luxuriant green.

February 17, 1976 Red Cedars

There is still fruit on our red cedars, which I probably wouldn't have noticed if it hadn't been for a flock of about fifty cedar waxwings that settled into a large tree this afternoon for a feast. They eat a variety of winter fruits but seem to be especially fond of the berries of the red cedar, from which part of the bird's name comes. Each dark blue berry, about one-fourth of an inch in diameter, contains two or three seeds that are distributed by the birds as they eat the fleshy fruit.

The eastern red cedar (*Juniperus virginiana*) is an evergreen that is tolerant of many soils and varied locations and grows abundantly even on dry gravelly slopes. Its distinctive characteristic is the variation in form of its small leaves that are both awl-shaped and scale-shaped. The awl-shaped leaves always appear on the young plants, but on mature trees the two forms occur on the same branches. The awl-shaped leaves are prickly, pointed and spreading on the stem while the scale-shaped ones are thick and blunt, closely overlapping the twigs to form a flat sprig of foliage. The tree foliage is dark green in summer and turns reddish for the winter.

With any luck, a red cedar could live for perhaps three centuries. In Tennessee and Kentucky this species may reach a height of one hundred feet, but here we seldom find a tree over thirty feet. They are often planted as ornamental trees and wind-breaks and do well in dry areas where other evergreens will not grow.

Red cedar wood has a nice fragrance and a distinct color contrast between the red heartwood and the creamy sapwood. It is used often in the linings of moth proof chests and closets, although it is not certain how repellant the odor is to moths. The cedar splits easily and can be planed and worked for fences, shingles, benches and tables, pails and lead pencils.

February 18, 1976 Gray Squirrels

My students have been wondering about the hibernating habits of gray squirrels, but the truth is, they don't hibernate. During a cold spell they stay in their homes for a few days, eating from the supply of seeds they have stored there. However, when milder weather returns, they are out again looking for food and sunning themselves in sheltered spots. Since today is mild, we have nearly twenty at our feeding station here. We do not discourage them from coming. They have been the subject of several library research papers and the reason for countless trips to the forest to see how they live.

The eastern gray squirrel grows to about eighteen inches including its bushy tail, and it weighs about one pound. In winter the soft light gray fur becomes long and dense. Albino and melanistic gray squirrels occur, and sometimes these mutations, either partial or complete, are so common that they become the dominant color phase in an area. Gray squirrels are not fully grown until their second year although they may breed as yearlings. Their potential life span is six to ten years, and, although few live that long, a number kept as pets have lived to be fifteen years old. They usually have home ranges of about two acres, but some shift their homes as different foods attract them and may roam over as much as a five-mile area. For this reason, squirrels that raid gardens or for some other reason are a nuisance and are live-trapped, should be moved at least five miles.

Their home is in hardwood forests and forests where deciduous trees are mixed with pines and other conifers. They will also live in city parks and suburbs where large nut and shade trees offer food and denning sites. In winter natural holes in older trees probably give the most protection, and if they suit the exacting standards of the wary squirrel, they will become dens and may shelter a group of six or seven. When den trees are scarce and leaf nests are built, they are close to the tree trunk in a fork or on a strong limb and are usually thirty to fifty feet above ground. The nests are only ragged balls of twigs and leaves about one to two feet in diameter but are waterproof with inconspicuous side openings. When the leaf nests are abandoned, they quickly fall to pieces.

Individual gray squirrels consume about two pounds of food a week or one hundred pounds a year. Usually they are vegetarians, eating various kinds of nuts, seeds, fungi and wild berries and even bark and twigs when food stores run out in later winter. In early spring they lick the sweet sap and eat the swelling buds of trees. Occasionally the squirrels will eat eggs or a young bird in a nest or a bit of carrion, and, like other rodents, they are fond of gnawing on shed antlers or bones.

In August and through autumn they store acorns and other nuts singly in small holes dug in the ground where one to three minutes is spent on each acorn cached. A hole a little more than an inch deep is quickly dug, the acorn is put in, and soil and leaves pushed over it. They may also cache food in hollow trunks or fallen logs.

Naturalists have observed that the squirrels can remember where their food is stored for only about twenty minutes, and after that the food is found by odor alone. In this way food storage benefits the local squirrel population rather than any one digger. Gray squirrels have large nostrils, and the size of their nasal cavities suggests they have a good sense of smell. This can be observed as a squirrel hunts for food that lies under several inches of snow, its nostrils dilating as it digs. Not all acorns and other cached seeds are found, so squirrels become helpful agents in spreading the forests on which they depend for their food and shelter.

February 19, 1976 Red Squirrels

Most of the complaints about squirrels comes from their indefatigability in taking seeds from a birdfeeder. There are three options: quit feeding the birds, get a squirrel-proof feeder or join the ranks of the squirrel watchers, which can be fun! The only birdfeeder I know that squirrels can't raid is one mounted on a smooth metal post with a cone-shaped collar about two feet in diameter just beneath the feeder. The feeder itself should be at least five feet from the ground and away from overhanging branches, nearby fences or any structure that the ingenious acrobat can use to launch itself for an attack on the feeder.

Soon after 8 a.m. today I counted eighteen gray squirrels and four red squirrels at the feeding station. The red squirrels are smaller than the gray, have a rusty-red coat and a prominent eye ring. The temperature was near freezing, and the snow was coming down just fast enough to collect on their backs as they worked over the sunflower and corn seeds. Both squirrel species compete for woodland food, and both compete here at the feeding station. Neither will tolerate the other on the same feeder. Although they are smaller, red squirrels, apparently, are better fighters. A battle usually results in the retreat of the gray squirrel but seldom with any serious injuries to either party.

Like the gray squirrel, the red prefers to nest in a hollow tree but will build a nest of leaves if no tree cavity is available. Since they often line their leafy nests using red cedar bark as insulation, cedars stripped of their bark indicate that a red squirrel's nest is nearby. It may dig a burrow for a nesting site, which will probably be located under a tree or stump, and a single squirrel may have all three types of homes described. They, like grays, are active all winter but both hole-up in bad weather.

Red squirrels prefer evergreen forests and, consequently, are not as abundant in southern Minnesota as farther north. Although they store cones and nuts under tree roots or in under-ground burrows, they will also tunnel through snow to search for nuts on the ground or to have safe and easy access to a shrub or tree that has fruits. Individuals may eat eggs, young birds and the young of cottontail rabbits and gray squirrels, but in general they are vegetarians and do not deserve the bad reputation that a few have gained. They perform a service in forests since many of the seeds they bury remain in the ground, eventually becoming trees. The range of a red squirrel is small, seldom more than 400 feet in diameter. Like the blue jay, it is a sentinel of the forest. If anything unusual is going on in a red squirrel's territory, it responds with loud chattering and scolding.

February 20, 1976 First Nesting Bird

A great horned owl was seen today on a nest high in a tree near Victoria. This signals the beginning of the 1976 bird nesting season since the great horned owl is our earliest nesting bird in Minnesota.

Following a snow or sleet storm, it is not uncommon to see an owl incubating under a cover of snow or ice. It seems remarkable that its eggs should be laid before the last of the snow has melted because they would freeze if left unprotected, but the reason seems clear when one considers some facts. The incubation period is about twenty-eight days, the young remain in the nest about six or seven weeks, and they are unable to fly until they are ten to twelve weeks old. If the eggs are laid before the first of March, it will be mid-June or later before the young are partially able to care for themselves. During this time and probably for a few more weeks, they are fed by their parents. The

Great Horned Owl

young are voracious feeders and their food is difficult to obtain, so it is much easier for their parents to provide for their needs before the summer foliage becomes too dense.

Great horned owls nest in forest areas in hollow trees, or they make use of old hawk, crow and squirrel nests. No nest is prepared by the owl itself, and the only contribution the owl makes is a few feathers from its body. These have been found, together with the usual clutch of two eggs, in a nest that is thirty to seventy feet above the ground.

Owls require an enormous amount of food as all birds do. They have an extremely high metabolism and can process the equivalent of their own body weight in food each day. Owls are also killers by nature. They take all manner of prey, from insects, earthworms, fish and amphibians to birds and quite large mammals. As predators, there are fewer owls than the food they eat, which is a necessity or they would eat themselves out of business.

The great horned owl is nearly two feet in length, with a wing-spread of five feet, and it weighs about three and one-half pounds. It is the only large owl with ear tufts. The female is larger than the male, but otherwise they resemble one another with conspicuous white throat collar, dark-streaked breast and yellow eyes. It is common throughout the timber country in the United States and Canada up to the edge of the tundra.

The horned owl has been called the "tiger of the air" because of its large size and ravenous feeding habits, but it also is a very generous provider for its young. The tiger comparison applies well to the owl's way of hunting, for the sweep of its great wings in the silent air is as noiseless as the tread of a big cat's padded feet on the soft earth. A great horned owl glides as silently as a shadow through the forests and over the meadows, and to an unwatchful cottontail rabbit or striped skunk, that shadow means certain and sudden death from the powerful talons. Because of its great strength, it does not hesitate to attack birds and mammals much heavier than itself. Occasionally even domestic cats are preyed upon.

Although active and formidable by night, the great horned owl passes the day concealed in a large tree. It can see perfectly well in bright sunlight, so when pressed by hunger, it may be found hunting for food in the daytime. During the day owls are objects of persecution by birds in general with crows and blue jays leading the noisy charge as they caw and scream but are seldom bold enough to strike. The owl will move from place to place, trying to shake off the tormentors and find a place where it can doze in peace. It is doubtful that an owl ever strikes the boisterous rascals in the daytime, but it will have its revenge when they are in their roosts at night. I have read that great horned owls prey on blue jays, crows, various black birds, plus large birds such as red-tailed hawks and pheasants.

When Norway rats, gophers, mice, rabbits and other small mammals are scarce in the area, it is forced to live on fish, birds and domestic poultry. Night raids on poultry yards have given this owl a bad name, but there have also been numerous cases recorded where great horned owls have lived and raised a family in close proximity to farms without molesting poultry.

February 21, 1976 First Chipmunk of the Year

The first active eastern chipmunk in the Arboretum area appeared:

February 18, 1971
March 11, 1972
February 27, 1973
February 19, 1974
February 28, 1975
February 21, 1976

The temperature was only in the mid-20s this morning, so I was surprised to see the year's first active chipmunk, which wasted little time getting to the feeders. Beginning in 1971 I started keeping a record of the first appearance of the eastern chipmunk, and today's observation compares well with the other early spring sighting dates.

February 22, 1976 Tapping Maple Trees

About one-half of the landscape is still covered with snow, but with warm temperatures the last few days, the sap has started running. The gardener at the University of Minnesota Horticultural Research Center said that the sap ran from boxelders (in maple genus) he has been pruning lately. We are starting to see icicles forming on the ends of sugar maple twigs that have been browsed by deer as the sap runs from the small wounds. People who are interested in maple syrup production have been looking for these signs and are now busy tapping maple trees. They know that quite frequently the early sap flows are the largest.

Sap flow is triggered by thawing days followed by freezing nights. The ideal weather for tapping is cold, crisp nights with temperatures near 20°F, together with daytime temperatures reaching into the 40° to 50°F range, but people have learned not to expect the sap to run on schedule. Late afternoon is a good time to collect the day's flow, and, although some days there will be very little, on others the buckets may overflow, depending upon the weather. Sugar maples (*Acer saccharum*), black maples (*Acer nigrum*) and boxelders (*Acer negundo*), also known as ash-leaved maples, are tapped. The red maple (*Acer rubrum*) and silver maple (*Acer saccharinum*) can also be tapped, but their sap is less sweet.

The taphole is made by using a carpenter's brace with either a three-eighth or seven-sixteenth inch bit. Trunks smaller than ten inches in diameter should not be tapped. Holes about three inches deep are bored into the tree trunk about three feet above ground level. A small metal or wooden tube called a spile is inserted into the hole and tapped lightly with a hammer so it fits snugly. The spile supports the container and carries sap into it. The old wooden buckets and metal pails have now largely been replaced by plastic bags and plastic tubing, which are easier to use and store and which inhibit the growth of microorganisms when sunlight filters through the plastic. A plastic pipeline can be used to collect sap from trees on a hillside, enabling the sap to be carried directly to the storage tank by gravity.

Once sap is collected, it must be boiled to drive off most of the water. The amount of water that needs to be evaporated to reduce sap to syrup varies with the amount of sugar in the sap, but usually thirty to forty gallons of sap are needed to make one gallon of syrup.

February 23, 1978 Another Sign of Spring

Today at 11:11 a.m. we broke the long string of below freezing days. The Twin Cities area temperature hasn't been above 32°F since December 18, sixty-six days ago, a record string of consecutive below-freezing days in this century, but we had a high of 33°F today.

Driving on a gravel road near Lake Waconia, I noticed a few muddy spots, the first for this year. Other years I've also seen muddy spots on our country roads around this time, even when we had had days when the official temperature was not above freezing. This is because the sun's rays are hitting us directly enough at this time of the year and for long-enough periods to warm some spots, like exposed road gravel, to points well above freezing. Melting of ice and snow near the warm spots results, and even some frost comes out.

As the warming trend continues in the next few weeks, we will have more and more muddy stretches with the usual big ruts on our country roads, inconvenient and annoying, but, nevertheless, a sign of spring.

A Muddy Country Road

February 24, 1976 The Call of the Red-bellied Woodpecker

Today while I was hiking in the forest areas southwest of Lake Minnetonka, I heard red-bellied woodpeckers calling. They were doing the "whicker" call like that of the flicker, which is the usual call we hear as the nesting season approaches. These showy and now-noisy woodpeckers enjoy a wide distribution throughout much of the eastern half of the United States, except in the most northern parts, but birders hiking here fifty years ago would not have heard these sounds.

This handsome zebra-backed woodpecker is one of the species of birds that has extended its range northward into Minnesota during the last 100 years. Thomas S. Roberts reported that the first one on record in Minnesota was seen in 1893 at La Crescent, but by 1930 this species was beginning to breed as far north and west as the Twin Cities.

Red-bellied woodpeckers are about the same size as red-headed woodpeckers, but their outstanding black and white ladder-back is a distinguishing difference. If they live in your neighborhood, they will be fairly shy, and you will see them only in the tree-tops during the summer. In winter and spring, however, they are easily attracted to feeding stations to feed on seeds and beef suet. Their natural food consists of about equal portions of animal and vegetable matter. Insects, acorns, juniper berries and wild grapes are among their favorite foods.

February 25, 1976 Smells Like Spring

This is our third consecutive day with temperatures above the 50°F mark. The Twin Cities had a record high of 58°F, and people certainly responded to our unusual weather in positive ways by opening windows, going bicycling, etc. I wanted to see how plants and animals were responding also to this respite from the cold weather, so I went for a hike under blue skies and feather-like cirrus clouds. I stopped for a few moments on a woodland trail to enjoy the scented air, and inhaling deeply I sensed spring. The pleasant earthy smell is back!

My field notebook contains these entries from this memorable day:

The sap is running from the wounds in the sugar maples.
Red squirrels are chattering.
White-breasted nuthatches, black-capped chickadees and blue jays are breaking forth with spring songs.
Skunks are out.
Tree sparrows are singing, not just twittering.

Red-bellied woodpeckers are calling.
Many snow fleas can be seen on the north slopes.
Mosses are lush green.
Eight gnats can be seen hovering in a group.
Single strands of spider silk, with active spiders, are hanging on tree branches.
Red-osier dogwood bark is extremely bright red.
Canada geese are vocal; the first migrators returned February 23.
A pygmy grasshoper was sunning on a grassy slope.

I know we will return to winter weather again, but one season slides into another, and today we witnessed spring in winter.

February 26, 1979 Solar Eclipse

I would have liked nothing better than to have been in Montana or North Dakota this morning to view the sun's corona and large prominences and to experience the awesome beauty associated with a total solar eclipse. Today is especially interesting because the next total solar eclipse visible in the continental United States won't be until 2017 although there will be one in Hawaii in 1991. I saw a total solar eclipse on June 30, 1954, from a hill near Minneapolis, and I would have liked to have seen one again today. Since that wasn't possible, the next best thing that we could have here was a view of a 91 percent eclipse.

The sky was clear over the Arboretum at 7 a.m. Statistically this is the sunniest day of winter in the Twin Cities area, according to meteorologist Bruce Watson, author of the WEATHERGUIDE '79. Today we had a few cirrus clouds early in the morning and afternoon, but during the partial eclipse from 9:30 until noon, the sky was clear. I set up a small reflecting telescope and screen at the Lowry Nature Center so the staff and students could get a good indirect view of the sun as the moon moved across its surface. The clear sky darkened as we viewed the sun as a crescent, and with light from less than 10 percent of the sun's surface in our area, we felt a drop in air temperature. Roger Stein, our Nature Center director, said that he observed a drop in temperature from 24° to 16°F in his Excelsior area yard.

The time went fast. We had a 91 percent eclipse for only a couple minutes, and then the hidden areas of the sun's surface started to appear again. We could easily see sunspots with the small telescope and screen. At the darkest time at 10:47, we still heard black-capped chickadees and cardinals calling, but many of the other birds did not become vocal until it got brighter, many minutes later.

A friend from Argyle wrote, "We didn't see a total eclipse here but it was mighty close (about a 98 percent eclipse). The twilight was fascinating although it wasn't totally dark, of course. Birds were silent, and it was noticeably colder."

February 27, 1975 Sounds Like Spring

We haven't had a really warm day, we still have one to two feet of snow on the ground, and yet the air is filled with avian strains. The cardinals and chickadees continue their whistling, woodpeckers their drumming, and white-breasted nuthatches together with nearby blue jays continually break forth with their special spring songs. We have been hearing these sounds building up in intensity for several weeks. Now the resident Canada geese from Carver Park have started their spring displays and are often seen flying and making their honking sound, which is fine music to my winter-worn ears.

February 28, 1977 Red-tailed Hawks

It is believed that red-tailed hawks remain mated for life. They often return each year to the same patch of woods to nest, and today a pair was spotted over the area where they or another pair of red-tails had nested last spring in Baker Park Reserve near Maple Plain. Late February or early March is the time for these birds to arrive and begin their nest-building duties. Today's arrivals show us that nature is on schedule.

The red-tailed hawk is a large bird that is quite common in the vicinity of the Arboretum where it can often be seen soaring with little movement of its wings in great circles high in the air. The adult can be recognized by the bright reddish-chestnut color on the upper surface of the tail that is fully expanded like an open fan and can be seen when the bird dips and turns to bring its upper half into view. The red tail is not acquired until the bird is a little over a year old. Until then it is immature and does not mate, and it is nearly two years old when it does.

They nest in woodlands and feed in open country. The large nest is well made of sticks and twigs and is usually built high in one of the tallest trees. It is believed that both the male and female help in building the nest. Two eggs are usually laid and have an incubation period of about twenty-eight days. Since the red-tail's food consists mainly of rodents, it does very little damage to domestic poultry or wild birds.

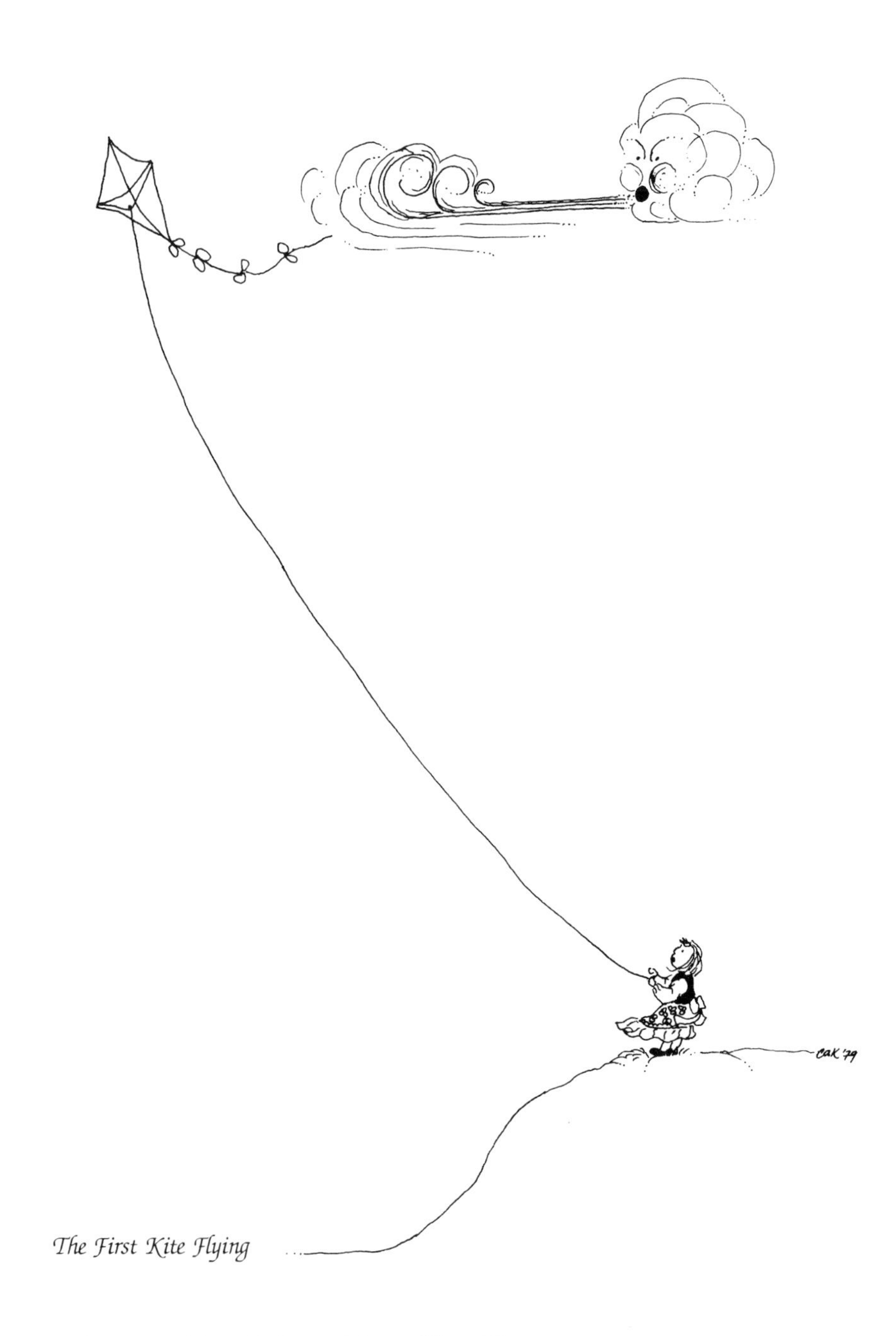

The First Kite Flying

February 29, 1976 First Kite Flyers

Kites have been on display in our area stores for about two weeks, and today we saw the first ones in the air, a true sign of spring. We had partly cloudy skies, and a temperature high that was in the low 20s with a cold north wind. The wind was in the correct speed range as experts tell us that for ideal kite-flying weather the wind should be seven to twelve miles an hour, but with no mention of what the temperature should be! We usually buy and fly kites early in the spring in Minnesota. It's one of those sports that we engage in to welcome spring and that fits in well between the end of cross-country skiing and the beginning of baseball.

Kites did not originate in Minnesota nor in America, for that matter. China is the birthplace of kites, and from there kite-flying has spread in the past 2,500 years to Korea, Japan, Thailand, India, Europe and finally America.

The kite is really an anchored airplane, and, although the comparison is not exact, the two have much in common. Both the airplane and the kite stay aloft because of the movement of air against or across a nearly plane surface. The airplane has a motor to pull it through and against the air by means of a propeller, thus making its own breeze, and the kite has a string to hold it in position while the wind pushes against its surface. Both actions hold the heavier-than-air objects off the earth, overcoming the force of gravity. In the case of the airplane, the action of the air passing over the curved surface of the wings gives a lift. Kite surfaces are subject to the action of the air moving steadily against the kite, opposed by the pulling of the line in a nearly opposite direction, and the result is support for the kite.

Kite-flying can be a fun, safe sport if one follows a few suggestions. Don't fly your kite in a storm or fog. Stay away from powerlines, TV antennas and trees. Stay five miles from an airport. To put up a kite, don't run with it. Let the wind take it from your hand, or from someone's hand about seventy-five feet away, and hold the kite overhead for you. Keep the wind at your back. Keep your eyes on the kite, so that if the string breaks, you can mark the spot where the kite falls.

Tapping for Maple Syrup

March 1, 1976 March Came in Like a Lion

March came in like a lion so, according to folklore, it will go out like a lamb. Today we had a strong east wind, temperatures in the low 20s, freezing rain and, finally, two inches of new snow.

Four days ago over 100 Canada geese arrived in Carver Park Reserve. These dedicated optimists returned early, certain that spring warmth and new life would come soon. People listen for the geese in late winter, and a surge of inner warmth goes through their bodies, much like a warm south wind across a chilly landscape, when the calls are heard. The first honkers are back, kite flyers have been out, snowdrops have buds, the maple sap ran a few days ago, but we still must wait to shed our heavy parkas and clumsy boots. We remember from years past that March 1 to March 14 is traditionally the snowiest time of the year.

March went out like a lamb.

March 2, 1979 Starlings' Bills

While magnolias bloom in New Orleans, we look for more subtle happenings here to indicate that spring is on its way. Among other things, we have noticed that the starlings' bills , which have been dark since last summer, are now changing to bright yellow as the nesting season approaches. Some starlings have black beaks, some are changing from black to yellow, and some are all yellow. Naturalist Kathy Heidel observed that the bills begin changing color at the base, and lately she noticed some that were yellow at the base and still black on the tips. From early spring until summer the adult starling can be singled out at a distance since it is the only black bird having a rather long, sharp, yellow bill. After the breeding season, the entire bill darkens again until it is nearly black.

There is still another noticeable change in the birds. In winter the starlings have a spotted appearance because the feathers of the head and underparts have white tips, but, as spring approaches, most of the white tips wear off, revealing the bird's glossy black plumage.

Since many people ask how they can keep hoards of starlings from bird feeding stations, I can say that starlings are easily discouraged if you will withhold their favorite foods. You can do this without seriously inconveniencing your other bird guests, too. If you keep on supplying sunflower seeds, whole kernels of corn and hard suet, you can accommodate most birds while discouraging starlings. It should be remembered that, under stress of hunger during very bad weather, starlings will eat anything, however.

I have found a list of appealing foods to use at feeders that are designed especially for starlings, which should not be put out during your anti-starling campaign:

table scraps	mash for chickens
bacon grease	peanut butter
halved apples	mashed potatoes
bread	potato chips
cracked corn	sauerkraut
soaked dogfood	

March 3, 1977 March Snowstorm

March is the time of transition from the cold season to our warm growing season. Although winter's bitter cold has passed, storms and snow are still a part of the first half of the month. Yesterday there was little snow on the ground, but today we are in the midst of a snowstorm that may leave a foot of snow. Nature proves again that this is the snowiest time of the year.

Familiar voices on WCCO Radio are listing the school closings, the most since the big storm in January, 1976. A big snowfall gives us a sense of coziness or camaraderie; coziness, if one can stay home in comfort and just look out, camaraderie, if we make our way to work or attempt to keep appointments. People get a chance to tell how much trouble they had clearing the driveway or walks, shoveling out and pushing the car or just walking to the bus stop.

The snow we are getting is wet and has a high water content. Since forty-five inches is the normal amount the Twin Cities can expect in a winter season, we may be receiving about one-fourth of our normal allotment. Heavy snow can be hazardous to motorists, to people shoveling, to weak roof structures and to wildlife, but it can also be a blessing. About 150,000 acres were burned in Minnesota during the dry year of 1976, and it could be worse in 1977 if we don't get sufficient moisture. Perhaps today's snow will help correct this.

Birdfeeder birds are extremely active picking up cracked corn, millet, sunflower seeds and bits of beef suet. They depend on the feeders until their natural food is easier to find. For the past few days there has been an increase among the horned larks, which are a ground-feeding species. It is difficult for them to find food as they don't come to the feeders. We can be sure, however, that most of our wild friends including the early-arriving horned larks will survive as nature provides them with adaptability for many circumstances.

We received twelve inches of snow today.

March 4, 1977 Bald Eagles

The bald eagle, our national bird, can be seen now in its winter territory along the Mississippi River below Hastings. One of the best locations nearby to observe them is in the Reads Landing area where the Chippewa River flows into the Mississippi. In a short time thir-

Bald Eagle

teen of these magnificent birds with their seven-foot wingspan were seen today.

Because dead fish are the usual food of bald eagles, birds and mammals are rarely attacked unless they are wounded or weakened by disease. Eating dead fish that are found on beaches and river banks, however, has caused many birds to absorb large amounts of pesticides that interfere with their calcium metabolism and result in thin-shelled and often infertile eggs. In presettlement times bald eagles nested in big trees on the shores of nearly every large lake and along rivers throughout the wooded parts of the state, but hunting with guns, disruption of their habitat and now pesticides in the birds' environment have caused them nearly to disappear from Minnesota. The area producing the most young now is the Chippewa National Forest, but the best place to observe eagles is along the lower Mississippi River.

March 5, 1974 Return of the Wood Ducks

The temperature rose to 53°F today. Chipmunks are in the forest, the maple sap is running well, and willow pussies (catkins) are out. I saw my first American robins, male red-winged blackbirds, eastern bluebirds, fox sparrow and a pair of wood ducks, all in one day.

Unquestionably, the drake wood duck is the most beautiful of all wildfowl, with the female also being more colorful than the females of other species. Both are crested, multicolored ducks. The male is patterned in iridescent greens, purples and blues and has a distinctive white chin patch while the duller-colored female has a broad white eye-ring. Weighing one and one-half pounds, they sit lightly on the water with their long tails well above the surface.

Appropriately named, the wood duck is found near wooded lakes and streams, feeding on certain insects and plant materials from duckweeds to acorns, which are crushed in the gizzard. Although woodies winter mainly in southern United States and southward into central Mexico, a few stay in Minnesota. I don't know where the pair I observed this morning came from, but it's nice to have them back.

Wood ducks nest in trees but only in natural cavities in the trunk or large branches. They prefer hollow trees close to water, but, if trees are not available, they will nest further away and will also use nesting boxes set up in the right locations. The hole chosen may be close to or as high as fifty feet above the ground. No outside material is transported to the nest by the bird, but it makes use of any chips or other material that may already be there and mixes down from its breast with it.

During the first of April wood ducks can be seen checking nesting boxes and tree trunks with natural cavities, after which nesting begins. The usual clutch contains fourteen eggs with an incubation period of about thirty days. Males normally desert females at the beginning of incubation, and the females rear their young alone. The young leave the nest soon after hatching, jumping from the nesting cavity to the ground, and in early June we look for broods of very young wood ducks following their mothers through wooded ponds and similar habitats.

Wood Ducks

March 6, 1976 A Welcome Sight

Meadowlarks are sometimes seen in the southern half of Minnesota throughout the winter, but, to my knowledge, none was seen in the Arboretum area this winter, so the two along the roadside snowbanks this afternoon lifted my spirits. I don't know if they were eastern or western meadowlarks because I can only distinguish between the two species by their songs. They look nearly alike, but their songs are different. I hope they can find enough roadside weed seeds to survive until the snow melts and exposes good feeding spots on meadows and prairies.

March 7, 1979 Winter or Spring

Winter is still here, but spring is on its way. Area lakes are covered by over twenty inches of ice, and the snow blanket is about twenty-four inches thick. At Isabella, Minnesota, snow depths average thirty-three inches while Lake Superior still has a good cover of ice. On the other hand, American robins are bunched up in Missouri and will soon be here, a few chipmunks are out, skunk and raccoon tracks are numerous, our country roads are muddy most days, the common crows are returning to northern Minnesota, and American goldfinches are turning more yellow each day.

December 1 to February 28 is the winter season for meteorologists. As a student of nature, I agree, and so our spring season is a week old. The first signs of spring appeared in January, as the days lengthened, but by now the list of signs is long enough to declare the presence of spring. Almost. I try to get outdoors as often as I can escape from the chains that bind me to a pattern of living, partly of my own making and partly the result of our busy society, that keeps me indoors. I may step out only a few feet from our back door, or I may have time to wander only half-a-mile, but I need to get outdoors to keep pace with the awakening season. I may fail to glimpse an event that will have passed tomorrow and that I will have to wait another year to observe.

March 8, 1977 A Certain Feeling

The temperature is 57°F in Hastings and Bethel, 56°F in Duluth, 58°F in International Falls, 82°F in Council Bluffs, Iowa, and 46°F here in the Twin Cities. In our area we still have eight or nine inches of snow, but on this beautiful sunny day it's melting fast.

At 8 a.m. two male red-winged blackbirds were singing "O-ka-leeee" over and over while perched in trees above the feeding station. A little later we heard the first robin singing, and then I saw my first chipmunk of the year. Soon other hikers were reporting them. This is the first day eastern chipmunks have emerged, as far as we know. The first meadowlark was spotted by Kathy Heidel, several birders reported seeing a great blue heron at Hyland Lake Park Reserve, and my students and I saw ants on the sidewalk on the south side of Hopkins Burwell Elementary School.

Orwin Rustad wrote the following phrase concluding his observations for this day: . . . "a feeling spring really moved in." Later I called to ask him what, specifically, that feeling was. He said his impression was triggered by a combination of warmth and high humidity as he could smell the dampness and had a comfortable feeling in being outside. No doubt many people in the Upper Midwest would agree that today they, too, had a feeling that "spring moved in."

March 9, 1978 Ants on the Sidewalk

A high of 39°F was recorded in Minneapolis today. Motorcyclists and bikers were out, and I even saw the top down on a car. We still have about ten inches of snow, and over thirty inches covers the Gunflint Trail area in Cook County. But most of the snow has melted from the sidewalks and other spots close to the south-facing walls of Burwell School in the Hopkins School District. At 1 p.m. I checked these sun-warmed sidewalks for ants and saw six medium-size, black ant workers traveling along a sidewalk groove.

An ant is an insect, by definition, because it has six legs and three body parts (head, thorax, and abdomen), and it belongs to the order *Hymenoptera,* which also includes wasps and bees. About 6,000 different kinds of ants are known, and since they are social insects, they live in colonies and are found all over the world. Each colony has three castes: males, queens and wingless, sterile workers. The males die soon after mating, and the queens shed their wings, form new colonies or enter an established colony. Ants are relatively long-lived insects. The workers may live for three years or more and queens, an average of about twelve years, but males ordinarily live only a few weeks.

The ground is the great winter resort for the majority of northern ants. Snow insulates the ground so that ants are able to hibernate in relatively moderate temperatures and in an environment where moisture and relative humidity are fairly constant. They are exposed less to the rigors of weather than the mammals and birds that remain active through the winter. Below the frost lines ants cluster together in their underground cities and remain quiet until spring comes or winter temperatures are favorable. Most are not in a deep dormancy so could forage at any time during the winter when the surface temperature of the soil rises above freezing. I'm sure that the six black ants I encountered this afternoon were simply taking advantage of a momentarily favorable microclimate and may have been out on the sidewalk on a few previous occasions. But it was the first time I had seen any this year in my constant search for signs of life in the awakening season.

March 10, 1977 Red-winged Blackbirds

Several V-shaped flocks of Canada geese were seen high overhead today, headed northwest. I was able to check with several observers and found that today the migrating Canada geese returned to the Hennepin County Park Reserve. Since the honkers are home, we can now be sure that spring warmth and new life will come. I later saw squadrons of geese flying low over frozen lakes, honking noisily and even landing on ponds where open water occasionally awaited them.

The first common grackle appeared at our feeder. Lesser scaup, eastern bluebirds, a rough-legged hawk and a marsh hawk were also firsts on our spring lists. The spring bird migration has also started in Faribault. A friend who had been watching saw flocks of killdeers, American robins and red-winged blackbirds come in on southeast winds there today.

It was reported that the first flock of red-winged blackbirds arrived in the large marsh off Ferndale Road in Wayzata, and then this afternoon I saw a swift-moving, compact band of about twenty-five adult male red-wings as they passed low and headed for a marsh in Carver Park. I was doubly rewarded when I heard them break forth with their cheery "O-ka-leeee" songs when they landed.

It is not always easy to distinguish among grackles, cowbirds and rusty blackbirds at a glance, but the male red-winged blackbird proclaims his identity from a distance with his solid black plumage and showy scarlet wing patches. We look for these harbingers of spring about the second week in March with the females spotted about a month later. The female looks very different from the male as she is brown with well-defined striping on her lower body. Red-wings prefer to nest in marshes and swamps, but they will nest near any body of water and occasionally have been known to settle in upland pastures. They like to feed in open fields and plowed lands. Although they have been condemned as grain eaters by farmers, only about one-eighth of their whole diet is made up of this food, the remaining food being weed seeds and insects.

The first male red-winged blackbird flocks have appeared in the Arboretum area on the following dates:

March 15, 1968	March 9, 1973	March 21, 1978
March 22, 1969	March 5, 1974	March 19, 1979
March 18, 1970	March 18, 1975	March 18, 1980
March 17, 1971	March 15, 1976	March 1, 1981
March 13, 1972	March 10, 1977	March 14, 1982
		March 2, 1983

One or two of these birds usually show up earlier than these dates at the area feeding stations, and we have also had a few red-wings winter over some years.

Red-winged Blackbird

March 11, 1978 The Sap is Running

The ice was out of Lake Minnetonka on this day 100 years ago after the warmest winter on record. This year our ponds and lakes still have thick ice, but we enjoyed a high temperature of 41°F and saw the sun for a while this afternoon. Spring is moving ahead today with the appearance of the first woodchuck or so-called groundhog, and the first sap is running from the maple trees.

It's sapping and sugaring time in New Hampshire, Vermont and here in Minnesota. The snow may still lie deep in the forests from Quebec and New England to Ontario, Wisconsin and Minnesota, but cold nights and warm days mean that the sap is running. During the past two generations, the art of tapping maple trees and preparing syrup and sugar has been largely forgotten, except by a few who follow this as a trade. Earlier generations looked forward to spring days when the sap would begin to flow, and they and their neighbors could gather for sugaring. Tapping maple trees and making syrup and sugar is an American tradition, and early European settlers learned the art from the local American Indians. Before the 1860s maple products were the principal sweetening material used in the United States, but now Americans like maple products for their unique flavor.

During the summer months sugar is manufactured in the leaves of the maple tree. The process is a complicated one involving the chemical action of water supplied by the soil, carbon dioxide from the air and chlorophyll from the leaf plastids. Within the plastids these raw materials undergo a chemical change with sunlight providing the energy. The result is glucose, a simple sugar that is later stored in the trunk and roots of the tree as starch. By the time the sap drips from the tapholes, the compound has again been transformed; this time into sucrose. Sap contains from 1 to 6 percent of this sugar with water making up the remainder of the volume together with a fractional percentage of organic acids and other compounds that account for the maple flavor.

March 12, 1979 Awakening Woodchuck

Much of a woodchuck's life is spent in hibernation. Unfavorable times are avoided by the ability of this ground-dwelling squirrel to become dormant. Here in our area they hibernate close to six months each year.

The pudgy woodchuck or groundhog does not appear above ground on its official day, February 2, but its own internal clock awakens it in early March when we begin looking for the first one. Yesterday the first one was spotted in a woodpile, sunning itself above the snow covered ground, and since today is sunny also, perhaps it will be seen again.

In early July woodchucks begin to take on weight, acquiring a blanket of fat that becomes nearly one-half inch thick during the next three months and causes the lethargy that is believed to be a motivating factor in hibernation. By late September they are seldom seen as most are already curled up asleep in underground nests. Older, fatter adults are the first to yield to sleepiness, followed by the leaner adults and the young. Sometimes two woodchucks hibernate in the same den.

Before going to sleep for the winter, the woodchuck seals itself in by plugging the hiberating chamber with earth from the main burrow tunnel. The tunnel is usually in a well-protected spot, occasionally beneath the tangled root system of a tree, which makes it almost impossible for a predator to find.

The curled-up woodchuck's body temperature may fall as low as about 38°F, with the heartbeat reduced to about four per minute (seventy-five per minute is normal in summer), and breathing is slowed to about one breath every six minutes. Waking a woodchuck by warming it up requires several hours. In March when they normally emerge from hibernation, it is the largest ones that are first to awaken. Stored body fat has been used to keep the animals alive, and they are now lean. The weight loss averages nearly 40 percent of their previous weight, but they are forced to remain thin for several more weeks as there is little green food available this early in the season.

The woodchuck is the largest member of the squirrel family, and it may weigh up to ten pounds or more as an adult, and measure one and one-half feet long. It feeds on green vegetation and other plant material, consuming as much as a pound of food a day. Clover, alfalfa, peas, beans, corn, melons and apples are favorite foods, to the dismay of gardeners and farmers. They sometimes damage trees by eating the bark. However, their construction of dens that serve as homes for animals that are important in controlling insect pests and rodent populations benefits the wildlife community as a whole.

Woodchucks are found throughout Minnesota at the edge of open woods and especially in hilly areas where they dig an extensive burrow system. Around 700 pounds of subsoil may be removed in the excavation of a single burrow system, contributing to the aeration and mixing of the soil. The burrow system provides refuges and homes for skunks, raccoons, foxes, cottontail rabbits, weasels, chipmunks, white-footed mice, shorttail shrews, pheasants, quail, ruffed grouse and various snakes. Often when areas have been burned over, woodchuck burrows have saved the lives of many animals. Because of their daytime habits, woodchucks are easily observed and provide enjoyment for anyone whose garden, cornfield, or orchard is not in a woodchuck's feeding territory.

The first woodchuck was observed out of hibernation in the Arboretum area on these dates:

March 4, 1973	March 11, 1978
April 2, 1974	March 11, 1979
March 7, 1975	March 3, 1980
March 18, 1976	February 24, 1981
March 11, 1977	March 4, 1982
	March 1, 1983

March 13, 1979 Honey Bees' Cleansing Flights

This afternoon I talked to a fellow amateur radio operator from Lovelady, Texas, on the fifteen meter shortwave band. He mentioned that last week they planted potatoes and radishes, and today he was transplanting tomato plants into the garden. Spring has arrived in Texas and will continue to move northward. He also mentioned that the peach trees were in full bloom, with the pear trees just beginning to blossom. I have read that honey bees visit pear blossoms primarily for pollen and that peach blossoms are so attractive that honey bees visit them from surrounding areas. Honey bees and wild bees are necessary for pollination to make sure a good crop of fruit will follow.

Area honey bees are still living off their honey reserves, and I like to think they are waiting for their chance to get out and collect some early pollen and nectar. It probably will be another month of waiting, but in the last couple days our honey bees have been leaving their hives on short cleansing flights. I found some dead and chilled bees stranded in the snow as far as 300 feet from the hives.

Dead bees in the snow worry new beekeepers who wonder why the bees are in the snow and how they got there. This occurs when winter or early spring sunshine raises the temperature on the inside and the front of the hive sufficiently to cause bees to fly out a short way to void themselves, the excrement causing dark spots on the snow. Bees that fly even a few feet from the hive sometimes become chilled, and in moments their bodies cool down so their wings are unable to get them back to the hive. They drop to the snow, casualties of the cold, but a common occurrence in the bee cycle.

I have seen them out of the hive on sunny days with temperatures in the 20s and 30s even though they must realize it is too cold for them. They often choose to fly rather than foul up the combs and hive when they have been forced to remain inside for a long time. Ideally, they should have a warm flight day every four to six weeks. Beekeepers hope for a few warm days in December, a mid-January thaw and a few more warm days in February and again in March. Confinement for over six weeks becomes serious, and disease becomes a problem if feces are discharged within the hive.

March 14, 1977 Pocket Gopher Mounds

Ruffed grouse have started drumming in the Superior National Forest, and the first American woodcocks just started their display flights in the Arboretum. It was reported that the first pocket gopher mounds were seen in Faribault today.

The pocket gopher's presence is revealed by mounds of earth a few feet apart in grassy areas. They are often confused with mounds deposited by moles, although the earth pushed up by a gopher is well-pulverized rather than in clods. Since gopher mounds are an excellent source of potting soil, we can remember this positive attribute when someone complains that the mounds interfere with haying.

Because pocket gophers are solitary animals, it is only during the breeding season that more than one will be found in a burrow system. This is very extensive since it is through these tunnels that gophers move about and gather much of their food. They are well-suited to subterranean life with large heads, tiny ears and eyes, fur-lined cheek pouches for carrying food, a stocky body, short legs, and strong forefeet and claws for digging. They are usually brown, up to thirteen inches long and weigh up to nineteen ounces. Their food consists of roots, tubers, grasses and succulent parts of other plants, which makes them unwelcome pests in gardens.

Pocket gophers are seldom seen out of their burrows, yet they are active day and night, often tunneling into the snow in winter to have access to vegetation above ground. Now that the frost in the ground is just about gone, I'm sure we will be seeing those gopher-made mounds of earth in our area soon.

March 15, 1977 A Western Meadowlark

Lakes and ponds have a ring of open water around them, and the ice is turning dark. I added two more firsts to my list of 1977 spring signs today — street cleaners were out in Hopkins and I saw new growth on grasses next to the east side of Hopkins West Junior High School. Area

Canada geese and red-winged blackbirds could be heard as I also enjoyed the song of the western meadowlark.

On the prairie the western meadowlarks take the place of robins in leading the morning chorus. As a child my mother lived on a farm in northwestern Minnesota in Kittson County, where she loved the clear flute-like jumble of gurgling notes of the meadowlark. Her enthusiasm for these sounds was so contagious that I have been able to recognize the voice of the western meadowlark and thrill to its unique characteristics since I was a boy.

The distinctive pose of a meadowlark perched on a fence post, its bright yellow breast with bold black V facing the sun and its head thrown back in song, is familiar to many people. One may judge how well the bird and its song have won people's affection by noting the states that have chosen the western meadowlark as their state bird.

Western Meadowlark

These include North Dakota, Nebraska, Kansas, Montana, Wyoming and Oregon.

It is hard to describe the waves of melody that make up the western meadowlarks' songs, and although attempts to express the songs in human words are inadequate, they at least indicate the rhythm and serve to recall them. Phrases like "now's the time to plant the corn," or "U-tah's a pretty place" or "tra la la traleek" help one to remember the songs that are made up of seven to ten notes.

March 16, 1977 First Gopher

For several days a female cardinal has been attacking the Lowry Nature Center windows, trying to drive the "other" cardinal out of her territory. Today a pair of ruddy ducks and a dozen ring-necked ducks arrived in Carver Park — where we saw them on one of the shorebird ponds that has open water now. An afternoon temperature of 45°F and a sunny sky were enough to encourage a gopher to emerge from winter hibernation, the first one I have seen in 1977.

The Minnesota gopher, famous symbol of the University of Minnesota, is actually the thirteen-lined ground squirrel. It is known by several other common names, but its scientific one is *Spermophilus tridecemlineatus.* The gopher, which is found in pastures and other short grass areas, is common throughout the state except in the northeast. Weighing from five to nine ounces, it is seven to eleven inches long, buff-colored with light and dark stripes and rows of spots down its sides and back. Seeds and insects are its main food. While many burrowing animals leave piles of soil about their burrows, gophers scatter the soil widely, so that entrances to burrows appear on the surface only as small holes.

Since my students and I are very interested in animals that spend Minnesota winters in hibernation, we have observed and recorded over the years that the gophers in the Arboretum area become quite scarce in October although a few may keep appearing in November. Apparently these are the younger and thinner ones who are active longer as they try to accumulate fat on their bodies.

Some facts, which I have learned by reading several sources, provide information about them: A gopher plugs the burrow opening before beginning its long sleep, then curls into a ball, nose touching its belly and tail over its head. The heartbeat drops from a normal of about 200 per minute to an average of seventeen beats, and respiration is reduced to as low as seven per minute. Oxygen consumption is decreased to about 7 percent of the amount used when it is active. At the same time the body temperature sinks to 37°F. Severe cold with freezing temperatures penetrating deep into the soil can awaken them from their dormancy several times during the winter. This causes their body temperature to rise and prevents their freezing to death, but unusually warm temperatures may also awaken them occasionally.

The first gopher (thirteen-lined ground squirrel) was observed out of hibernation in the Arboretum area on these dates:

March 14, 1973	March 16, 1978
March 17, 1974	March 31, 1979
April 6, 1975	April 7, 1980
March 21, 1976	March 2, 1981
March 16, 1977	March 22, 1982
	April 1, 1983

March 17, 1974 Scarlet Cup Fungus

Mycology is the branch of botany dealing with fungi. About this time of the year several of my naturalist friends and I become active amateur field mycologists in our search for a cup fungus that, like the skunk cabbage among flowering plants, is one of the harbingers of spring. The fungus is the scarlet cup (*Sarcoscypha coccines*) that we saw today for the first time.

The cup structure is the spore-producing part of this fungus species. The fruiting bodies range from saucer to cup shape and are roughly the size of a quarter to a silver dollar, with a white exterior and sometimes a short stalk. The inner surface of the cup is deep red, which makes it striking at this time of the year as it contrasts with old brown leaves, green mosses, the remaining snow or the dark forest soil. On an early spring day a few years ago, I saw at least twenty-five scarlet, shallow cups in a small maple-basswood forest near the Arboretum, each one attached to a fallen branch that was partly buried in the humus. They are most commonly found through April near basswood trees, singly or several on a buried stick.

The edible qualities of the scarlet cup are unknown, and it is not recommended that anyone try eating it.

March 18, 1978 Return of the First Great Blue Heron

First great blue herons returned to the Arboretum area:

March 27, 1971	March 17, 1975
March 21, 1972	March 19, 1976

March 26, 1973	March 8, 1977
March 7, 1974	March 18, 1978

Today's temperature highs in the 40s brought back the first great blue herons. They always return to their breeding range and, specifically, to their nesting rookeries early in the season. The great blue heron, or "blue crane" as it is often called, is the largest and best known of American herons. Like most of the heron species, it is very sociable, preferring to nest in congested communities that vary in size from a few pairs to hundreds of birds.

They are stately, graceful birds, flying with slow steady wingbeats, necks drawn in and legs stretched out behind. They stand over three feet tall, with much of their height made up of long legs and a long neck, and have wings that measure six feet from tip to tip. The blue-gray color with largely white neck and head and six-inch yellow bill are distinguishing characteristics in addition to their height. They seldom weigh more than seven pounds.

Many times while vacationing on the shores of beautiful Lake George in Hubbard County, our family has seen a great blue heron standing motionless on a distant point, silhouetted on the shore against the sky. Its artistic outline adds a touch of mystique to the broad expanse of water and dark forest.

Although I have grown up thinking of great blue herons as belonging to the northern Minnesota lakes, we also see many in the southern part of our state. In fact, the largest nesting colonies are found in the southeastern and central regions. As the nesting gets underway in April, the large nests, loosely constructed of sticks, are added to and used from year to year. The nests are built in groups, sometimes as many as a hundred or more, usually in the tops of tall trees in some isolated location but occasionally in shrubs or concealed in a reedbed. Three to five eggs are normally laid, and the incubation period is about twenty-eight days. Although herons nest in groups, they ordinarily feed alone, spreading out from the home heronry as they fly many miles to procure food for their young. When they find food, they gather enough to fill their large crops to capacity and then return to feed their offspring by a process of regurgitation.

As it hunts, the heron is often seen standing in shallow water, motionless as it patiently waits for the approach of prey. When an unwary fish or frog comes within striking distance, the heron's sharp beak shoots forward and downward with lightning speed, seldom missing its mark as the fish or other animal is seized crosswise between the mandibles. Hunting, which may be done by day or night, also involves stalking on dry land for field mice, shrews, grasshoppers and other insects, or the bird may alight on water and swim for its food when necessary.

One of the best-known colonies was once located on Crane Island in Lake Minnetonka where this heavily wooded, eleven-acre island was home to a mixed colony of herons and double-crested cormorants until 1907. When a number of people built summer residences on the island that year, the entire mixed colony moved to another and larger island not far away.

We have seen great blue herons in the Arboretum area in November, but usually most of them have left by September for places such as Texas, Mexico and Panama, with only a few stragglers occasionally seen in the southeastern part of the state during the winter.

March 19, 1978 Arrival of the First Robins

Dates of first American robin arrivals in the Arboretum area area:

March 13, 1971	March 21, 1975
March 14, 1972	March 18, 1976
March 5, 1973	March 8, 1977
March 5, 1974	March 19, 1978

For many people the sight or sound of a robin, now officially called the American robin, signals the beginning of spring. Several people in this area spotted some today, just as I was beginning to think that the robins were going to be abnormally late this year, held up by the snow in Iowa and Missouri. Although their arrival depends largely upon the weather conditions, they are usually here by mid-March. They arrived today, Palm Sunday, together with other obvious signs of spring such as tulips showing tender four-inch leaves, snow disappearing fast, country roads oozing with mud and people flying kites.

When robins come, they feed on wild berries such as those of the Virginia creeper and the sumacs, but as soon as the frost is out of the ground, they begin eating earthworms and insects. The males arrive first but do not sing much until their mates appear. After the first few, which may have spent the winter not far off, arrive, the real migrants from the South appear in large flocks and continue to pass through in successive waves until the middle of April as the earlier, now-resident birds settle down to domestic duties.

The male robin is more sharply colored than the female. His head is black; back, slate-brown; and breast, a brilliant red-brown. The throat is white streaked with black, and he has a white ring around his eye with a white spot above it and a yellow beak. The female is similarly marked but with a paler back and breast and no black on her head.

The American robins winter chiefly in the southern part of their breeding range that includes the Gulf States, Florida and northeastern

Mexico. In limited numbers they sometimes winter in the southern part of Minnesota in sheltered areas and have occasionally been seen as far north as the Lake Superior region. I have received reports of robins wintering in large numbers along the shore of Lake Superior from Duluth to Grand Marais, where the mountain ash grows and its fruit can provide food throughout the winter. We have had a robin or two wintering here, where they were observed feeding on crabapples and Russian olive fruit. When they do winter over, their numbers are often reduced later in the season when the food supply fails as the severe cold and deep snows make living conditions difficult.

Their food consists of about 43 percent animal matter, including May beetles, corn weevils, cutworms, armyworms, cabbageworms,

American Robin

codling moth larvae, white grubs, grasshopers, crickets and earthworms, and about 57 percent vegetable matter. More than one-half of the vegetable is fruit, and four-fifths of this is wild. In more densely populated areas where wild fruits have disappeared or the crop has failed, the robins can damage cultivated fruits. We should note, however, that it has been proved that robins are far more beneficial than damaging to the farmer and gardener when they continue to destroy many noxious insects throughout the year.

March 20, 1978   Yellow Crocuses

Astronomers tell us that spring began in the northern hemisphere at 5:34 p.m. today. There is an exact second each year when only a tick of the clock separates spring and winter. This second occurs on March 20 or 21, the vernal equinox, when the sun reaches the celestial equator, an imaginary line through the sky above the earth's equator. As the sun's center crosses this line, the season officially changes. From now until June 21, nights in the northern hemisphere continue to grow shorter than twelve hours and days to grow longer.

Our seasonal changes are regulated by the movement of our planet in its annual orbit. Tilted on its axis, the earth presents its southern half and then its northern half to the direct rays of the sun in the course of a yearly tour. As the tilted earth swings through space in its half-billion-mile annual orbit, it causes the days to shorten or lengthen and the seasons to change. The orbit around the sun (a star) is so enormous that successive days vary by only about two minutes in a twenty-four hour period, about one minute in the morning and one minute at night; however, these minutes that are gained or lost are among the most important for all life. Their steady advance or decline affects the sprouting, flowering, fruiting, migration, courtship and mating of our planet's living things.

If the axis of the earth were straight up and down rather than leaning 23½° to one side, there would be no spring, summer, fall or winter. The earth would have varied climates but no varied seasons. In any given spot on earth during twelve months of the year, the seasons would be the same. It's interesting that there are always twelve hours of sunshine on the equator.

Although officially spring began the same moment today in all parts of the northern hemisphere, conditions were different in all parts of the country. Azaleas are blooming hundreds of miles south of us, but we had sunshine, rain and snow today, along with the return of the first migratory Canada geese and flocks of American robins and the blooming of the first crocuses. Since spring development advances north in the United States at an average of about fifteen miles a day, the azaleas will be blooming here in two months.

To many people, gardeners or not, a crocus is a synonym for spring. A friend from Waconia called to say that on the east side of their house, yellow crocuses began to bloom today, the first day of spring, astronomically speaking. The crocuses came into bloom in this location on March 10 last year and have even been known to begin blooming in April during a late spring. There are also species that bloom in fall here, and some that flower in winter in mild climates. All are wildflowers native to southern Europe and Asia Minor.

Usually hybrid bulbs or corms are sold for fall planting in Minnesota, and plants grow about six inches tall with flower colors ranging from white to yellow to blue. Spring blooming crocuses should be planted in September for best results. It's very simple to plant the bulbs two to six inches apart and cover with about four inches of soil. Some gardeners dig up and separate the bulbs in early summer every three years, but this is not necessary as undisturbed clumps, fed with a little fertilizer, will increase in beauty from year to year. For the earliest spring bloom, crocuses should be planted in a sunny protected spot and for later bloom, on the north side of a wall, hedge, or building, in very light shade or even in the lawn. Then, however, the first lawn mowing should be delayed until the leaves of the crocuses die.

March 21, 1978 Killdeers Arrive

More American robins have arrived, the first flock of red-winged blackbirds was spotted, and Canada geese in pairs are checking out nesting sites. In the Arboretum snowdrops are up, with one plant already budding, and the maple sap is running. The snow was melting fast under a blue sky and with a 50°F temperature this afternoon. Surrounded by these signs, I still had a feeling that something was missing from the spring scene. It's another early harbinger that has to appear in sound or sight before spring can move ahead.

Late this afternoon I finally heard the sound. It was a bird repeating its name as a call — "killdeer, killdeer, killdeer." Most early spring observers first only hear the lonely-sounding overhead cry of a solitary, unseen killdeer, but I was fortunate to hear and to see seven killdeers in a group.

The killdeer is easily recognized by its distinct color pattern. It is olive-brown on its upper body and pure white on the lower, with two black bands across the breast. It is the size of a robin, with long legs that are used extensively for running. When it runs, the bird holds its body rigid, and its legs are a blur of motion. When standing, it often teeters or bobs. Although the killdeer is a shorebird, it is often found far from water in plowed fields, pastures, golf courses and short-grass prairies. Killdeers are common throughout the state except in deep forest areas.

The early returning birds frequently encounter belated winter weather with snow and freezing days and nights, which they endure surprisingly well, but since their diet is made up almost entirely of insects, finding food on cold spring days is a real job for them.

First killdeer observed in the Arboretum area:

March 26, 1971	March 14, 1975	March 18, 1979
March 18, 1972	March 18, 1976	March 16, 1980
March 12, 1973	March 11, 1977	March 15, 1981
March 6, 1974	March 21, 1978	February 25, 1983

March 22, 1978 The Mourning Cloak Butterfly

About ten years ago someone first alerted me to some butterfly species that spend the winter as adults in hibernation. On extremely warm winter or early spring days, it is possible to observe one flying about the landscape, and today a mourning cloak butterfly was out under a sunny sky with a few clouds and a high temperature of 49°F. Half the area is free of snow cover now, robins are busy hunting for food on area lawns, aspens are budding like pussy willows, and a friend reported that the skunk cabbage plants have started blooming in Minnehaha Park.

About 140 species of butterflies are found in Minnesota of which seven are known to hibernate in the adult stage. These seven include the painted beauty, red admiral, question mark, comma, mourning cloak, Compton's tortoise-shell and Milbert's tortoise-shell. They hibernate under loose bark, in hollow logs and trees, under eaves or in buildings, and they appear on spring days when the temperature reaches 50°F. These adults feed on nectar of flowers, tree sap and decayed fruit.

The mourning cloak is a long-lived, hearty species that is plentiful throughout Minnesota and practically everywhere throughout the eastern half of the United States and Canada. It is also a familiar sight in many temperate areas of Asia and Europe, and in England it is called the Camberwell beauty.

It is an exceptionally beautiful butterfly, dark velvety-brown with a yellow-gold border on its wings and blue dots on the margins between the brown and gold. The wing spread is about three inches. Like all butterflies, it has four stages in its life cycle:

egg — the female lays eggs on willow and elm trees and sometimes poplar species
larva — (caterpillar stage) usually feeds on leaves of willow or elm
pupa — (chrysalis) very angular and black with tawny spots
adult —

The first new adult generation emerges in late June or early July, and the second-generation adults appear in September. Some fly about through the month of October, and I have occasionally seen them as late as mid-November. They then hibernate and appear again in March (sometimes February) during warm, sunny weather. However, it is not until mid-April that they appear with regularity. They can then be seen sailing about leafless trees and shrubs of wooded ravines and forest clearings. These are the ones that produce a new generation.

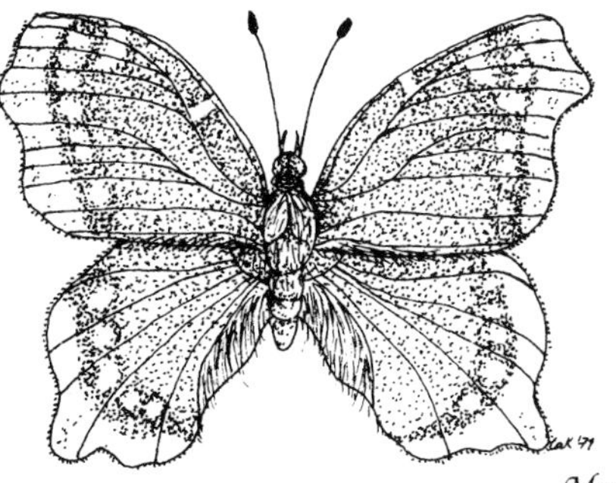

Mourning Cloak Butterfly

March 23, 1978 Singing Robins

To see a robin may be the sign of spring most people anticipate and then enjoy telling others about. Some, however, regard the rich caroling of the male, usually from high in a leafless tree, as the true herald of spring. Today, with twenty-nine inches of ice still covering Lake Waconia, I heard an American robin singing and saw my first meadowlark of the year. The robin's song consisted of clear rising and falling phrases with the words "cheer-up, cheer-up, . . . cheerily." I have been hearing at least two distinct call notes since the robins first arrived March 19, but this is the first singing I have heard.

March 24, 1976 Sound of the Woodcocks

Our Arboretum area landscape is now about 95 percent free of snow, and a pair of pintails and the first belted kingfisher arrived today. I returned to these spring-like signs after I had led a bird hike and taught a unit on stream life at the Environmental Learning Center near Isabella where three feet of snow still covers the ground. The first robins and killdeers just returned to Isabella, so our area is far ahead in spring development. There was something special about travelling south into an area where spring had moved in.

The ground is thawing and unlocking the food supply of earthworms and insects for the American woodcock, so we weren't totally surprised to hear the first "peenting" sounds this evening. Woodcocks are stocky birds, with long bills, short necks and a deadleaf pattern on their upper bodies, who begin their calling and display flights soon after they return from the southern states.

The arrival of spring is widely announced by the noisy courtship displays and vocalizations of birds, and the American woodcock adds its special music at a quiet time of day. Its performance usually begins soon after sunset and ceases when the glow in the western sky disappears, only to begin again in the morning twilight or on moonlight nights when it continues through the night. A person wanting to attend a woodcock concert must find the correct habitat. Woodcocks nest in wooded or brushy uplands not far from wet lowlands, and they perform their courtship displays on open pastures or fields. The bottom lands of the Minnesota and Mississippi Rivers provide good observation spots.

The loud nasal peenting sound is uttered every few seconds as the woodcock struts about on the ground. Suddenly he rises and flies off at an angle, circling higher and higher until he reaches a height of perhaps 200 to 300 feet and looks like a speck in the sky. The upward flight is accompanied by twittering musical notes, probably produced by the vibration of three outer wing feathers that are narrow and stiff. Both sexes have the same wing structure, but practically all records assume that the bird in the air is the male, performing for the benefit of his mate. As the bird flutters back down to earth, a series of chipping whistles completes its elaborate performance. He soon begins his peenting notes again, and the whole act is repeated until it is time to quit for the night or morning.

March 25, 1976 Song Sparrows

A cheerful song that often begins with three clear notes, "Sweet, sweet, sweet," followed by a lower one and then a rapid jumble of sounds was heard today in our area for the first time this spring.

The music, which is familiar to bird observers, comes from the song sparrow that lives on forest edges and thickets near wetland areas. It is a small bird with a brown upper body, heavy brown streaks on the white underparts and a prominent central breast spot.

My field notebook tonight has many entries from this 60°F. warm day in the awakening season. Some observations include:

First song sparrows return
First wood ducks appear
Build-up in the number of common grackles
Juncos singing, with hundreds seen in area
Open spots in the ponds
Canada geese very noisy and active
Both eastern and western meadowlarks singing
Maple sap running well
Swamp tree (cricket) frogs started calling

March 26, 1978 First Bluebirds

Naturalist Dale Rock spotted two eastern bluebirds next to the Lowry Nature Center building. We have been looking for them the last few days, and I was glad to hear that at least two have returned.

The female is a dull version of the male, which has a bright, completely blue back and rusty throat and breast. This beautiful bird is a favorite of many people, but in the past twenty-five years bluebirds have seldom been seen for reasons not altogether clear. Competition for nest sites from house sparrows or starlings may be a critical factor, together with spraying practices and the subsitution of metal fence posts for wooden ones.

Eastern bluebirds are observed along roadsides, in farmyards, on farmlands with scattered trees or old orchards and in the pine barrens of northern Minnesota. They nest in natural tree cavities, old woodpecker holes, wood fence posts and bird boxes. Insects make up the greatest part of their diet, but fruits and seeds are eaten during the months when insects are scarce.

March 27, 1978 Blooming Common Snowdrops

An Arboretum gardener and I are constantly on the lookout for the first snowdrop flowers at this time of the year. It's the first perennial flower to bloom here each year and signifies the beginning of the growing season. Three of the inch-wide, white, bell-like flowers opened today, announcing the end of winter and the beginning of the gardening year.

In gardening books snowdrops are described as hardy bulbs with nodding flowers that bloom while lingering patches of snow are still seen. The type grown in the Arboretum is called the common snowdrop (*Galanthus nivalis*) and is native to Europe and the Caucasus region. Each plant has two slender leaves about three to eight inches long from which the flowers rise. A bloom period of about two or three weeks is expected, and then the leaves will wither in late spring.

Snowdrops are easy to grow and will increase naturally when comfortably located. They like rich soil that retains moisture in a lightly shaded location, such as beneath deciduous trees or shrubs. The bulbs can be planted three inches deep and two inches apart in large patches in early fall and then left undisturbed for years.

March 28, 1976 Blooming Hepatica

The skunk cabbage is in full bloom at Minnehaha Park in Minneapolis where it grows in seepage areas, but, unfortunately, we don't

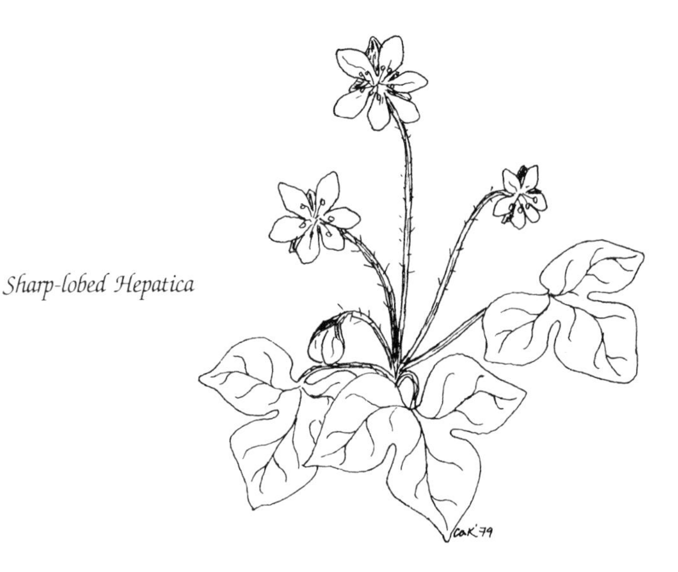

Sharp-lobed Hepatica

have the correct habitat in the Arboretum for it. This odd wildflower has a pointed brown or purplish spathe four to six inches high that encloses a club-like stem on which there are tiny flowers. The plant has a distinct skunk-like odor. The sharp-lobed hepatica is flourishing in the maple-basswood forest and came into bloom today. Hepatica flowers are white, pink or purple and appear on three-inch fuzzy stems above last year's partly dead leaves before the new leaves appear. The name hepatica is derived from the Greek word meaning liver, in reference to the shape of the leaves.

It must be spring. All the obvious signs are present. Robins sang their rain songs, and several were seen on lawns hunting for food. Leopard frogs are on the move, nightcrawlers are out, the rhubarb is up about an inch, Canada geese are flying, and mourning doves are calling. Late this afternoon a good steady spring rain began.

March 29, 1979 First Spring Thunderstorm

March 23, 1975 March 26, 1977
March 19, 1976 April 3, 1978

Meteorologist Bruce Watson, with his accumulated Minnesota weather data, has stated that in the Twin Cities area we can expect an average of thirty-eight days with thunderstorms annually. International Falls can expect thirty thunderstorm days and Rochester forty-one days during which thunderstorms are likely to occur.

A thunderstorm is a towering cloud system with violent upward and downward air currents, containing enormous amounts of energy that are disbursed in various forms of lightning, thunder, wind, rain and hail. It is formed under unstable atmospheric conditions when warm moist air is lifted vertically into cooler air at great heights. The conditions were right today, and early this evening the first spring thunderstorm brought us about one-half inch of rain.

As the air temperature rose during the day from an overnight low of 27°F, the sugar maples ran well. We still have twenty-one inches of ice covering Lake Waconia, but many gulls have returned and must be counting on sunny weather and warm rains to melt the ice soon. Today was cloudy with an east wind, and weatherwise people were expecting rain. The robins were expecting it too as I heard them singing "cheer-up, cheer-up . . ." for the first time this year. Many birders interpret this as the robins' rain song.

March 30, 1978 Where the Grasses Grow Green

These are the dates that I first observed grasses turning green on south slopes and in ditches in the Arboretum area:

April 9, 1971	April 18, 1975
April 16, 1972	March 26, 1976
March 30, 1973	March 25, 1977
April 12, 1974	March 30, 1978

To winter weary eyes, big patches of green look good and can lift one's spirits. For several years I have been recording the day when green grasses, probably of several species, are first noticed on south slopes and in roadside ditches. These green carpets remind us that the earth on which we live is green and that the green comes from plants that are essential to the life and welfare of mankind. People and animals could not exist on this planet without the green coloring found in plants and without the activities of the leaves containing this pigment.

Green plants possess the ability to manufacture food from raw materials derived from the soil and the air as they make their own food inside their bodies. Photosynthesis is the production of sugar (food) from carbon dioxide and water in the presence of chlorophyll, the green coloring matter in plants. The sunlight is the energy source, and oxygen is released in the process. All living things require energy for growth and to maintain life. This energy comes from the chemical energy in the food consumed, and the food in turn has its origin in photosynthesis. Photosynthesis has sometimes been called the most important chemical process known to man.

What else happenened today? The last common redpoll left, juncos arrived in great numbers on their way north together with the first tree swallows, blue-winged and green-winged teal, the first lesser scaup, shovelers and hooded mergansers. In addition, a bat was spotted flying over Lake Calhoun in Minneapolis this evening, and this was a good day to cut pussy-willow branches.

March 31, 1976 Common Snipe

You, snipe, "winnowing" in flight,
making a whistling sound with your wings and tail,
your display flight is like the first crocus,
a sure sign of spring.

JIM GILBERT

MARCH

March is the peak of the snow season. It's the time of transition from the cold season to the warm season, and by the end of the month, storms bring rain more often than snow.

33 34 35 36

Historically, the first three weeks of March are the snowiest of the year. **(33)** With melting, temporary ponds are part of the March landscape. **(34)** The first migratory robins **(35)** and red-winged blackbirds **(36)** return by mid-month.

37

38

39

40

The first migratory Canada geese return. **(37 & 38)** Canada geese are paired and claim nesting territories early. **(39)** Students check for the first sidewalk ants of the awakening season. **(40)**

The sap is running. **(41)** It's time to tap the maple trees and catch a drop of the sweet sap. **(42)** Maple trees run best when night temperatures are around 25°F and days reach about 45°F. Close to 40 gallons of maple sap must be collected and evaporated to produce one gallon of syrup. **(43 & 44)**

45

46

47

In late March, pussy willow twigs are showy. **(45)** The scarlet cup fungus seen in maple-basswood forests is a harbinger of spring. **(46)** Snowdrops bloom as lingering patches of snow are still seen. **(47)** Crocuses bloom in protected spots. **(48)**

48

APRIL

Mild days with occasional rain or snow in preparation for the new growing season characterize the month of April.

49

50

51

52

In April: Garter snakes come out of hibernation to bask in the sun. **(49)** We still can expect snow. **(50)** Ice can form on open ponds again. **(51)** But Canada geese are nesting. **(52)**

In April: Pasqueflowers bloom on prairies. **(53)** Snow trillium **(54)** and bloodroots **(55)** bloom in forests. Farmers begin working the soil for spring planting. **(56)**

57

58

Ice on shallow ponds and marshes goes out first. Soon painted turtles are sunning. **(57)** Ice generally leaves most Minnesota lakes in April. **(58)**. American toads start to call. **(59)** Snowshoe hares in northern Minnesota are now brown. **(60)**

59

60

61

62

63

At the end of April or early in May, in the U of M Arboretum and area, sugar maples bloom **(61)** magnolias have large showy flowers **(62)**, we enjoy the pink Nanking cherry blossoms **(63)**, and the overall landscape is softened by green grasses and newly emerging leaves. **(64)**

64

For several years we have checked the sky diligently night after night, after the spring thaws, to pick up the "winnowing" sound of the first returning snipe. Tonight the first snipe was heard high over the Arboretum under a colorful display of the aurora borealis. It was flying in a broad circle so that the direction of the sound continually shifted. This began the season of the always delightful but weird wind music. Soon we will hear the snipes during the day and see their lofty flights that are made up of a series of lengthy undulations or swoops.

All through the spring migration and nesting season we may hear the winnowing sound of the snipe's courtship flight that, some biologists have suggested, is indulged in by both sexes. Just as the bird is about to swoop downward, the tail is spread to its fullest, and the bleating or winnowing sound accompanies the descent. The sound is never produced except on the downward rush with the tail widespread.

The common or Wilson's snipe is a nine-inch long, brown shorebird with a striped back and long bill. It is an early migrant, leaving its winter quarters as the frost begins to go out of the ground in the north. A few birds may winter in the southeastern quarter of Minnesota in the valleys, but the winter range is usually the southern United States and through the West Indies, Central America and into Brazil.

Bloodroot

April 1, 1976 Blooming Trees

Lotus Lake in Chanhassen lost its ice cover today. Comma butterflies were on the wing, garter snakes were sunning themselves, and fox sparrows were scratching in forest leaves for food.

Although there are no leaves on the hazelnut shrubs yet, I did notice that the male catkins are extending and about to shed pollen, and the tiny scarlet, star-like female flowers are appearing. These two signs of spring are some assurance that there will be hazelnuts in late summer.

All trees and shrubs have flowers. Most of these flowers are not as showy as apple blossoms or roses, but they appear for the same purpose: to produce seed for another generation. Trees and shrubs produce many times more fruits and seeds than are necessary, another example, not of nature's waste but of providing for animal life.

Quaking aspens, which are the most widely distributed trees in North America, and silver maples are both starting to bloom. Both trees bloom before they leaf out each spring. Male and female aspen flowers appear in drooping grayish catkins with each sex on different trees, but the small yellowish-green male and female flowers of the silver maple may both appear on the same tree or each on different trees.

April 2, 1974 Influx of Spring Birds

Today in Carver Park Reserve we saw an Eastern phoebe, golden-crowned kinglet, several song sparrows, a garter snake and a woodchuck for the first time this year. We don't have much open water yet, but in one small area in Sunny Lake that had been kept open by a bubbler I counted a pair of canvasbacks, five shovelers, seven wood ducks, nine lesser scaup and sixty-two ring-necked ducks in among hundreds of Canada geese and mallards. Many of the geese and mallards had spent the winter here, but the others are migrants.

There's still snow on the north slopes, but change and expectation are in the air. One evidence of the expectation is the large number of robins, juncos and ducks that have arrived the last two days and are waiting for more spring-like weather before continuing their journey.

April 3, 1978 Calling Cricket Frogs

The swamp cricket frogs (*Pseudacris nigrita*), also called swamp tree frogs, can now be heard calling regularly from grassy ponds and roadside ditches although I heard them first on March 27. The great volume of the mating trills produced by these tiny frogs, which have bodies a little over an inch long, suggests that it is coming from much larger frogs. The sound is like that of a metallic clicker.

It's the males that call, and I have watched them at night with the aid of hip boots and a flashlight. Only their tiny heads with extended bubble-like throat sacs stick up above the water. With many males calling in a small pond, their combined chorus is continuous and quite deafening, but in the daytime the slightest disturbance causes them to remain quiet. A person walking near a pond of singing frogs causes the chorus to stop short. However, if one is perfectly quiet and doesn't move, soon an individual frog will begin singing, and in a few seconds the whole chorus will again be in full voice.

April 4, 1977 Whistling Swans

Lake Waconia is about 75 percent clear of ice. As big wet snowflakes fell at 7:20 a.m., more than sixty whistling swans took off from the lake and headed north with muffled musical whistles.

People in widely separated areas saw these majestic, white, long-necked waterfowl today, also, so I can accurately report that whistling swans are migrating through Minnesota. They migrate by day and night, flying in long V's from their winter range on the Atlantic coast where they are most abundant between Maryland and North Carolina. Whistling swans breed on the seacoast within the Arctic Circle.

Trumpeter swans are the largest North American waterfowl, and whistling swans, the second. The whistlers are snow white with black

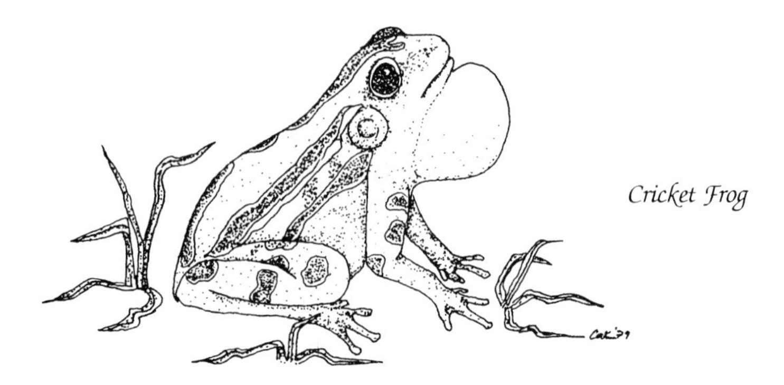

Cricket Frog

feet and bills, and the adult's black bill often shows a bright yellow spot at the base. They weigh ten to nineteen pounds and have a seven-foot wingspan.

When traveling long distances, whistling swans fly in V-shaped wedges in the same manner as geese and for the same reason. The resistance of the air is less as each bird flies in the widening wake of its predecessor. The leader has the hardest work to do as he or she "breaks the trail" but is relieved at intervals and drops back into the flock to rest.

April 5, 1972 Sugarbush Learning Experiences

We still have snow on the north slopes, and honeycombed ice covers Green Heron Pond except for a ring of open water, but there are signs of spring. Red-winged blackbirds can be heard, wood ducks are back, eastern bluebirds are singing, garter snakes have been out to bask in the sun the last two weeks, willow catkins are furry, and today I saw the first active leopard frog.

From a below-freezing temperature early this morning, we reached a high of 49°F in the Arboretum sugarbush, and the maple trees ran freely. For a few moments this afternoon, I stopped to watch Marion Couper, a devoted Arboretum volunteer, work with a group of young girls. She showed them how one identifies a maple, taps a tree and collects the watery sap. Her enthusiasm rubbed off on the girls as the group explored the sugarbush, eagerly caught a drop of sap on their fingers to taste and ended up at the sugarhouse to savor a small cup of the final product, the amber-colored syrup. Several thousand people, mostly elementary school students, had the opportunity to visit the sugarbush this spring where they learned about the art of tapping maple trees and preparing syrup.

April 4, 1972

Tapping of sugar maples began on March 13, and April 13 was the last day for syrup production. We have had a long season this year.

April 6, 1978 Life of a Wood Tick

The ice went out of the Freshwater Biological Institute marsh near Lake Minnetonka and several other local ponds today. Area lakes have rings of open water, and red-breasted mergansers, fish-eating, diving ducks, are already making use of open spots. For the first time this year I heard a common snipe "winnowing" in flight. Eastern phoebes are returning, robins began hunting for earthworms on lawns, leopard frogs started calling, and the first active wood ticks were found.

There is a superstition that wood ticks crawl up trees and drop down on people and animals. Another supersition contends that ticks twist their mouthparts into the bite wound and have to be unscrewed to be removed; neither is true. In the adult stage, ticks attack people and are common in spring and early summer but are seldom encountered after the first of August. The name wood tick is a poor one, too, because they are grassland animals. After an adult has mated, it climbs a blade of grass, sometimes as high as eighteen inches above the ground, and sits in the sun, hooked front legs held out like the claws of a crab as it looks for big game, perhaps a deer or a person. As a person walking through the tall grass brushes against the waiting hooks, the wood tick reacts instantly, releases its hold on the grass blade and latches on to the clothing or skin. It then crawls up looking for a quiet spot such as legs, stomach or hairline, and soon it drives in a probe and begins drawing blood.

Wood ticks are flattened, gray-brown, tough-skinned creatures with eight large legs and bodies about three-sixteenths of an inch long. They have a life cycle of a year during which young ticks become adults by fall, and those that survive the winter reproduce the next spring. Some biologists believe that if adults don't find a host, they may live for nearly three years. Although both female and male adults feed, the male can hold only a little blood. If the female is left undisturbed on an animal, she will expand as she draws blood, and when she is the size of a junebug, drop off to lay eggs; 3,000 to 5,000 of them. Two stages of immature wood ticks follow the egg stage, and in each stage they must find a host, usually mice, on which to feed. For this they lurk low in the grasslands and with their little hooked legs catch rides on their hosts.

Because wood ticks can bite without being felt, a person is often surprised to find one attached to his body and must examine himself carefully at night before retiring if in a tick-infested area. Among the animals, dogs, especially, must be examined for ticks during the tick season. If a tick is found attached to a person or a dog, it must be grasped close to the skin with a tweezer or tissue paper and then pulled off. Since the mouth parts are short, if this procedure is followed, they will not be left in the bite wound. Untreated tick wounds often become infected, so it is important to apply iodine or a similar disinfectant. Ticks should never be destroyed by crushing them in the fingers as infection can occur.

Since ticks can carry diseases, prompt removal of them can help prevent infection. In some parts of the country, they can carry Rocky Mountain spotted fever, which is not usually serious if treated promptly; its symptoms — reddening of the eyes and blotches on the extremities — are hard to ignore. There have been a few cases in South Dakota and Iowa, but Minnesota has had none in several years. I read that the ticks must be attached for four to six hours before they can transmit the disease.

The simplest way to avoid wood ticks is to stay out of their habitat, which is the long-grass areas, although this isn't absolutely foolproof either; they sometimes ride into homes on pets and children. When walking in tall grass during the wood tick season, a person must watch his legs and remove the ticks as soon as they are detected. Long pants should be tucked into socks or boots. Often ticks can be felt and removed before they grab hold, and if a person is a preservationist like me, he will return the wood ticks to their habitat.

April 7, 1979 Spring Chores

Lawns should be cleaned up in the spring, and for this Dr. Snyder recommends using a broom type of lawn rake and avoiding the use of a steel rake that digs into the soil and exposes the roots. Some people took advantage of the 44°F high temperature today wanting to be among the first to rake and clean up their yards, but we are waiting for a few days as our lawn is still quite wet. There is some lingering snow left from the sixty-eight and one-half inches the Twin Cities area received this past winter.

It's interesting to note that the cherry trees, magnolia, and dogwoods are now blooming in Washington, D.C. Most of these plants could never survive a Minnesota winter. We may not have big splashes of colorful blooms at this time, but we do have skunk cabbages, snowdrops and a few crocuses.

April 8, 1979 Fox Sparrows and Sapsuckers Arrive

Fox sparrows, one of the eighteen or so species of sparrows we see in this area each year, and yellow-bellied sapsuckers, one of seven locally seen woodpecker species, appeared today. Both species are migrating through.

The fox sparrows' summer home is the dense coniferous forests in Canada. In our area we see them twice each year for a few weeks as they travel from their wintering range near the Gulf Coast to their breeding grounds in spring and back again in the fall. They are one of the largest sparrows and are easy to recognize with their bold, brown-streaked underparts, bright orange-brown rumps and tails and a central breast spot like the song sparrow. They scratch in forest floor leaves with both feet and often make so much noise that one expects to find a large animal.

A few yellow-bellied sapsuckers may attempt to winter in Minnesota, but most go south to the Gulf Coast, Panama and the West Indies. In the summer they are residents throughout the state although I have seen very few in our area other than during migration times. They seem to like the mixed deciduous and conifer forests north of us. I have observed them and seen evidence of their work in the Itasca State Park and Aitkin areas. Both sexes have dull yellowish bellies and red forehead patches, but the males have red throats and the females, white. Their drumming is distinctive. Several rapid thumps are followed by several slow rhythmic ones. They get their name from their habit of boring holes into the inner bark of a tree and letting the sap run before wiping it up with their brush-like tongues. They will return again and again to the same tree for the sap and to consume the insects that have been attracted to it.

April 9, 1978 Arrival of the Loon

The ice went out of Green Heron and Wood Duck Ponds yesterday, and today it is leaving the surfaces of some small lakes in the area. People have reported seeing loons as the water opens.

The common loon, officially designated the Minnesota state bird in 1961, is a summer resident throughout most of the state except the southern regions and the Red River Valley. Loons appear in spring shortly after the disappearance of the ice, and their fall migration peaks in mid-October although many linger until driven away by the freezing lakes. They are beautiful black and white birds about two feet long, the size of a goose. Loons are known for their diving ability and have been caught in fishing nets as far as 200 feet below the water surface. They treat us to echoing calls and yodel-like laughing and are the symbol of the Minnesota wilderness for many people.

Each pair together selects an open expanse of lake where no other loons are tolerated during the period of nesting and raising the young. Only one pair will be found nesting on a small lake, but on large lakes with islands and bays there may be several pairs. An exception to this desire for seclusion is the occasional social gathering of ten or more loons, sometimes seen in noisy, active performances in the early morning and the evening. Most nest building occurs in June in Minnesota with the peak of nest establishment in the northern part of the state between June 15 and 18. A simple nest of vegetation is built a few feet from the shoreline, and the incubation period of the two olive-brown, lightly spotted eggs is twenty-nine days with both parents taking turns sitting on the eggs.

Fish, which are the loon's principal food, are pursued beneath the surface of the water with great speed and power. A loon acquires the speed to overtake fish by powerful strokes of its webbed feet, and the wings are probably only used underwater for making sharp turns. Frogs and other aquatic creatures are also part of its diet. The feet are located back on the body, which aids in diving, but when a loon comes up on shore to nest, it must propel itself forward on its belly. Water, both salt and fresh, is the loon's real home, and it only rarely comes up on land to sleep.

The name loon means lummox or awkward and refers to its on-shore movements and perhaps to its inability to fly from the ground. To lift its eight-or-nine-pound body from the water, it must use both feet and wings and requires a great effort. Once in the air, however, flight is swift and powerful even though this bird has a very small wing area in comparison to its body weight.

April 10, 1977 88°F

Naturalist Kathy Heidel reported that the pasque flowers are at bloom peak on the Chaska Prairie, and writer Dick Gray planted onions, bibb and leaf lettuce, carrots, beets and radishes in his garden today. He also recorded the official Lake Minnetonka ice-out at noon. On my way to church, I observed aspen catkins fully extended, my first darner dragonfly of the year, early tulips blooming near an east-facing foundation, elm bud scales and common purple lilac leaf buds starting to open.

Today was Easter and our temperature was 88°F as officially recorded at the Minneapolis-St. Paul International Airport. It set a new record high for this date and broke the old 81°F set in 1910. This was also the highest temperature ever recorded so early in the spring. Children asked to play indoors because it was too hot outside, which shows, I guess, that it takes us winter-worn Minnesota people a while to adjust.

About 10,000 acres of land were burned in the state during the weekend with the biggest fires in the Virginia and Hibbing areas. But on a more positive note, someone reported that spring peepers started calling today around Anoka, and an Arboretum gardener saw the skunk cabbages in full bloom in Minnehaha Falls Park.

The ice has been out of Lake Waconia for only five days, but the water is warming up. I recorded a surface temperature of 48°F, and in the shallow water next to shore it was 65°F this afternoon, almost warm enough for wading.

This was a beautiful day and will be long-remembered for many reasons. I recorded several species of birds I had heard singing, among them the mourning dove and the western meadowlark, and my last bird entry mentions that our area robins sang until after 7 p.m. CST.

Oh yes, the mosquitoes were out, too.

April 11, 1977 Barn Swallow

Although most barn swallows arrive in late April or early May, frequently a few come in mid-April, and today I saw my first one perched on a powerline next to a small barn on the north side of Lake Waconia. As I watched, it left its wire perch several times and glided through the air with the ease and grace of an Olympic figure skater, its long, deeply forked tail enabling it to make the quick changes of direction so necessary for catching insects in flight and for eluding enemies.

Like other swallows, the barn swallow migrates during the daytime, catching its food as it goes. They are abundant summer residents that nest throughout Minnesota, most numerous in farming areas with fewer in heavily wooded spots. The barn swallow is certainly a candidate for the greatest traveler among land birds as it winters in South America as far south as Tierra del Fuego, writes Roger Tory Peterson. The breeding range extends from northwestern Alaska to Mexico and from the Atlantic to the Pacific coast, including much of Canada and the United States.

Barn swallows nest in barns or other buildings and also in hollow trees, caves and crevices in rocky cliffs. We seldom find more than six or eight nests in one place although an observer reported once seeing twenty-seven in a single barn. The nests are constructed from pellets of mud reinforced with straw and grass, lined with feathers and fine grasses and attached to vertical surfaces, with male and female working together in the construction.

It was once noted that a pair worked eight full days for fourteen hours each day to complete their nest. They began their workday as early as 5 a.m., and a load of material was brought to the nest construction site about every two or three minutes.

Each nest usually contains four or five eggs that both sexes help to warm. After the eggs hatch in fifteen days, the young remain in the nest for twenty days while they are fed and cared for constantly by both parents. After leaving the nest, the young remain in the vicinity

Barn Swallows

for several days and return to the nest each night. An observer in New York state found that barn swallow pairs that used old nests constructed in previous years would raise two broods; those that built new ones had only one brood. After the nesting season is over, they gather with other swallow species and perch in long lines on telephone and power wires before they migrate in September.

Barn swallows are swift, strong, tireless flyers. They spend most of the day catching insects; house flies, horse flies and robber flies are the favorites, but other foods may include beetles, ants, wasps, bugs and a few grasshoppers. They obtain water by flying close to the surface of a pond or lake and dipping down to scoop up mouthfuls. They also bathe this way.

I love to hear the cheerful, musical twittering as the barn swallows swoop and glide about our landscape or rest on wires. They are attracted by grazing cattle and moving farm machinery in the fields and like to follow anything that moves in order to feed on the disturbed insects. Anyone who has walked through a field of waving grasses has probably noticed the swallows following behind, catching insects in the air and reducing the fly and mosquito population.

We are having a very early spring. The Dutchman's breeches began blooming today, and I saw my first bumble bee, beeflies and American toad. In a quick jaunt around the Arboretum, I made the following notations in my field notebook:

English sparrows are nest building in the martin house.
American elms and snow trillium (*Trillium nivale*) are at bloom peak.
A few bloodroots have started blooming.
Atlantic leatherwood (*Dirca palustris*) began to bloom today.
Early forsythia (*Forsythia ovata*) is blooming profusely.
The native tamaracks are starting to leaf out.
Scarlet elderberry shrubs have leafed out.

First barn swallow arrived in the Arboretum area:

April 18, 1974	April 11, 1977	April 26, 1979
April 15, 1976	April 14, 1978	April 21, 1980

In his migration records for Hennepin County, 1921–1961, E. D. Swedenborg notes the return of the first barn swallow on these dates:

April 29, 1923	April 26, 1933	April 16, 1944
April 21, 1929	April 11, 1941	April 17, 1949

April 12, 1979 Purple Martins Return

Soon we will be hearing the purple martin's rich, gurgling warbles. In fact, it's time to put up the martin house to welcome back the largest member of the swallow family. Millard Skarp, who lives on Browns Bay of Lake Minnetonka, is our local authority on martins. He waits each year for their appearance and then immediately puts up one or two martin apartment buildings. He is following the custom practiced by early settlers who put up martin houses, and before them, southern American Indian tribes who hung clusters of hollow gourds in trees near their gardens. In the wild, martins nested in tall trees filled with woodpecker holes, but these early colonies did not reach the size of colonies in large martin houses today where as many as two hundred pairs may congregate.

During the winter purple martins are found in South America, apparently concentrated chiefly in the Amazon valley in Brazil. They are migratory birds that spend each spring and summer nesting throughout most of the United States and southern Canada. They live exclusively on flying insects and arrive in our area each year when insects start flying. The first martin scouts were seen in the Lake Minnetonka area today, an average date for their arrival. Over many years the spring migration period in Minnesota has been from late March through late May with the bulk of them arriving from mid-April through early May. Most will leave the latter part of August.

First purple martins returned to the Lake Minnetonka area:

April 20, 1971	April 16, 1975	April 12, 1979
April 14, 1972	April 9, 1976	April 7, 1980
April 15, 1973	April 12, 1977	April 6, 1981
April 15, 1974	April 15, 1978	March 31, 1982
		April 13, 1983

April 13, 1976 First Mosquito Bite

The arrival of the mosquito is a sign of spring, usually greeted with something less than enthusiasm, that occurs in April or May.

A friend called this evening to report a mosquito bite. I told him it was the first I had heard of this year, so I recorded it in my field notebook. There are many insects that are active now because of the warm weather we have been having. Honey bees are visiting red maples and other blooming plants, the mourning cloak and Milbert's tortoise shell butterflies are out of hibernation and on the wing, and clouds of gnats are flying.

Admittedly, mosquitoes are a nuisance. I swat at them myself, but a closer look at these insects and their way of life proves them to be quite interesting. With the help of several entomology books and literature from the Metropolitan Mosquito Control District in St. Paul, I have come up with some fascinating information:

1. Mosquitoes are widely distributed and well-known. Males have very plumose (bushy) antennae and do not bite; females, which have only a few short hairs on the antennae, do bite and are often serious pests. Females need a blood meal to develop their eggs, but the males feed on nectar and other plant juices.

2. The next time a mosquito comes in to attack, if you refrain from swatting it, you can watch the mouthparts in operation. Similar to the hypodermic needles used by doctors, the mouthparts are capable of piercing the skin through which they release a chemical to stop blood from clotting. It is this substance that causes the itching. The mosquito will then fill up on blood, sucking through its tubular mouth.

3. Although fifty species are found in Minnesota, only twenty-eight kinds bite humans.

4. Adult (flying) mosquitoes frequently rest in grass or on shrubs, but they never develop there. They need water to complete their early life stages.

5. Water is their breeding place. This can be a tin can of water lying beside the road, holes in trees and stumps, a puddle in the backyard or a large pond. Eggs are often laid on the surface of water, either singly or in rafts of 100 to 300. Many mosquitoes lay eggs near water, and eggs may hatch into small larvae (wrigglers and or wigglers) within days, or they may remain unhatched for weeks, months or years until they are covered with water. The wigglers feed upon minute plants, animals and organic debris. They are fed upon in turn by fish and waterfowl. They grow quickly and turn into pupae or tumblers, and soon their backs split open and adults emerge.

6. Mosquitoes begin developing in March when the melting water from snow drains into depressions in wooded areas. During the summer they develop, for the seven to ten days required for their growth, in depressions that hold runoff water collected from thunderstorms. With the exception of only one kind of mosquito that develops under water and breathes through cattails, they do not develop in lakes.

7. According to Metropolitan Mosquito Control District information, the life span of snow-melt mosquitoes ranges from three to five months, but those hatching from summer thunderstorms live an aver-

age of only four weeks. Flight ranges vary from less than one-fourth of a mile by the species that can transmit the LaCrosse encephalitis virus to more than fifteen miles for the most common pest mosquito (*Aedes vexans*).

8. Mosquitoes serve as vectors of several severe diseases such as malaria, yellow fever and encephalitis. Although these diseases are mainly tropical, three forms of encephalitis viruses are mosquito-borne in our area, and the dog heartworm parasite is carried to dogs in Minnesota by twelve species.

9. There are several things that people can do to control the disease-bearing and pest mosquitoes. If you live in a wooded area, rid your yard and neighborhood of breeding sites, such as containers that could hold water, and fill low tree holes with cement. Residents of non-wooded areas should also empty, remove, cover or turn over any container that could hold water, to reduce breeding sites. Measures aimed at adult female mosquitoes are mainly in the nature of preventives, such as wearing protective clothing, screening windows, using repellents or spraying with approved insecticides.

April 14, 1978 Ice Out of Lake Waconia

On March 27 there was a ring of open water around the shoreline of Lake Waconia, and we have been awaiting the sights and smells of an open lake ever since. Ice-out is an exciting time, and today it occurred. Yesterday about 75 percent of the surface of Lake Waconia was free of ice. By this evening less than 5 percent of the lake had ice on it and that only on the east side where ice was piled up from winds yesterday and the day before. People were anxious to get on the lake, and this evening I spotted two boats with fishermen in them. Soon docks will go in, and sailboats will appear as we are off and running into summer.

In talking with many people who live near lakes, I have found that there is disagreement about dates when lakes actually freeze over or open up each year. The disagreements refer to the amount of ice cover and open water. Some observers record the ice-out date as the day when most of the ice is gone, and others wait until the lake is completely ice free. There are similar problems in the fall when people say a lake is frozen over when most of its surface has a coating of ice, and some observers wait to record the freeze-up date until no open water is left. I like to simplify my recording as much as possible, and so in the spring I record the date when at least 90 percent of the lake is free of ice. In autumn I record the first day when at least 90 percent of the lake is frozen over and stays that way.

Since 1971 I have logged the ice-out dates for Lake Waconia, a lake close to 3,000 acres in Carver County. Mary and Stan Giesen from Waconia gave me their list of observations, which they have kept since 1955. Listed below is the twenty-nine year record of the ice-out dates:

April 12, 1955	May 1, 1965	April 19, 1974
April 18, 1956	March 31, 1966	April 27, 1975
April 16, 1957	April 7, 1967	April 3, 1976
April 10, 1958	March 30, 1968	April 5, 1977
April 5, 1959	April 17, 1969	April 14, 1978
April 13, 1960	April 17, 1970	April 23, 1979
April 13, 1961	April 15, 1971	April 18, 1980
April 26, 1962	April 25, 1972	March 25, 1981
April 3, 1963	April 5, 1973	April 18, 1982
April 15, 1964		April 13, 1983

April 15, 1976 First Flowers on Rue Anemones

We continue to be amazed at our early spring. This morning I saw dandelion flowers on a south-facing slope, the first I have seen out in the open and away from buildings. Red cedar trees are shedding pollen, common purple lilacs and crabapple trees are leafing out, hardy magnolias are starting to bloom, and there is a green tinge to the forest canopy.

In the Arboretum woodland wildflower ravine the Pennsylvania sedge is blooming, wild leek leaves are up about six inches, both bloodroots and sharp-lobed hepaticas are still blooming, and the rue anemone has its first open flowers. In contrast, the rue anemone first bloomed on April 22, 1974, and May 2, 1975.

Rue-anemone

The rue anemone (*Anemonella thalictroides*) is a slender, delicate perennial herb that grows four to eight inches high from a cluster of thickened tuberous roots. One-inch wide pink, white or purple flowers are found on slim stalks above a whorl of small three-lobed leaflets. It grows in rich upland forests from Maine to northwest Florida and westward to Minnesota and Oklahoma. It is a wiry-stemmed member of the buttercup family and seems to prefer the upper edge of a ravine slope where air currents tend to keep it continually in motion; hence, the other common name, windflower. The rue anemone, which starts blooming a few days after the bloodroots, is common in this area, and it and the cultivar with double flowers can easily be grown in wildflower gardens.

April 16, 1979 Farmers in the Field

A spring sign I look for each year is the first Carver county farmer working the soil for spring planting, which may be plowing, cultivating, disking or toothing. It's a good indication that the frost has left or is leaving the soil and that some of the fields are becoming dry. The farmers with high, well-drained land are the first to be out and are the envy of others who are also anxious to get ready for a new growing season.

In addition to a farmer doing fieldwork, there were many other spring signs today. The tree swallows are beginning to claim their nesting boxes, the sharp-lobed hepatica and vernal witch hazel started blooming in the Arboretum, grasses are turning green in ditches and on south-facing slopes, and beekeepers are installing packages of honey bees.

First Carver county farmer was seen working the soil on:

April 17, 1972	April 2, 1976	April 14, 1980
March 27, 1973	March 26, 1977	March 13, 1981
April 9, 1974	April 15, 1978	April 23, 1982
May 2, 1975	April 16, 1979	April 25, 1983

April 17, 1976 Minnesota Dwarf Trout Lily

Today was a cloudy day with traces of rain off and on, and temperatures were in the 60s.

At 7:30 a.m. a wide-awake group of birders gathered in the Arboretum to begin a hike around the bog trail and other good birding spots. Although a strong wind made it difficult to bird, we observed over twenty-five species. We thrilled to the sound of a common snipe winnowing in its display flights and heard the musical phrases of the first brown thrasher. Ruby-crowned kinglets, chipping sparrows, swamp sparrows, song sparrows and both male and female red-winged blackbirds filled the air with sounds of rhythm and melody. Since this is an unusually early spring, the sugar maples, American basswoods, paper birches, red oaks and ironwoods are all starting to leaf out. Birders usually also like to botanize, so we stopped to look at the bright rose-purple flowers of Korean rhododendron and the fragrant blossoms of several magnolia trees. American twinleaf, false rue anemone and trillium were starting to bloom. Early forsythia (*Forsythia ovata*) shrubs loaded with yellow flowers, Korean abelialeaf with its white flowers, marsh marigolds about to bloom along the bog boardwalk . . . where else could one go birding in such a colorful, fragrant setting?

This spring quarter I have been taking Plant Materials I (Horticulture 1021, University of Minnesota) from Albert G. Johnson. The class meets for three and one-half hours each Saturday at the Arboretum where he is also taxonomist and plant breeder.

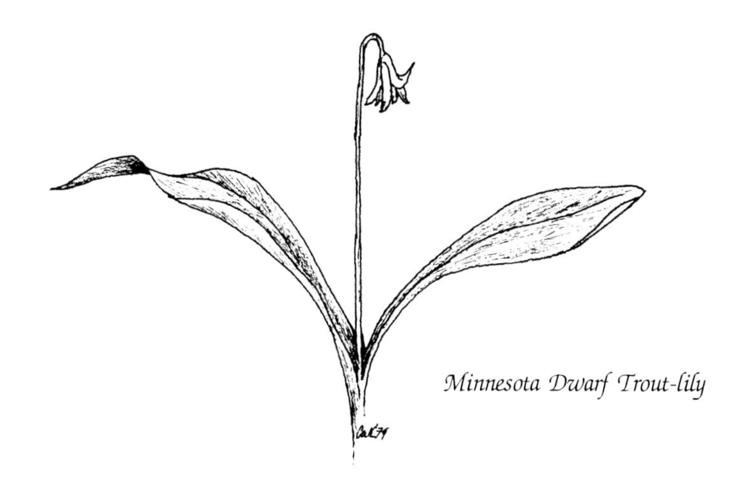

Minnesota Dwarf Trout-lily

After some preliminary lab work and a short lecture, Al took his class out on the grounds where, being a keen observer and an excellent botanist, he was at his best. His store of knowledge was tapped many times as students constantly questioned him. How do you tell a black spruce from a white spruce; when will the redbuds bloom; which species of forsythia has hardy flower buds; is a clump of aspens generally one clone and so genetically the same?

The answer to the last question was yes, and he continued: Black spruce has pubescent branchlets and ovid cones about one inch long;

white spruce has smooth branchlets and cones that are one to two inches long; *Forsythia ovata* is the species to plant, and one usually looks for eastern redbud flowers the third week in May.

As we hiked along, he showed us a Nanking cherry that had just started to bloom, telling us that the fruit is mild and good eating. As we looked at the sugar maples blooming, he said that this is the earliest spring he has seen here. Al mentioned that the river birch (*Betula nigra*), which had started to bloom, is a good tree because it has tolerance to the bronze bark borer. Today I took notes on forty different plants he mentioned on our hike, but the stop I remember best was the one along the stream valley in the sugar maple forest where we saw the Minnesota dwarf trout lily (*Erythronium propullans*).

The dwarf trout lily is Minnesota's only true endemic plant species, growing naturally only in this state. This rare plant occurs on its own only in Rice and Goodhue counties, but Al planted a few clumps in the Arboretum, so now hundreds of people will be able to view them there. The plants are six inches tall, with two leaves and single pale pink flowers, one-half inch across. Spring is early this year, and they started blooming April 15, but usually they bloom from about May 1 to May 15. About two weeks after flowering is over, each plant will dry up but will reappear the following spring.

April 18, 1979 Appearance of the Painted Turtles

Today we had our warmest temperature so far in 1979 as the mercury rose to 68°F under a sunny sky. It was just yesterday that the last snowbank in our yard melted away. There are still people fishing from the ice cover on Lake Waconia, but I'm sure it's not very safe there as the ice went out of several small area lakes and ponds today. A neighbor is out in the garden planting onions and potatoes, common grackles are nest building, eastern phoebes are calling, and painted turtles are basking in the sun. Yesterday we saw the first turtle sunning itself, and today there are several up on logs. Painted turtles are usually first seen sunning a few days before the ice cover leaves our larger lakes in Carver County.

The painted turtle, commonly called a mud turtle, is a small turtle with an upper shell up to about six inches long and bright yellow and red markings on its under side. There are more painted turtles than any other of the eight turtle species living in Minnesota. Ponds and lakes where aquatic vegetation is abundant are their habitat. Their diet consists of about two-thirds water plants and one-third animal food including dead fish, dead clams, worms and various aquatic insects.

After a nest cavity is dug by the female with her hind legs, usually six or seven eggs are laid, and an incubation period of about one hundred days follows. The female leaves the nest site soon after laying the last egg and filling in the cavity with soil. During the nesting season in June and early July painted turtles wander about the landscape, often at a great distance from water, and as they slowly cross roads and highways many are killed.

Although it is not easy to approach the painted turtle closely, it is probably the least wary of all Minnesota turtles. Its habit of sunning on floating logs or any object projecting just above the water level makes it easy to see. Since my students have sometimes asked why turtles bask in the sun with outstretched necks, legs and tails, I have found out from reptile biologists that they do this to raise their body temperatures enabling their food to digest. Turtles also receive ultraviolet light for the manufacture of vitamin A, but there is no certain evidence that sunning removes their parasites.

First painted turtle observed sunning in Arboretum area:

April 14, 1971	May 1, 1975	April 17, 1979
April 20, 1972	April 2, 1976	April 14, 1980
March 26, 1973	April 7, 1977	March 22, 1981
April 17, 1974	April 21, 1978	April 15, 1982
		April 21, 1983

April 19, 1975 Flowers and Snow

For an hour this afternoon I walked slowly along the Arboretum trail between the woodland garden and the witch hazel shrubs, stopping often to listen and look.

The sky was cloudy, a cold west wind was blowing as a few drops of rain fell, and the temperature was not quite 40°F. Lichens were bright and mosses at the bases of trees a lush green. As I watched, a red squirrel chattered and two gray squirrels ran past me. It's a late spring, but I see many signs of the awakening season. Although a week ago a foot of snow covered most of the area, now the snow patches are only a few inches deep. Nearby a small stream is running with a sound of its own as it flows over rocks, soil, twigs, logs, roots and other resistances.

Two hermit thrushes, five golden-crowned kinglets and a lone ruby-crowned kinglet flew by, and a dozen juncos searched the wet leaves and soil for food. A pair of white-breasted nuthatches and a lone brown creeper were hunting for hidden food in the bark of trees. The creeper explored sugar maple and American elm trees, starting at the bottom of each tree and moving up. Several times it flew back to the bottom of the same tree and worked its way up. Finally it flew to another tree. Deer tracks in the snow were a special treat before my last stop next to a vernal witch hazel that is just starting to bloom. The new small flowers with crumpled yellow petals join last year's dried red-brown leaves, which are still clinging to the shrub.

April 20, 1979 Bloodroots Blooming

It smells like spring. Lawns seem to have turned green overnight under the influence of warm temperatures and light rain. Our last snowbanks disappeared, and the ice sheets left Lake Virginia, Lake Zumbra and Stone Lake today.

The first bloodroots (*Sanguinaria canadensis*) have just come into bloom. Like the crocuses in our gardens, the bloodroot on the woodland slope means spring. Each fragile white flower rises from the center of its curled leaf, opening in full sun and closing at night. Flowers remain closed if the day is dark, perhaps to save the pollen for pollen-gathering insects as the plants have no nectar. Each flower is about one and one-half inches wide and has eight to twelve petals, usually eight. Like most members of the poppy family, the flowers don't last long, and the petals soon drop and an elongated seedpod develops. After the petals have fallen, the leaf grows much larger, often measuring six inches across, and a petiole or stalk ten inches long develops. It becomes one of the most beautiful leaves of the forest.

The name bloodroot is derived not from the root but from the thick horizontal underground stem that yields a red-orange sap. Other parts of the plant have much smaller amounts of red-orange juice. The generic name comes from the Latin word *sanguinarius*, which means bleeding. The sap was used by American Indians as a dye for baskets, clothing and war paint as well as for an insect repellant.

First bloodroot blooming in the Arboretum area:

April 14, 1971	April 26, 1975	April 20, 1979
April 18, 1972	April 7, 1976	April 18, 1980
April 13, 1973	April 10, 1977	March 29, 1981
April 18, 1974	April 16, 1978	April 18, 1982
		April 20, 1983

April 21, 1979 Leopard Frogs Calling

Our family spent this warm sunny day, 67°F, raking and cleaning the yard, and I sunburned the top of my bald head for the first time this year. More than fifty tree swallows circling overhead reminded us to get the nesting boxes up. The air was filled with bird music; the loud rattling sounds of belted kingfishers, the pumping noise of the American bittern, the "ker-wee" whistles of a sora and a snipe winnowing in flight. Add to that the songs of American robins, the trills of the newly arrived chipping sparrows, the hoarse rasping notes of yellow-headed blackbirds and calls of various gulls riding on Lake Waconia ice sheets, and we were treated to a fine concert. By early afternoon a new sound was heard coming from a flooded grassy meadow just north of our yard and continuing all afternoon; the sound was the low, guttural croak of male leopard frogs.

In breeding ponds the deep snore of the male leopard frog, a sound somewhat like that of a person rubbing his thumb over a wet balloon, can be heard from late March until early May. Several thousand eggs frequently constitute a single mass, which is usually placed around dead twigs or grass stalks or any similar support, from a few inches to a foot beneath the water's surface. Males fertilize the eggs as soon as they are laid in the shallow water. Weather conditions have a marked effect on the period of development of the eggs and tadpoles, but about twelve weeks are required for the passage of the two stages until the one-inch long new frogs leave the ponds.

The leopard frog (*Rana pipiens*), a large green or brownish frog with black spots, is common in Minnesota. Its maximum body size is about four inches. The frogs usually become active in late March in our area after spending the winter on the bottoms of permanent ponds and lakes. Almost immediately they become conspicuous by starting out for temporary meadow ponds for breeding, often crossing highways as they go. Warm, foggy or rainy nights impel them to move in great numbers, and at such times thousands are killed by cars. In the fall, large numbers cross the roads again on warm, wet evenings as they

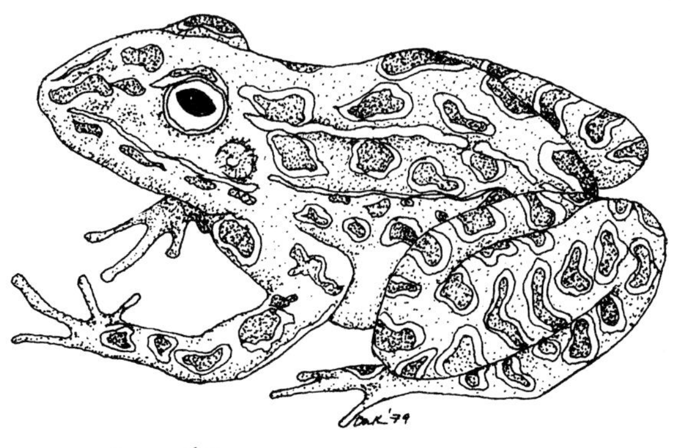

Leopard Frog

head toward their winter homes. Insects and spiders make up 90 percent of their food, according to researchers.

I have been keeping records on five of the thirteen species of frogs and toads found in Minnesota. One thing I observe and record is the first time each is heard calling in this area.

First Heard Calling

Amphibian Species	1977	1978	1979	1980	1981
swamp cricket frogs *Pseudacris nigrita*	March 26	March 27	April 12	April 5	March 22
wood frogs *Rana sylvatica*	—	—	April 15	April 14	March 29
leopard frogs *Rana pipiens*	April 9	March 31	April 21	April 17	April 2
American toads *Bufo americanus*	April 15	April 27	May 6	April 30	April 26
common tree frogs *Hyla versicolor*	April 26	May 10	May 19	May 4	May 3

April 22, 1979 Nest-building Robins

While people are still skiing in northeastern Minnesota, the first robins in the Twin Cities area have started gathering nesting material. On this damp afternoon I have been watching a robin on our front lawn as it picked up material to construct a nest after following certain ritual steps.

Selection of an appropriate site is just as important as the actual construction of the nest. The choosing of a nesting site, a matter of considerable deliberation, is undertaken primarily by the female. She may even show a bit of indecision by beginning nest construction at two or more separate places before settling on her final choice, which is usually five to twenty feet above the ground. Sites on the ground itself or as high as sixty feet above the ground may be used, but a firm foundation seems to be a more crucial requirement than concealment as the nest is supported primarily from below.

Old orchard and shade trees suit the robin's needs quite well. Some robins nest deep in the forest, some build on the edges of forests and in trees and shrubs near human contacts, and some even choose artificial sites. Artificial sites might be window ledges, rain pipes under eaves, fire-escape steps, bridges and fences. They are attracted to areas of homes because of earthworm-filled lawns and gardens. Food is always a concern of nesting robins since their babies consume enormous amounts as they grow toward independence. The first nest, built in early spring when deciduous trees are still leafless, is frequently constructed among the branches of evergreens.

Robins usually take five to six days to build a nest for their first brood of the season, and in nest construction as with site selection, the female assumes primary responsibility although her mate aids by bringing material. The actual shaping of the nest is done entirely by the female as the male usually drops his load haphazardly on the edge of the structure. First, a firm foundation of twigs, grasses, rootlets and occasionally strips of cloth or paper or string is laid down, with slightly finer materials used to shape the sides. After the sides of the nest have been fairly well made, the female shapes the nest to the exact contours of her body by turning around and around in it.

Since the second stage of actual construction is the mud plastering, a rainy day is generally chosen. The female brings pellets of mud in her bill, peppers them onto the nest walls and flattens the mud with her body while turning around in the nest. All that remains now is the lining, which is made of soft grasses that adhere to the mud as it dries. Average nest measurements are: outside diameter, six and one-half inches; inside, four inches; and inside depth, two and one-half inches.

Sometimes a female robin repairs an old nest or adds a layer of new material rather than build a new nest from scratch. She may reoccupy the same one for successive broods within a season and, in even rarer cases, use the same nest year after year. Probably the reason for repetitive use is not fondness for a certain nest but rather loyalty to the site.

One or two days after her nest is completed, the female robin begins laying eggs at the rate of one per day. These glossy, sky-blue eggs are usually laid in the morning with three to five the usual clutch. Incubation usually begins when the clutch of eggs is complete, but if the weather is cold, the female will start sooner. It is performed by the female with the male standing guard. The eggs hatch in twelve to thirteen days with the usual departure time from the nest about thirteen days after hatching.

Since robins raise two or three broods each year and usually construct separate nests for each, the female may begin building a second nest before the first brood has flown. The male parent takes practically full charge of the fledglings, allowing his mate to prepare for the next brood.

Extra robin notes:

American robin is now the name sanctioned by the American Ornithologists' Union as there are other birds of different species in the world also named robin.

An observer can tell robin sexes apart since the female robin has a paler back and breast and no black on the head.

Robins are primarily monogamous and are normally devoted to only one mate at a time. They usually rear two or three broods in spring and summer and almost always remain with the same mate for successive broods within a nesting season. They probably don't mate for life because of scattering during migration. However, since both sexes return to their previous northern territories each spring, there is a chance of successive remating.

One observer reported that a robin built her nest five consecutive years in a woodbine vine trailing up a porch. The robin was identified by a white mark on the side of her head.

The domestic cat is the most destructive enemy of birds that nest in our yards. It has been estimated that a cat will capture an average of fifty birds in a season. Helpless young robins provide a large part of the kill.

April 23, 1979 Ice-out of Lake Minnetonka

Bloodroots continue to bloom, and the first flowers of the Dutchman's-breeches are opening. Comma butterflies took advantage of this beautiful sunny day, with a high in the upper 70s, to swoop about the landscape. Streets and sidewalks covered with newly fallen American elm bud scales showed that the elms are blooming. Wild raspberry and gooseberry shrubs are leafing, and the persistent brown leaves from the red oaks are falling. As strong south winds removed big sheets of ice on Lake Minnetonka, spring pushed a few more steps toward the summer season.

Naturalist Dick Gray reported that the official ice-out for Lake Minnetonka was today. I have been puzzled for years about determining the date when ice leaves such a large lake that contains so many bays. He said that the criterion is based on being able to navigate a boat from Cooks Bay in Mound, through the Narrows, circling Big Island and touching the shoreline in Excelsior and Wayzata. All ice sheets must be gone from the lake, as well.

Mid-April is the average time for the ice to leave Lake Minnetonka. Dick Gray has compiled a list of ice-out dates for the lake containing entries for more than one hundred years. March 11, 1878, was the earliest and May 8, 1956, was the latest date on the list. Part of the list follows:

March 27, 1910	April 4, 1973	April 17, 1978
March 30, 1945	April 19, 1974	April 23, 1979
May 2, 1950	April 28, 1975	April 19, 1980
April 19, 1970	April 3, 1976	March 27, 1981
April 17, 1971	April 10, 1977	April 19, 1982
April 26, 1972		April 22, 1983

April 24, 1979 Ice Cover Leaves

The ice on the shallow marshes and ponds goes out first, then on small lakes and shallow bays, and finally the main ice sheets of the large lakes give up to the spring winds and warmth. Today the ice went out of Traverse, which is a large lake in western Minnesota.

People living near ponds and lakes are fortunate as they can directly observe the ice-out process. Although it is sometimes thought that ice sinks when it goes out, this is not possible because ice is lighter than water. Ice begins its retreat from the shore and provides a belt of open water around the lake with the ring having a temperature of about 45°F. Then a wide band of ice beyond the open water becomes soft and rotten while the rest of the ice cover gets dark. At this time turtles and leopard frogs begin to break their winter hibernation and to emerge from the bottom sediments although they are still sluggish in the cold water.

Finally a strong wind moves the main ice sheet, which weakens and begins to fracture along great stretches. The next stages were explained to me by Dick Gray, who said that ice crystals on the edges of the floating sheets give up and fall over, melting rapidly in the water, which is above freezing. Then one day the wind will sweep the remaining ice sheets from the lake. As the ice sheets are pushed ashore by the winds, the remaining ice chunks are up to seven inches thick and honeycombed. These sheets are composed of long six-sided ice crystals whose strength is gained by being side-by-side with other crystals until moved and crushed by the breaking up of the sheets.

Some loose floe ice along a shore doesn't constitute the condition of ice still being in because a boat can easily be pushed through it. When someone wants to send me an ice-out date of a particular lake for my records, I ask that person to record the first day when at least 90 percent of the lake is free of ice.

We say that spring moves north in Minnesota about twelve miles per day, or as Earl Kuehnast, Minnesota state climatologist, found from a study he did for the area from St. Louis, Missouri, to northern Minnesota, spring moves north one-half mile per hour. This tells us that a certain mean temperature is moving north. The Twin Cities usually reaches a mean temperature of 45°F on April 15, which is the average ice-out date for Lake Minnetonka. The same mean temperature reaches International Falls about May 5, the average ice-out date for lakes in that area.

Listed below are ice-out dates for twenty Minnesota lakes in 1979, a year that had a late spring, and by looking at these dates, we can easily see the progression of spring from south to north. Actually, spring comes last to the Lake Superior (drainage) Basin in northeastern Minnesota.

Lake	*County*	*First day when at least 90 percent of the lake was free of ice in 1979*
Lake Jefferson	LeSueur	April 18
Cottonwood Lake	Lyon	April 19

Lotus Lake	Carver	April 19	
Lake Shetek	Murray	April 19	(April 2, 1977)
Lake Harriet	Hennepin	April 20	
Lake Minnewashta	Carver	April 20	
Lake Owasso	Ramsey	April 20	
Lake Virginia	Carver	April 20	(March 29, 1977)
Buffalo Lake	Wright	April 23	
Grindstone Lake	Pine	April 23	
Traverse Lake	Traverse	April 24	
Darling Lake	Douglas	May 3	
Lake George	Hubbard	May 3	
Kabekona Lake	Hubbard	May 4	
Lake Itasca	Clearwater	May 5	
Woman Lake	Cass	May 6	(April 21, 1977)
Kabetogama Lake	St. Louis	May 10	
Flat Horn Lake	Lake	May 11	(April 17, 1977)
Sea Gull Lake	Cook	May 12	
Caribou Lake	Cook	May 17	

April 25, 1978 Dutchman's-breeches

One of the most attractive woodland spring wildflowers, the Dutchman's-breeches (*Dicentra cucullaria*), opened its first flowers today on an east-facing, wooded hillside containing rich, well-drained soil. The white, yellow-tipped pendant flowers droop in a row from an arched stem. Each flower has two inflated spurs that suggest the legs of tiny trousers, ankles up, that are actually nectar pockets formed by two petals. From what I have observed, the flowers are pollinated by early bumble bees that have tongues that are long enough to tap the nectar. In fact, I usually spot the first spring bumble bees on the day Dutchman's-breeches come into bloom. Nature's plan for pollination of this species is sometimes defeated by some insects that eat holes in the spurs from the outside, stealing the nectar and not touching the stamens.

Dutchman's-breeches grows from a cluster of grain-like tubers crowded together in the form of a scaly bulb. Finely cut leaves, each of which comes directly from a stem underground, have three chief divisions, which in turn are divided into three parts. Since the plant grows in the forest, it takes advantage of the spring sunshine by spreading its leaves early before the trees leaf out. Thus it makes food for the maturing seeds and also stores some food in its underground parts for use the following spring. By mid-summer the leaves have entirely disappeared.

First flowers open on Dutchman's-breeches plants in the Arboretum area:

April 18, 1971 May 6, 1975 April 23, 1979

April 27, 1972
April 18, 1973
April 24, 1974
April 13, 1976
April 11, 1977
April 25, 1978
April 19, 1980
April 8, 1981
April 23, 1982
April 24, 1983

April 26, 1977 Early Crabapple Blossoms

Something unusual is happening. We normally look for the first common purple lilac flowers and first crabapple blossoms in mid-May, but both started blooming today, this being the third warmest April on record. This is a very early spring with plant development ahead of schedule, according to my ten years of note taking. I heard a report from the Stillwater area that the apple trees are flowering, the earliest in sixty-seven years.

Twin Cities area homeowners have been mowing their lawns for a

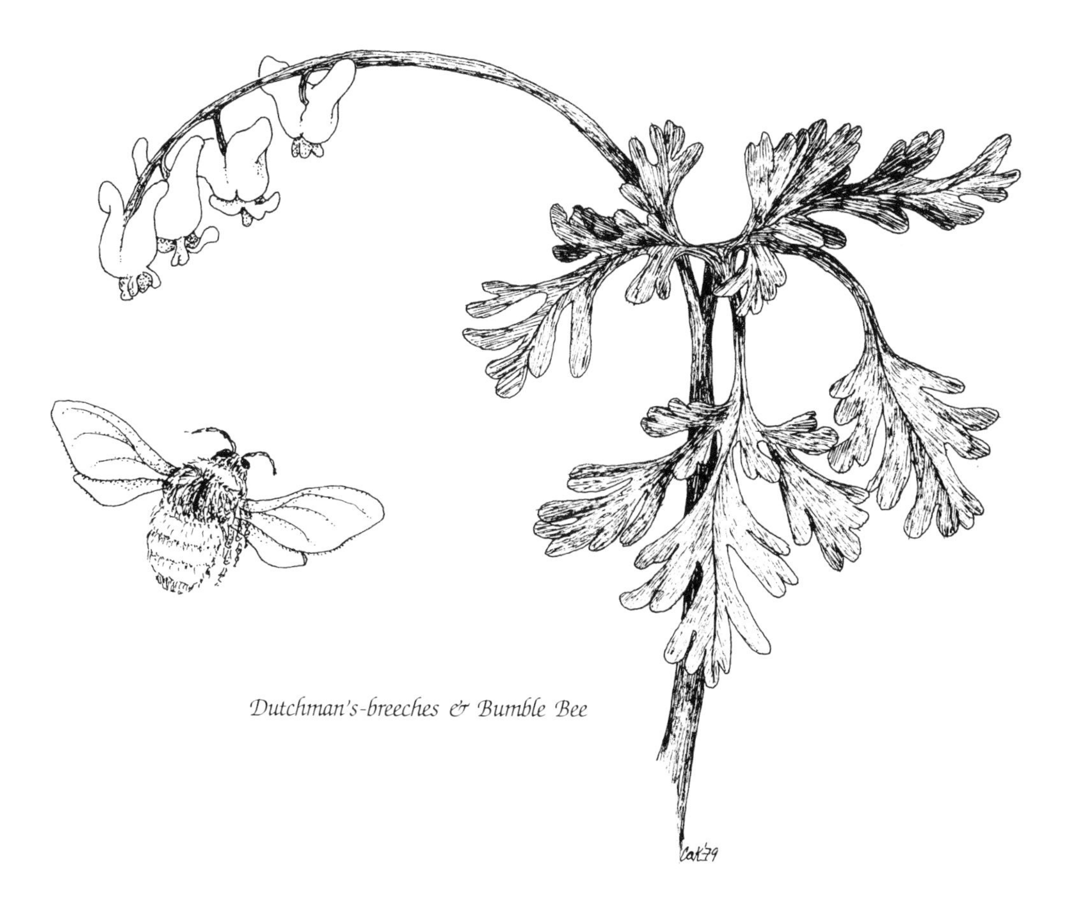

Dutchman's-breeches & Bumble Bee

week, it's the beginning of the Lake Superior smelt run, and aspens are leafing out in Moss Lake in Carlton County.

In 76°F weather I hiked around the Arboretum for an hour. I wanted to record a few happenings on this rare, early spring day and some of my observations include:

Red Splendor crabapple leaves are out about half-way, the trees are loaded with flower buds and a few flowers have opened.

Forest areas are quite shady now that the canopy leaves have reached about one-third of their mature size.

Poison ivy is leafing out with red leaves.

The wildflowers, violets, wood anemone, rue anemone and red baneberry, are now in full bloom.

Honey bees and wild bees are buzzing around and visiting the fragrant white flowers of the native American plum trees.

Virginia creeper is leafing out.

April 27, 1978 A Banded Bird Returns

While trapping and banding birds today at the Lowry Nature Center, I caught a male red-winged blackbird that was wearing a band. A quick check of the numbers on the band with our bird banding records showed that this bird had been banded here on April 25, 1977, at one of the feeders. I had banded the bird then, and now a year later, I recaptured it.

Several other bird banders in Minnesota have had the same experience. While banding near the shore of Smiths Bay, Lake Minnetonka, during the 1920s, Frank and Marie Commons trapped and banded 1,254 red-winged blackbirds. Of this number, 176 returned in subsequent years; six making a three-year record, two, a four-year record, and one, a five-year record. They also reported that fifteen red-wings were recaptured by others and were listed as recoveries. One of their birds was recovered in Arkansas, one in Oklahoma, two in Louisiana and four in Texas.

The red-winged blackbird is found throughout North America in summer and in winter as far south as Costa Rica, with a few wintering in southern Minnesota. There are many in Carver Park and the Lake Minnetonka area in the spring, summer and fall. Undoubtedly they come in large numbers because of the availability of marsh lands, which provide nesting sites. The banding records tell us that they return to the same nesting areas and also give us some information on where they go in winter.

A 1980 report issued by the non-game office of the Department of Natural Resources stated that the red-winged blackbird is Minnesota's most common bird. Among the other top ten species in decreasing number are the common grackle, house sparrow, starling, western meadowlark, mourning dove, American robin, cliff swallow, common crow and common yellowthroat.

April 28, 1979 Lawn Mowing Time

Usually seven to fourteen days after the ice leaves our area lakes and about the time bloodroots are blooming in the woodlands, it's time to take out the lawn mower. Dr. Snyder recommends beginning to mow as soon as growth starts in the spring and continuing whenever the grass has grown one inch above the height set for the mower. The frequency depends on the fertility of the soil, the moisture available and the air temperature. Lawns should be mowed well into the fall season as long as there is grass growing. In the spring any debris on the lawn should be cleaned up using a broom type of rake. Although a couple of neighbors mowed today, I caught up on the raking and pruned a few apple trees.

The yard work finished, I took our two young sons Andrew and Christian to the Arboretum for a hike. They enjoyed running and hiking on the trails and covered about three times the distance I did while I also cleaned birdhouses and recorded a few observations. We heard the swamp cricket frogs calling from several tiny ponds and a brown thrasher singing a succession of deliberate notes and short phrases. We watched honey bees working over the fragrant white flowers of alpine rockcress, and I saw the first open wild ginger flowers, which are dark, solitary, red flowers found at ground level between the stalks of the paired heart-shaped leaves. I was reminded again of the myriad beauties to enjoy and the countless mysteries to explore in nature's new spring season.

April 29, 1978 First Chimney Swifts

Smelt are running in the streams on Lake Superior's North Shore. Rainbow smelt are not native to Minnesota waters. They were accidentally introduced when they were planted in several Michigan lakes as food for the landlocked salmon and then escaped into the Great Lakes. Although they are the common smelt found along the Atlantic coast and on the Pacific coast from British Columbia north to Alaska, their presence in Minnesota waters was not verified until 1946 when specimens were caught in the mouth of the French River.

Dipping for smelt at the mouths of the tributaries of Lake Superior has become a popular sport. The smelt move into the streams at night to spawn, and in the morning most of them drift back to the lake, repeating the run on successive nights until they are through spawning. Many are taken by people who are crowded on the stream banks at night using dip nets and minnow seines, but this seems to have little effect on the number of smelt since they are very prolific.

Equally as spectacular as the smelt runs that attract thousands of fishermen to the North Shore at the end of April and into May is the migration of chimney swifts into Minnesota for the annual nesting season. Birdwatchers throughout the state are on the lookout in April and May to see the first "flying cigars." With crescent wings the chimney swifts circle far overhead as they glide and sweep through the sky. They are among the fastest and most aerial of all birds, courting, feeding, drinking and bathing on the wing and each year fluttering down chimneys after a long journey from a wilderness thousands of miles away.

Swifts, aptly named because of their fast flying, are a worldwide family of seventy-six species. Four species are found in the United States, but only the chimney swift is found in Minnesota. Its winter range was unknown until 1943 when a few banded birds were recovered from the Amazon valley in Peru. When they travel north in spring, the first ones reach the southern part of the United States the third week in March when spring is well under way in the deep South. The insects that swarm high in the warm air provide them with their food. However, chimney swifts do not reach the southern part of Minnesota until a full month later, which seems a long time for birds that fly sixty to seventy miles per hour. The chief reason for their slow northward push is the uncertain weather at that time, so they spend their days flying and feeding and often not making much migratory progress. They travel many extra miles during migration as they don't want to arrive before insects fill the air. Chimney swifts have five-inch long bodies and a twelve-inch wing spread. They feed exclusively on flying insects and fly continuously all day except in heavy rain, sometimes covering 500 miles a day.

The noisy chatter of chipping notes discloses their presence overhead. This morning as I heard their friendly voices for the first time this year, I looked up and saw two dark-colored birds with long narrow wings and very short tails twisting and turning in their flight.

Swifts gather in communal roosts in tall chimneys, entering in huge funnel formations at dusk. I have taken our children to the Prairie Farm, Wisconsin, Elementary School or Waconia High School on many evenings to count the chimney swifts as they funnel down into the chimneys for the night.

It is interesting to note that the species is most numerous where people live, because the birds nest in chimneys and abandoned buildings, but some can also be found in large forested areas following their natural pattern of nesting in hollow trees.

The first chimney swifts were observed in Waconia area on these dates:

April 28, 1972	May 5, 1976	May 1, 1980
April 30, 1973	May 3, 1977	April 28, 1981
April 27, 1974	April 29, 1978	April 24, 1982
May 9, 1975	May 6, 1979	April 28, 1983

April 30, 1977 Early Swim

Ever since I began taking notes on plant development ten years ago, this is the earliest spring I have recorded. Professor A. C. Hodson's thirty-year record (1941–1970) of spring in the vicinity of the St. Paul campus of the University of Minnesota was published in the May, 1971, issue of *The Minnesota Horticulturist.* Dr. Hodson (U of M Department of Entomology, Fisheries, Wildlife) points out that the spring of 1946 was the earliest he had recorded, but in looking through his records I see that spring 1977 is even earlier.

During an early spring some plants bloom several weeks sooner than during a late spring. This should be remembered when looking through the charts and logs in this book. Plants that appear at well-separated intervals in an early spring may bloom more closely together in time during a late spring. Dr. Hodson notes that the most striking characteristic of Minnesota spring seasons is their great variability from one year to another. Spring plant observations recorded since 1908 in the St. Paul campus neighborhood indicate, however, that the general progress of spring has shown no tendency to become either earlier or later in spite of occasional great variability from year to year. But then in terms of geological time, seventy years isn't very long.

Plants, animals and people were busy taking advantage of this uniquely early spring day with clear skies and a high temperature of 76°F. I am sure that my brother David, who went swimming in Lake Waconia, was the first swimmer for 1977. The lily-of-the-valley and bleeding heart have started blooming, honey bees actively worked crabapple flowers today, and great numbers of May beetles (junebugs) are flying tonight.

A few entries from my Arboretum field notes provide more examples of how early spring is today.

> Sugar maples have finished blooming, seeds are forming and leaves are half-way out.

Bur oaks are blooming, and leaves are about one-fourth of their mature size.

Juneberry collection is at bloom peak.

Eastern redbuds (*Cercis Canadensis*) have started flowering.

First dandelion seedheads appeared in open spots.

The large-flowered trillium (*Trillium grandiflorum*) is close to bloom peak.

MAY

In May warm temperatures and showers work to green-up our landscape. It's the month of flowers with delightful weather, neither too hot or too cold.

65

66

Broods of new Canada goose goslings are seen in early May. **(65 & 66)** Orange halves and nesting material put out the first of May will help attract orioles. **(67)** Al Zander, from the Minnetonka area, sets out oranges for the orioles but he has found that grape jelly mixed half-and half with water and put in small jars will attract them from May until early September. **(68)**

67

68

69 70 71 72

In May: Marsh marigolds bloom in wetlands. **(69)** Jack-in-the-pulpits **(70)** and violets **(71)** open in moist woods, and interrupted fern leaves appear. **(72)**

73

74

75

Common dandelions bloom in great numbers **(73)** and lawn mowing begins in May **(74)**, while daffodils **(75)** and tulips **(76)** flower.

76

Forests in May are a treasury of bloom. Hikers can easily observe the large-flowered trillium **(77)** and columbine **(78)**, but the large yellow lady-slipper and showy orchis are scarce. **(79 & 80)**

81

82

83

84

Farmers continue to cultivate **(81)** and plant **(82)**. Gardeners set out annual flower plants. **(83)** The Arctic phlox blooms in rock gardens. **(84)**

May is the month of apple **(85)** and crabapple bloom. **(86)** The fragrance of the common purple lilac fills the air **(87)** at the time common morel mushrooms are found. **(88)**

85

86

87

88

89 90 91 92

During the month of flowers: The first broods of robins hatch. **(89)** Killdeers nest. **(90)** Willets **(91)** and many other shorebird species stop to feed as they migrate north to nesting areas. Snowshoe hare babies arrive. **(92)**

93

94

95

96

Azaleas **(93 & 94)**, including the newly introduced Northern Lights azalea shrubs **(95)**, and the old favorite bridal wreath spirea **(96)** end the month of May with numerous flowers in the U of M Landscape Arboretum area.

Monarch & Lilac

May 1, 1976 Oriole Day

Every year on this day area people put out orange halves to welcome the northern (Baltimore) orioles returning from Central America. I expected to see some orioles today as we searched the Arboretum for them, but none could be found. I had all but given up when Al Zander, a birder from the Glen Lake area of Minnetonka, called to report that he had seen the first one for 1976. Hundreds more will be joining this one during the next couple of days, and from the tops of the American elms and sugar maples these orange and black birds will sing their spring songs.

Although the orioles may have missed coming to the Arboretum today, spring was definitely in the air as I picked up the fragrances of the first open lilac and crabapple flowers. Several species of Juneberries are at bloom peak, and the leaves are about half-way out on forest trees so that the shade is noticeable. Plant development this year is ahead of the average year, but the first oriole was on schedule.

May 2, 1977 Crabapple Collection

Scattered frost was seen this morning, but luckily it missed the crabapple trees in the Arboretum. The crabapple collection is at its peak of bloom, the trees having pink, white or dark red flowers. There are 150 different species, cultivars and selections, and more than 400 crabapple trees in bloom. Not only do people look forward to the crabapples blooming in their own neighborhood, but thousands come here to see and smell the profusion of bloom.

While hiking today, I saw my first green heron of the year flying over Green Heron Pond, and as I continued, I noticed Arctic phlox plants loaded with purple-pink flowers and the first shrub rose *(Rose primula)* and native choke cherry shrubs blooming. It is difficult to realize that so many plants are in bloom this early in the month.

In Carver Park Reserve we saw the first newly hatched Canada goose goslings together with the first black swallowtail butterfly on the wing. We were also treated to a series of joyous, bubbling phrases of the bobolinks in flight over the meadows as they return from their winter in southern South America.

May 20 seems to be the average date to view flowering crabapples at their best, but not always as the list shows.

University of Minnesota Landscape Arboretum Crabapple Collection at Bloom Peak:

May 16, 1969	May 21, 1974	May 30, 1979
May 21, 1970	May 23, 1975	May 7, 1980
May 20, 1971	May 11, 1976	May 9, 1981
May 21, 1972	May 2, 1977	May 16, 1982
May 20, 1973	May 20, 1978	May 24, 1983

May 3, 1978 Rhubarb Sauce Time

Silver maples and green ash trees are just starting to leaf out, and the first rhubarb is high enough to pull. Rhubarb *(Rheum rhabarbarum)* is a cool-climate perennial grown for the thick leaf stalks that are pulled and cooked in spring for their agreeable acid flavor. Native to southern Siberia and the Volga region, rhubarb has been cultivated for centuries. It was introduced to Europe about 1600, and by 1800 many different varieties were listed by horticulturists in America.

Rhubarb is most productive in the northern third of the United States. It is one of the few vegetables that can be grown in Alaska but cannot be successfully grown in the southern Gulf states as it requires a cold period of dormancy, preferably at freezing temperatures. In Minnesota rhubarb is a harbinger of spring and is ready about a month before the first strawberries ripen.

In harvesting rhubarb, a stalk is pulled, not cut, but the leaf is cut off as it contains toxic quantitites of oxalic acid and should not be eaten. The flower stalks should be removed and not allowed to produce seeds since seed production saps the energy of the plant. Harvesting of the thick reddish leaf stalks can continue for about two months, after which plants should be allowed to build up a large crown for the next year.

Propagation of rhubarb is by division of the root. Each division needs a bud and piece of root for a new plant. Six to eight plants set four feet apart in a row will provide enough rhubarb for average family use. Rhubarb will grow in sand, peat or clay soil if it is well-drained and supplied with humus and nutrients. Starting new clumps or dividing old crowns can be done very early in the spring when the soil is still in the best condition, but it can easily be transplanted whenever the tops are dead. It is best not to harvest stalks the first year that the plants are set out and only lightly the second year, but from the third year on, heavy pulling does not hurt the roots.

The first rhubarb was pulled for sauce in Arboretum area:

April 19, 1976	May 6, 1979	May 2, 1982
April 18, 1977	April 27, 1980	May 4, 1983
May 3, 1978	April 6, 1981	

May 4, 1978 House Wrens

House wrens winter in the southern United States and Mexico. The first ones arrive each year in our area in late April or early May, and three days ago the first ones returned and began their melodious songs. The male house wren arrives about nine days before the female, and, as soon as he appears on the breeding ground, he announces his arrival by the territory song. This establishes his definite area that is defended chiefly by song. Territory is important as a means by which birds become paired and mated and is an insurance for adequate nesting sites and food supplies.

Adult male house wrens that have previously nested are very likely to return to the same territory that they occupied the year before or may establish a new territory adjacent to it. The return of females to their former nesting areas is almost as regular, and wrens hatched the year before also tend to return to the vicinity where they were born. Nest boxes that are set out in yards near homes are generally used, but otherwise any nook or cranny in or on a building may serve as a spot to build a nest. A tin can, pail, empty stove pipe or old hat left hanging on a peg are other likely places that may be used.

Despite its tiny size, about four and one-half inches, and its drab brown plumage, the house wren is as well known as the American robin, for what it lacks in size and color is compensated for with voice and activity. It is common in populated areas in the state and also prevalent throughout wild places, particularly burned-over northern area forests.

The cavity of the wren house is filled with sticks or other material except for a hollow at the back for the eggs. If wrens return in spring to find an old nest still in place, they usually remove it stick by stick and then build it again, often using the material they have just discarded. Six to ten eggs are laid, and the incubation period is typically thirteen days. Later a second brood is raised. House wrens are not permanently mated and may form new pair bonds between broods. It is not uncommon for one male to be attentive to two females at the same time and to assist in feeding each of the broods.

House wrens sometimes pierce the eggs of other birds in their area, and in establishing nest sites, they may even destroy the nests or eggs of the same or different species. Aggression towards other birds is not a recently acquired trait but is an old trait activated to secure and dominate a definite area during the reproductive season, for the sake of preservation. It is probably evidence of their superior intelligence in the battle of the survival of the fittest. This behavior tends to be most intense during years when the total number of house wrens and other bird species is the highest.

They are diligent in the search for insects and spiders to satisfy their own hunger and that of their numerous offspring. Most of the food consists of grasshoppers, crickets, beetles, bugs and caterpillars, making them among the most valuable birds in gardens and orchards.

The first house wren returned to the Arboretum area:

April 27, 1976	May 5, 1979	April 27, 1982
April 19, 1977	May 2, 1980	April 30, 1983
May 1, 1978	April 28, 1981	

May 5, 1979 Rose-breasted Grosbeaks

Early migrant birds vary considerably in their times of arrival, but there are two colorful summer visitors to our state that we can expect to see early in May; the northern oriole and the rose-breasted grosbeak. Several birders spotted the first rose-breasted grosbeaks and the first northern oriole today.

The winter range of the rose-breasted grosbeaks is northwestern South America, Central America and parts of Mexico. Upon returning here, they will go to birdfeeders to eat sunflower seeds, but their choice habitat is moist woodlands near open fields containing shrubs. They also like overgrown orchards. Nests are made of twigs and grass, usually set in a low branch of a tree. The rich voice of the rose-breasted grosbeak is like that of a robin but softer and more melodious. The male can be easily identified as it is black and white with conspicuous rose-red patches on its breast and underwings while the female has no colorful patches and is heavily streaked with brown on white.

Just to show that winter still has a small grip — today two inches of snow fell in Duluth and six inches in Park Falls, Wisconsin. Here in our area we had a temperature range from 42° to 60°F, which made it a great day for working in the garden.

May 6, 1979 First Calling of American Toads

Field corn planting is just getting started in the Annandale and Watertown areas, the first chimney swifts were seen in Mound and Wayzata, and marsh marigolds began blooming along the bog boardwalk. During twilight tonight while listening to a chorus of robins, I heard the American toads *(Bufo americanus)* singing. The toads are out of hibernation, and the males have started their trill calls. Each trill is high-pitched, has a whistle quality, continues on the same notes and is maintained uninterruptedly for about twenty seconds or longer. The song is so unique that it is worth obtaining a recording of it or finding someone to teach it to you.

Contrary to popular superstition, you won't get warts on your hands by picking up a toad, but you will learn something about this remarkable amphibian. It feels cold to the hand because it is a cold blooded animal, which means it is an animal with blood the temperature of its surroundings; this is different from the warm blooded animal that has a temperature of its own that is maintained whether the surroundings are cold or hot.

Toads have a dry, warty skin, a wide waist, flattened triangular head, a fleshy tongue attached only near the front of the lower jaw and jaws without teeth. When first metamorphosed (leaving the water from the tadpole stage), it is only about one-half inch long, but an adult grows to nearly four inches. Although the warty skin of the toad suggests great age, it grows fast and reaches maturity in two to three years. It is recorded that one lived for thirty-six years.

Hibernation is accomplished by burrowing with the back feet into the ground to a depth below the frost line. Soon after emerging from winter hibernation, male toads move to grassy ponds for breeding, and when they reach the ponds in April or May, they begin their mating trills. This sound is made when the throat is puffed out, almost globular, but the actual sound is made by the air drawn in at the nostrils and passed back and forth from lungs to the mouth over the vocal chords, the puffed-out throat acting as a resonator. Females arrive at the breeding ponds a few days after the males and lay long strands of eggs, which are then fertilized by the males. One researcher has reported that a single female American toad laid over fifteen thousand eggs.

Toad eggs hatch in two to twelve days, depending upon the water temperature, and the period of time spent as a tadpole, breathing by gills and swimming with a long fin, also varies according to temperature and food available. It is possible for the tadpole to develop hind legs and front arms, absorb the material in the tail into the growing body and leave the water as an air-breathing toad within six to seven weeks.

The tadpoles feed mostly on vegetation, but the toads live entirely upon small animals, usually many insects that are injurious to grasses and other plants, making American toads useful creatures in the fields and gardens.

American toads in Arboretum area were first heard calling:

May 6, 1973	April 15, 1977	April 26, 1981
April 26, 1974	April 27, 1978	April 24, 1982
May 6, 1975	May 6, 1979	April 30, 1983
April 13, 1976	April 30, 1980	

May 7, 1979 Jack-in-the-Pulpit

This was one of those May days when there was so much going on out of doors that it was nearly impossible for me to concentrate on anything except the wonders of nature. At 6:30 a.m. I received a call saying that a large number of northern orioles had returned, and a few moments later when I opened a window, I heard the clear flute-like, whistled phrases of a male oriole from the top of a large green ash. Soon I was aware of a snipe winnowing in the distance, mourning doves cooing, a brown thrasher in full song and the dry, chipping rattles or trills of the chipping sparrows. I was glad that I could schedule time to be outdoors today.

Dandelions started blooming in the open, and boxelder trees are flowering and starting to leaf out. Alfalfa hay is up about six inches, Virginia bluebells have begun blooming, bumble bees are on the wing, and the first Harris' sparrow appeared at the feeder. In the Arboretum I saw apricot trees loaded with flower buds and the first Jack-in-the-pulpit open far enough for me to see the spathe and spadix.

The Jack-in-the-pulpit is a well-known perennial wildflower found throughout Minnesota. When it first appears in the spring, it looks like a pointed green peg with leaves rolled lengthwise to a point. At the center of the rolled leaves is a spathe, also rolled lengthwise, which enfolds the flowers. The spathe, a modified leaf, is a funnel-shaped structure that has an overhanging flap at the top like the old-style pulpit, and this hood over Jack, the little preacher, offers protection for the true flowers. The spathes, or pulpits, vary in color from pale green to dark green with purple stripes. Jack is a club-shaped stem with flowers on its lower part and is called a spadix. Occasionally both kinds of flowers may be found on one spadix, the pollen-bearing flowers set above the others, but usually they are on separate plants. Small flies and some beetles seem to be the pollen carriers for this plant.

Jack-in-the-pulpit usually has two leaves, each with three large leaflets. During the summer the spathe falls away showing the green

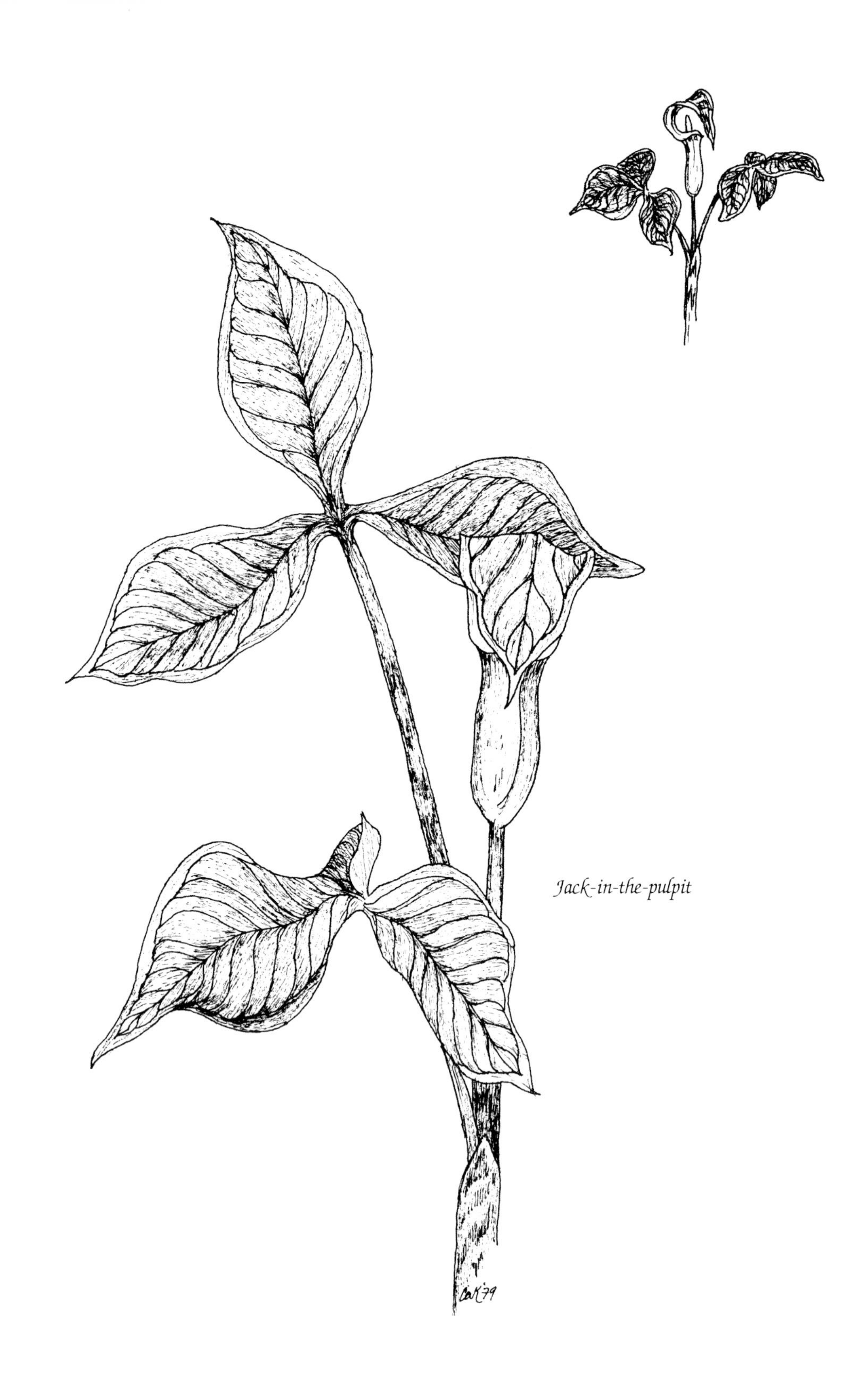

Jack-in-the-pulpit

berries, and by the end of August the leaves have withered and the green berries turn scarlet. Below ground the main corm (a solid food storehouse) gives off smaller corms that spread the plant by this means as well as by seeds.

I have listed the record for the opening of the Jack-in-the-pulpit in the Arboretum.

May 5, 1971	May 10, 1975	May 7, 1979
May 13, 1972	April 20, 1976	May 4, 1982
April 28, 1973	April 21, 1977	May 8, 1983
May 3, 1974	May 5, 1978	

May 8, 1976 Hike with Dr. Snyder

As a part-time naturalist on the University of Minnesota Landscape Arboretum staff for the past eight years, I have come to know Dr. Snyder, who is respected for his academic and practical knowledge and his dedication to excellence. He is the Arboretum director, recognized as an authority in the field of horticulture, and he is always willing to share his skill and wisdom.

During the growing season I often ask Dr. Snyder questions about plant identification, planting, pruning or watering as they occur in the course of our work. I don't often have the chance to walk around with him on the grounds, but this morning I joined a University student group as he took them on a field trip in the Arboretum. Some of my notes from that hike follow:

Dr. Snyder pointed out some red maples and mentioned that we should never buy seeds or plants from a source more than two hundred miles from our own area if we want hardy trees.

We noticed that the buds on a shellback hickory (*Carya laciniosa*, 55409A) are about three inches long and just starting to open. This particular tree was the first tree planted in the Arboretum, a seedling from a hickory planted by pioneer horticulturst Peter Gideon who brought seeds from a shellbark hickory in Illinois. Dr. Snyder planted the tree in July, 1957. This was not the time to plant a shellbark hickory, but the six-foot-tall tree had been bulldozed out of an area by mistake, and so he brought it to the Arboretum site although there was then only an option to buy the land. He mentioned that this specimen had not grown much for five or six years, but then it began to grow rapidly.

The marsh marigolds are at bloom peak, and the wild geranium is starting to flower. This spring is two weeks ahead of an average year.

The Ohio buckeye, one of his favorite trees, had been blooming for the last couple days and has leafed out. The leaves are about half their full size, and the beautiful yellowish flowers are in upright panicles.

The sweet birch (*Betula lenta*) and river birch (*Betula nigra*) are excellent trees to grow here as these are two of the few birches with resistance to the bark borer. Trees from local sources should be planted.

Dr. Snyder said that scrub oaks are stunted trees growing in soil with low fertility and could be any species. Oaks are beautiful trees that should be planted but not in stands and not pruned in the summer. This will help control oak wilt disease. We saw native bur oaks, white oaks and red oaks. He pointed out Mongolian oaks, pin oaks and swamp white oaks that were planted in the Arboretum and are doing well.

Gray dogwood (*Cornus racemosa*) is a fine native shrub that is often used in naturalized plantings and is attractive with its flowers, fruits and red pedicels.

The eastern redbuds (*Cercis canadensis*) are loaded with rosy-pink flowers. Seeds from a tree growing at the Horticultural Research Center are producing hardy seedlings. Dr. Snyder said that from other seed sources about 99 percent of the seedlings die. Native redbuds can be found as far north as southern Iowa.

May 9, 1979 Green Tinge

Yesterday a green tinge in the canopy of the forest areas began to show as leaf buds swelled and began opening. Ironwoods, American elms, boxelders, aspens and paper birches are all starting to leaf out, and for the next week or two we will be treated to a great variety of shades of green.

Today was overcast with occasional rain resulting in a final total of more than one inch. Migrating willets stopped to feed in one shallow pond, and I wasn't surprised to see them on a rainy day because they are shore birds. But it was interesting to see the behavior of other birds at the feeder on a cold rainy day. Two white-crowned sparrows, a single Harris' sparrow and a dozen white-throated sparrows fed for a long period on millet seeds I had scattered on the ground for them. I also noticed that red-winged blackbirds, common grackles, blue jays and cardinals came occasionally to feed during the rain along with the red squirrels.

Green tinge first noticed in tops of Arboretum area forests:

April 26, 1971	May 9, 1975	May 8, 1979	May 3, 1983
May 2, 1972	April 15, 1976	April 22, 1980	
April 21, 1973	April 15, 1977	April 13, 1981	
April 26, 1974	May 2, 1978	April 29, 1982	

May 10, 1978 Dandelions

The dandelion is a versatile and useful plant. One of its virtues is that young dandelion leaves are rich in vitamin A. If the leaves are gathered before the flowers appear, they can be added to salads or boiled for five to ten minutes before eating, but when fully grown, they become bitter. Roots, gathered in early spring and fall, have been used as a substitute for coffee after being baked in an oven until brown and brittle, ground and then perked like commercial coffee. Wine can also be made from the flower heads. However, dandelion plants should not be picked for eating if chemical weed killer or fertilizers have been applied.

I first noticed common dandelions blooming out in the open on April 29, but I have seen the yellow flowers next to south-facing walls of buildings since April 4. Today they are in full bloom with great masses of yellow spread across lawns and other open areas.

The edges of the dandelion leaf are noticed in a peculiar way that someone thought looked like lion's teeth in profile. Thus, the plant was called "dents-de-lion" (teeth of the lion) in France, and from this the name dandelion has come. It is native to Europe and Asia, and, like so many other weeds, it was brought to North America and to other parts of the New World by explorers and colonists.

Some of the tactics by which the dandelion conquers us and takes possession of our yards, parks and fields are listed.

It blooms early in spring and until November, producing seed for a long season.

It flourishes in most types of soil.

Its long taproot gets moisture and food not reached by many other plants.

Its leaves spread out from the base. They crowd and shade many neighboring plants out of existence.

Many insects visit it, and, therefore, it has plenty of pollen carriers. It can also develop seeds from its own pollen or can develop seeds without pollination.

It develops numerous seeds attached to parachutes that the wind can scatter to new areas.

Because it forms rosettes of leaves in the fall, it is able to begin growth early in the spring.

Dandelions are extremely persistent and flourish despite efforts to exterminate them, and yet I think the world would be lonesome for their golden flowers and fluffy seed heads if they were eliminated.

May 11, 1979 Yellow-rumped Warblers

To warble means to sing with trills and quavers, and this describes some of the songs of a group of birds known as warblers. About 160 species are known, of which forty-four can be found in the United States with twice as many in the eastern as in the western states. The wood warblers, the *Parulidae* family, are found only in America.

Warblers are small, active, colorful songsters with slender, straight, pointed bills. Most inhabit the woodland. Since they feed almost exclusively upon insects, they are highly migratory, and thousands of miles frequently separate their summer and winter homes. Most warblers are among the first birds to arrive in spring. They are largely nocturnal migrants whose long journeys in the dark over water and land expose them to many dangers. They often strike lighthouses, electric and radio towers and tall buildings, with fatal results. Several species migrate together, advancing northward in great waves during favorable nights. During the day they can be seen traveling slowly through the woods and orchards from tree to tree. During mid-May at the height of migration, warbler flocks, often made up of a dozen species, flit about in their bright plumage to the delight of birdwatchers.

The yellow-rumped is the most common of the warblers we are seeing now in the Arboretum area. There are many of them, and their cheery trills suggest the song of a junco. No warbler is more easily identified than this one with its four distinct patches of yellow on the crown, two sides and rump. Myrtle warbler was the name we used for it when I first studied birds, and this common name is taken from its fondness for the berries of wax myrtle (bayberry family). Yellow-rumped warblers nest in the coniferous belt in Alaska and Canada and in the northern part of the United States from northern Minnesota to Massachusetts.

May 12, 1978 Wild Violets

The word violet, like rose, has no translation, and, like the rose, violet became the word for a color although not all violets are the same color. The four species of native violets are at bloom peak. Two have blue flowers, one has yellow, and one, the northern white violet blooming along the bog boardwalk, has small white flowers marked with purple along the veins. In addition to these native violets, there are several cultivated species and hybrids blooming in the woodland garden.

Because of their abundance and beauty, the violets are among the favorite wildflowers. They are low herbs that can be divided into two distinct groups — those with the leaves and flowers arising directly from the rootstock and those with leaves and flowers that come from a common stem. The flower possesses five stamens and five sepals. There are also five petals, one pair above, a pair on each side, and a broad lower petal, which gives the bees and other insects a resting place when they are seeking nectar. This lower petal is prolonged backward into a spur that holds the nectar, and the purple lines on it are nectar guides that lead insects to the nectar buried in the spur. When it is gathering nectar, an insect becomes laden with pollen and carries it from flower to flower.

At the base of most of the species of violets, the small flowers that never open can be found. They have no petals, but within them the pollen and the pistil are fully developed. These flowers seem to be developed only for self-pollination and are called cleistogamous (closed marriage) flowers by botanists. Cleistomagous flowers appear after the showy ones are on the wane and continue to develop over a long period during the summer. This may be nature's way of assuring perpetuation of the pure species since allied species of some groups freely hybridize when growing nearby.

All violets have capsules that can shoot seeds as far as nine feet from the parent plant. The seed pods are three-lobed, each one dividing lengthwise with a double row of seeds within. The lobe curls back and scatters the seed when it is ripe. This expulsion of seed results in a new bit of soil area for the offspring and keeps the family from being crowded out.

Orioles have started gathering nesting material. Garden tulips and backyard plum trees are blooming. This is my mother's birthday, and since I have been a naturalist at heart from childhood, I have always thought that it came at the most beautiful time of the year. My parents joined me at the Arboretum for a lunch-hour hike, and together we enjoyed looking at the marsh marigolds, violets and other wildflowers, the daffodils and the newly leafed trees.

May 13, 1978 Large-flowered Trilliums

Today is the opening day of the Minnesota fishing season, and, in spite of strong north winds and cool temperatures, many fishermen got their limits of walleyes and northern pike. In the Arboretum area lawn grasses are a lush green, wild columbine began to bloom, I saw baby robins as they hatched, and the large-flowered trillium (*Trillium grandiflorum*) is at the peak of bloom.

Trilliums are in the lily family and are often called wood lilies because of their favorite haunts. They are perennial herbs coming up each spring from an underground stem and are named from the word triplum, meaning threefold; there are three leaves, three petals and three sepals. Thomas Morley, a professor of botany at the University of Minnesota, lists four native trillium species in his book, *Spring Flora of Minnesota* (University of Minnesota, 1969). The largest plant, usually about one foot tall and the most showy of the native trilliums, is the large-flowered trillium that likes the rich soil in moist woods in many parts of Minnesota. It is also cultivated in wildflower gardens, and hundreds have been planted in the Arboretum.

Large-flowered Trillium

The large-flowered trillium has three white petals, two to three inches long. The sepals alternate with the petals, so that when we look straight into the flower we see it as a six-pointed star, three of the points being the white petals and three the green sepals, which are narrower and shorter. This spring the first large-flowered trillium flower opened above its three deep green leaves on May 1. Once opened, the flowers turn with the sun for two or three weeks and become pink or purple as they age. The flowers are visited by bees and butterflies, and as the petals drop, three-parted seed pods form.

May 14, 1973 The Common Purple Lilac as an Indicator of Spring Development in Minnesota

Searching the lilac hedges in Excelsior and Waconia this afternoon, I found several shrubs of the common purple lilac with the first flower open or opening on a cluster. A lilac flower cluster is a grouping of many small individual flowers, so the date we record for bloom start is the day when the first small flower is fully open. The common purple lilac (*Syringa vulgaris*) has been used by phenologists throughout the United States and Europe to judge spring development.

Exactly when the common purple lilac was brought to America is in doubt, but we have records dating back to 1652 when it was found in the yards of early settlers. As pioneers moved westward, the lilac was often the first flowering shrub that bloomed beside the log houses in the frontier settlements. At the time of fullest bloom and greatest fragrance, lilacs were brought to country churches, and the fragrance of the flowers enhanced the worship environment.

This is a table showing spring development in widely separated parts of Minnesota in 1973, a fairly typical year, using the common purple lilac as an indicator plant.

Town	*County*	*Opening of first Flower in cluster*	*Peak of Bloom*	*End of Bloom*
Luverne	Rock	May 10	May 15	May 21
Mankato	Blue Earth	May 10	May 19	May 29
Winona	Winona	May 11	May 19	May 28
St. James	Watonwan	May 14	May 20	May 26
Faribault	Rice	May 14	May 22	May 29
Minneapolis	Hennepin	May 15	May 20	May 30
Boyd	Lac Qui Parle	May 15	May 23	May 31
Crookston	Polk	May 19	May 27	June 3
Argyle	Marshall	May 25	May 31	June 6
Roseau	Roseau	May 27	June 2	June 11
Shevlin	Clearwater	May 29	June 4	June 9
Aitkin	Aitkin	May 28	June 3	June 10
Moose Lake	Carlton	May 29	June 7	June 14
Duluth — 3 mi. uphill from Lake Superior	St. Louis	June 5	June 8	June 16
Lutsen — 50 ft. from Lake Superior	Cook	July 3	July 12	July 24

May 15, 1979 Trees Leafing Out

This year spring is about a week later than normal. The gray catbirds have just returned, and their songs of long, irregular musical and mechanical notes together with cat-like whines can now be heard from thickets of small trees and shrubs. Apple and crabapple trees are leafing out, and the red-berried elder is starting to bloom. In northeastern Minnesota the smelt are running in North Shore streams of Lake Superior.

At 5:00 p.m. I drove to the Arboretum to take a quick hike to see how spring is progressing. I observed:

Honey bees were feeding on thousands of dandelions.

Mandan apricots are loaded with light pink flowers, and three Northern orioles were feeding from the flowers. Since they didn't seem to be eating the flowers, they must have been getting nectar from each blossom.

Prickly ash shrubs are blooming, but no leaves are visible yet.

American basswoods, sugar maples and red oaks are beginning to leaf out. (May 10, 1978, and April 17, 1976)

The nodding trillium is starting to bloom.

Common yellowthroats were breaking forth with their loud, fast "witchity-witchity-witchity-witchity" songs from the edge of Green Heron Pond.

May 16, 1978 Apple Blossom Time

Warbling vireos are back. I first heard this drab summer resident that lives in tall deciduous trees two days ago. They are more easily detected by sound than sight as their song is long and warbling, somewhat like that of a purple finch but slower. Shorebirds and warblers continue to move through the countryside. This is the time when eastern bluebird eggs are hatching, tree swallows are laying eggs, and purple martins are building nests. Bleeding hearts are blooming, and I saw the first apple blossoms.

At this time of year apple blossoms fill the air with one of the best spring scents. It is a soft scent that permeates like mist, but this fragrance lasts only about a week since apple blossoms are fragile and fall with the first rain shower or hot wind.

The purpose of the apple blossoms is to produce apples that contain seeds to grow into more apple trees. The apple tree is classified as a member of the rose family, and the small apple-like hips found on wild rose shrubs in fall and winter show the relationship. A comparison of a wild rose blossom with an apple blossom will also show the close tie. Besides apples, the rose family includes pears, cherries, plums, apricots, raspberries and strawberries. All have showy flowers and are insect-pollinated. The petals and odor of the flowers attract the insects, which then gather nectar and pollen. Commercial honey bees do most of the pollination in orchards although some pollination is done by wild bees and other insects.

Each spring an average apple tree can produce from fifty thousand to one hundred thousand apple blossoms. Most are grouped in clusters of five or six and grow from the ends of short woody stems called fruiting spurs. Each blossom has five white or pink petals, and both male (stamen) and female (pistil) flower parts are found in each apple blossom. The many stamens, which contain the pollen, stand up like a column at the center of a flower. Five stigmas at the ends of the pistils can also be seen in the center of the flower. Each pistil contains two egg cells, making ten seeds possible in each apple fruit. Pollen must get from the stamens to the pistils for seeds to be produced.

It has been speculated that the same apple blossom might be both

Apple Blossoms

parents to its seeds. It is possible in some varieties of apples, but for the majority of apple varieties, it is not. Most apple trees have a chemical mechanism for rejecting their own pollen and pollen produced by other trees of the same variety. Generally speaking, there must be cross-pollination between two or more varieties, and the insects perform this job.

One of the most reliable pollinators is the honey bee whose body is covered with tiny hairs. As she goes into the blossom to get the nectar produced at the bases of the petals, her body brushes against the anthers at the ends of the stamens, the pollen sticks to the hairs, and at the same time she brushes against the pistil and leaves some pollen behind. As she flies from one tree to another, she takes the pollen from one to the pistisl of the next. Without bees the apple crop would be almost wiped out, and this would be true for almost every variety of fruit or vegetable.

Since there are ten eggs, it follows that ten pollen grains are necessary to fertilize completely any blossom. If this doesn't happen because the blossom is poorly fertilized, the entire blossom falls from the tree. If most or all of the eggs are fertilized, the petals drop and what remains develops into an apple. Later the tree will drop even fruit that has already formed if the crop is too heavy or if too many blossoms were fertilized.

In an average year no more than 2 to 5 percent of the blossoms develop into apples. As the apple grows, its final size, shape and color, as well as taste and aroma, are determined by the genetic structure of the mother tree. The seeds inside the apple could have been fathered by one or up to ten different trees. Each seed has its own genetic mixture, and when seeds grow into trees, they will produce fruit according to their own genetic makeups.

Grafting is necessary to produce apple trees of the same variety, since each apple seed, when planted, produces a new variety of tree and fruit. Thousands of apple varieties have been cultivated in the United States, and of those, some of my favorites are Beacon, Wealthy, McIntosh, State Fair, Regent and Haralson.

May 17, 1979 Ruby-throated Hummingbird

This afternoon I saw my first hummingbird of the season, a female ruby-throat that was busy visiting the pink flowers of a Mandan apricot tree. About four months from now these birds will leave, as they winter chiefly from Mexico to Panama and north Florida and southern Texas. In spring they leave their tropical or semitropical winter quarters for the north, keeping pace with the opening of their favorite flowers as the year advances. Bird watchers in the Lake George area, just east of

Itasca State Park, tell me that the ruby-throats usually arrive there about May 12 and leave about September 12.

Hummingbirds are found, in the Western Hemisphere, only in North, Central and South America and adjacent Caribbean islands. Out of some 300 species, only about a dozen are native to the United States, and only one species, the ruby-throat, nests east of the Rocky Mountains. It is a summer resident in Minnesota and is the tiniest of all the birds here.

Ruby-throated hummingbirds are only about three inches long and weigh a little over three grams each; about 150 birds would weigh a pound. Their feathers are metallic green on their upper bodies and mainly white on the lower, with the adult male having a bright red throat. Their top flight speed is just under thirty miles an hour, and the humming sound of their wings in flight accounts for their name. The rapidity of their wing beat registers as a blur to the human eye, but an analysis of high-speed motion pictures shows the rate to be about seventy beats per second for a male and fifty for a female. The difference in rate is because the female is larger.

Hummingbirds have the highest energy output per unit of weight of any living, warm-blooded animal. While hovering, a hummingbird has an energy output per unit weight about ten times that of a person running nine miles per hour. A normal person will consume two to two and one-half pounds of food per day, but to generate the energy output of a hummingbird, a person would have to consume 285 pounds of hamburger or 370 pounds of boiled potatoes per day. Hummingbirds must feed abundantly and regularly to keep up their energy supply, and they are well equipped for this. They can fly backwards as well as hover and have a highly extensible and tubular tongue with which they can reach deep into a flower for nectar for quick fuel consumption. Ruby-throats also consume small insects and spiders, and I have watched them drink tree sap from yellow-bellied sapsucker borings.

Hummers can be attracted to feeding stations with red glass tubes filled with a mixture of honey and sugar water, and there are many flowering plants attractive to them that gardeners can include in their plantings. A few are listed below.

bee-balm	cardinal-flower	columbine
coral bells	foxglove	hollyhock
morning glory	petunia	phlox
snapdragon	touch-me-not (*Impatiens capensis*)	trumpet honeysuckle

One of the best reference books I have seen on hummingbirds is entitled *Hummingbirds* by Crawford H. Greenwald (Doubleday, 1960). I have used this book for several facts for this entry.

May 18, 1974 Arboretum Bird Hike

Eighteen people joined me for the 7:30 a.m. Arboretum bird hike today. We saw or heard forty species in two hours, which was a good number considering the cool temperature and a little rain. Some of the species we observed were eastern green heron, common snipe, black tern, least flycatcher, house wren, short-billed marsh wren, catbird, brown thrasher, myrtle warbler, palm warbler, yellowthroat, Wilson's warbler, American redstart, bobolink, Baltimore oriole, rose-breasted grosbeak, chipping sparrow and white-throated sparrow. We have found the best birding areas to be the trail around Green Heron Pond, the woodland garden and up into the crabapple collection, and the ground covers out to the hedge collection.

Today most of the crabapple trees are starting to flower, Virginia bluebells and the showy orchis (*Orchis spectabilis*) are blooming, and the primrose collection is at its peak of bloom. Many of the daffodil plants are still flowering as the cool weather helps keep them a long time.

May 19, 1979 Wild Columbine Blooming

Thousands of yellow dandelion flowerheads can be seen, and a few of the seedheads are starting to appear. Backyard plum trees are at bloom peak, warblers are numerous, and scarlet tanagers and indigo buntings have returned.

In late afternoon a thunderstorm passed through here, after which we had a beautiful rainbow. While out enjoying it, I happened to look down and saw the first flower open on one of the many wild columbine plants growing in an open natural forest on the edge of our yard.

Columbine flowers are drooping bells with five, long, curved spurs that begin to bloom about mid-May in the Twin Cities area and continue into summer. The flowers are terminal and are yellow and red with petals prolonged into five hollow spurs that are knobbed at the end and contain nectar. There are many stamens and five pistils that become many-seeded pods. Wild columbine (*Aquilegia canadensis*) is a perennial, one to three feet tall, with two or three times compounded leaves and lobed leaflets. This is our only native columbine and is found throughout Minnesota in woodlands and on shaded rocky cliffs and ledges, but it can be grown easily in a wildflower garden and sometimes in ordinary garden soil if the site is shady. The long flower spurs explains the generic and common names. They are said to resemble the talons of an eagle (*aquila*) or to resemble a circle of doves (*columba*) drinking around a fountain.

Tonight I heard the strong trills of the common tree frog (*Hyla versicolor*) for the first time this year as this species is not an early breeder. The calls were coming from a dense forest nearby that has several undisturbed ponds. We often see those two-inch-long frogs, with their conspicuous finger and toe disks, on screens and windows as they come to feed on the insects that are attracted by the lights in the room on summer evenings. I have noticed that common tree frogs vary greatly in color at different times and in different conditions.

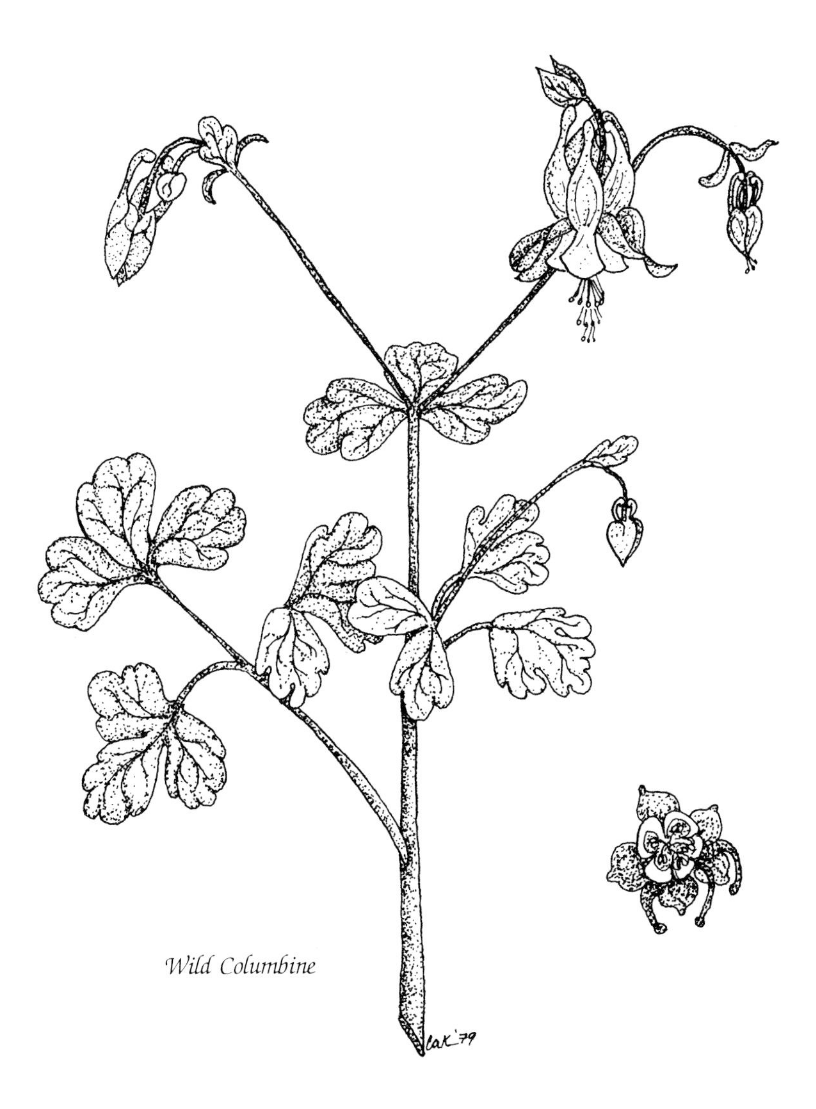

Wild Columbine

Their dorsal sides can change colors within a few minutes from tones of green to gray to brown.

The first flower was open on wild columbine in the Arboretum vicinity:

May 9, 1971	May 17, 1975	May 19, 1979
May 16, 1972	April 30, 1976	May 3, 1980
May 14, 1973	April 29, 1977	May 2, 1981
May 16, 1974	May 13, 1978	May 10, 1982
		May 13, 1983

May 20, 1974 What's Blooming

This morning I watched a male blackburnian warbler with a bright orange throat busily working over a large oak tree where he seemed to be catching insects that were on or close to the oak flowers. Next my attention was caught by a bumble bee that was visiting wild gooseberry flowers. Then I noticed that the tartarian honeysuckle shrubs and choke cherries were just coming into bloom, all this happening within a few feet of the warbler and me. Apple and crabapple trees together with the common lilac are fast approaching full bloom, and clove currant shrubs are loaded with fragrant yellow flowers.

In local wildflower gardens Jacob's ladder with its cluster of blue-violet bells and ladder of paired leaflets, bleeding hearts, a perennial from Japan, and the shooting star are in bloom.

In the forests nodding trillium at bloom peak, rue anemone covered with flowers, and violet flowers by the thousands surround us.

Our Minnesota spring flora, made up of native and cultivated plants, is extremely rich and diverse, which I enjoy as I get out with my plant identification books, camera and notebook as often as I can. There are about 1,700 species of flowering plants growing wild in the state and hundreds of cultivated ones to learn about and enjoy.

May 21, 1978 Flowers, Birds and People

This morning we watched a mother wood duck lead her newly hatched young across a busy street to a nearby pond where they will find food and safety. Not far away four killdeer eggs were hatching as the parent birds immediately carried the shells away from the nest. As soon as the moisture dried on their down feathers, the young were on their feet and left the nest with the parents leading the way. Naturalist Kathy Heidel recorded seventy-four species of birds today on hikes she led in Carver Park Reserve. Nine warblers species were seen, along with blue-gray gnatcatchers, eastern wood pewees, great-crested flycatchers, eastern kingbirds and many others.

This seemed to be a weekend for warblers. Naturalists at the Environmental Learning Center near Isabella saw many, and naturalist Mary Vanderford observed them north of Ely along the Echo Trail. She also reported that birches and aspens are now leafing out although they began leafing out on May 3 in the Twin Cities. The golden corydalis is blooming, and the black flies have appeared.

The Arboretum was a very busy place today, and later I learned that over 1,500 people entered the Arboretum between 9:00 a.m. and 4:30 p.m. Perhaps the reasons for so many people were:

Crabapples and lilacs are blooming, scenting the air with perfume.

Many wildflowers, daffodils and irises are blooming.

The Arboretum Auxiliary put on their annual spring plant sale.

The Arboretum Gift Shop was open, and Dr. Snyder was autographing copies of his new book, *Gardening in the Upper Midwest.*

The Minnesota Daffodil Society put on its first annual show.

Tonight about sunset I noticed common nighthawks migrating through. They are about the size of a blue jay and are dark, with long, pointed wings, slightly forked tails and white wing patches. They fly, glide and swerve with great ability, no doubt consuming enormous numbers of insects as they travel to their nesting grounds.

May 22, 1978 Choke Cherry Bloom

The choke cherry (*Prunus virginiana*) is considered to be a shrub or small tree and is seldom over fifteen feet tall. These woody plants grow in moist to dry thickets, on shores and on the edges of woods throughout the state. They are native from Newfoundland to Saskatchewan and south to North Carolina and Kansas, often growing abundantly and with fruit that is remarkably free from insect or disease damage. Growing in a variety of soils and being shade tolerant, the choke cherry is widely planted for conservation and for bird food. The fruits are also often used in making jelly.

Choke cherries began blooming on May 19, and today they are at their peak. The small white flowers are only about one-quarter inch across but are striking looking as they grow in dense, spike-like clusters (racemes) three to five inches long. The strong-scented flower clusters and the leaves appear on the ends of new stems. The dark red-purple fruit, in drooping clusters, is ripe in July and August.

Every day is interesting to a naturalist, but this one had been filled with fascinating happenings to record. Here are a few:

The common purple lilacs (*Syringa vulgaris*) are at bloom peak in Waconia and Excelsior. Our area is perfumed with a scent that Edward Bunyard, a British horticulturist, called "the very heart and soul of memory." Other writers have also stated that the common purple lilac essence is one of the most memory-stirring of all fragrances. Longfellow firmly declared, "I shall not go to town while the lilacs bloom," nor did he.

Edible morel mushrooms, a favorite of mushroom hunters, have appeared. Although a number of habitats can produce the fruiting bodies, folklore holds that an apple orchard is the favorite spot. They do grow in old orchards, but also in conifer plantations, maple and oak forests, in swampy grounds under elms, in grassy pastures and on lawns where they come up around recently dead trees or stumps. Morels appear in spring after a lot of rain, and I usually look for them when the common purple lilacs are blooming. They are delicious when fresh but can be either dried or frozen and kept for future use without losing any of their fine quality.

Honey bees are working the crabapple blossoms.

The fernleaf peony is at bloom peak. This is an old favorite perennial with double red flowers that was taken by pioneers to their new homes on the prairies.

Catalpa trees are leafing out, and bridal wreath spirea is starting to bloom.

While banding birds today in Carver Park Reserve, we recaptured a male common grackle that I had orginally banded at the same feeding station May 9, 1977. Yes, many birds return to their same territories.

May 23, 1977 Early Spring

"Properly recorded and correctly interpreted, there is nothing perhaps to equal the records of the dates of periodical events in plants and animals as indices to the bioclimatic character of a place or local area, because such events are in direct response, not to one or a few, but to all the complex elements and factors of the environment, which no artificial instrument, or set of instruments, yet available, will record."

A. D. HOPKINS, 1918

Phenology is the study of the chronology of natural events. A more exacting definition states that phenology is a branch of the biological sciences concerned with the timing of natural events in plants and animals from year to year and from place to place, and their relationship to season, weather and climate. Students of nature who keep records to help find order and meaning are called phenologists.

The term phenology was apparently first used in 1853 by the Belgian botanist Charles Morren. It was derived from the Greek word *phaino*, meaning to appear or to show. Although the term is relatively new, the use of nature's own weather bureau is old. Ancient Chinese and Romans had phenological calendars to guide agricultural activities. Phenology is more ancient than the categories that it transects; its first paper, published about 974 B.C., cuts across three sciences, meteorology, botany and ornithology, not yet born.

> "For lo, the winter is past,
> the rain is over and gone.
> The flowers appear on the earth,
> the time of the singing of the birds has come,
> and the voice of the turtle dove
> is heard in our land."
>
> The Song of Solomon 2:11-12

Although our weather instruments are better than they were sixty years ago, phenological observations still give us very meaningful information on how a season is progressing and how it compares with past years. Phenological data allow us to make predictions because one phenological event follows another, and many events in nature can be correlated. Here are some examples: crocuses bloom before tulips, wood ticks are seen before junebugs, the ice goes out of area lakes before we mow our lawns, bumble bees appear when Dutchman's-breeches start blooming, and we pick our first ripe garden strawberries about a week after the first alfalfa hay is cut.

Today the smooth wild rose (*Rosa blanda*), many cultivated roses and a number of peony flowers are blooming, together with the pitcher-plant in the Arboretum bog. The bearded irises are at bloom peak, and alfalfa haycutting is well under way in southern Minnesota.

The chart below with eight phenological happenings helps us to see just how early we had different spring events in 1977:

Spring Sign	*1975*	*1977*
Ice went out of Green Heron Pond in the Arboretum	April 24	March 28
Early forsythia (*Forsythia ovata*) at bloom peak in the Arboretum	May 10	April 16
First farmer in Waconia area observed cutting alfalfa hay	May 29	May 10
Ripe American elm seeds falling like snow	June 2	May 10

Red clover (*Trifolium pratense*) started to bloom	June 2	May 16
First ripe garden strawberry picked	June 7	May 16
Our state flower, the showy pink and white ladyslipper (*Cypripedium reginae*), started to bloom in Arboretum	June 12	May 21
Russian olive (*Elaeganus augustifolia*) started to bloom	June 12	May 21

The information for this entry in the book is being put together in August, 1979. Examining the records as far back as 1819 when weather observations were first recorded at Fort Snelling (Minneapolis), Bruce F. Watson, consulting meteorologist, and Earl L. Kuehnast, Minnesota state climatologist, both agree that 1977 was the earliest spring on record. The warmest March and April period came in 1878, but the warmest April and May period was 1977. The warmest March, April and May period was also 1977, with the year 1878 coming in second, 1910, third, and 1946, fourth.

May 24, 1972 Lily-of-the-valley

When the lily-of-the-valley (*Convallaria majalis*) blooms, its exquisite scent is always refreshingly new and spring-like, the favorite flower fragrance of many people. On a still day a bed in bloom will fill the air with its distinctive sweetness, and to the French this flower is the symbol of spring. Many people in the Upper Midwest feel the same.

The lily-of-the-valley is at its peak of bloom in our area now. A native of Europe and Asia, this hardy herbaceous perennial has been a favorite in Minnesota gardens for many years. The six-inch flower stems are slightly curved and carry an inflorescence in the form of a one-sided raceme bearing up to twenty pendulous, bell-shaped white flowers with the petal tips recurved. The leaves are glossy green, oval-oblong in shape and grow in pairs. Both the leaves and flower stalks rise directly from the root stock that is found just below the ground level where it is in the form of small rhizomes or tubers.

A shade-tolerant plant that is often grown on the north side of buildings, the lily-of-the-valley is an excellent ground cover in a shaded or partially shaded place. Overcrowded plants should be divided in the fall, but overcrowding may not occur for many years, and plants should be left undisturbed as long as possible. The small horizontal rhizomes should not be planted too deeply. It is sufficient for their upper surface to be only slightly covered with soil.

May 25, 1978 First Monarch Butterflies

I had been waiting for the monarch butterflies to return since May 13 when the common purple lilacs started blooming in Minneapolis and St. Paul and on the shore of Lake Waconia on May 17. Monarchs and lilacs seem to go together. A naturalist friend reported seeing monarchs and lilac flowers April 15 in Joplin, Missouri. Today was the first time I saw a monarch this year and was reminded again of the miracle of their lives.

Today was hot, the first day this spring that the mercury rose into the 90s with Hutchinson having 97°F. A strong south wind was blowing as I entered the Arboretum about 5 p.m. Nature was ready for the return of the monarchs from Mexico. Common milkweeds were up several inches and many wildflowers and garden plants were in bloom, and, of course, the lilacs were still blooming. The fragrant yellow flowers of the Father Hugo rose, blooming hawthorns and jack pines shedding pollen were all things for me to ponder momentarily, but I was intent upon looking for a monarch. For several different springs I had seen the first monarchs in the ground cover area on the Chinese lilac hedge, and when I reached there, I noticed that the hedge was at peak bloom and very fragrant. Then I saw them, black and orange wisps. I saw three monarchs strong in flight but nervously visiting the lilac flowers for sips of nectar.

Several telephone calls to other interested people revealed that the first returning monarchs had also been spotted in Richfield at the Wood Lake Nature Center and in Burnsville, Mound and Northfield. After supper I spotted several more in our yard and decided it must have been the strong south wind that brought them back to Minnesota for the growing season.

The first monarch butterflies returned to the Arboretum area on these dates:

May 30, 1971	May 20, 1975	May 29, 1979
May 20, 1972	June 3, 1976	May 28, 1980
June 1, 1973	May 14, 1977	May 14, 1981
May 21, 1974	May 25, 1978	June 11, 1982
		June 10, 1983

May 26, 1978 Bridal Wreath Spirea

Bridal wreath is the popular name of the Vanhouette spirea *(Spiraea x vanhouttei)*. This hybrid shrub, resulting from a cross between *S. cantonensis* and *S. trilobata*, originated before 1866 and has been planted more than any other spirea. Early in this century traveling nursery salesmen must have covered every Minnesota town and farm, selling nearly every householder a few plants, for that is the only way one can account for the large number of Vanhoutte spirea shrubs seen throughout the populated parts of the state. Maybe the earlier over-planting makes some present day gardeners ignore this shrub now.

Spring wouldn't be quite complete without the bridal wreath in full bloom as it is at the present time. Myriads of little three-eighths inch florets in one and one-half inch diameter, flat-topped clusters grow along the gracefully arching branches. When blooming, a shrub stands like a great white fountain, and although the oval leaves are barely noticeable now, in autumn they will change from green to orange before falling.

Bridal wreath is one of the best spireas to grow for several reasons. This shrub, which is about six feet tall, can be grown in either sun or light shade, preferably the former, in average soil that is well-drained but retains moisture. It is a good border shrub and can also be used in foundation plantings. The only attention it needs is to cut the oldest stems to the ground after flowering to promote stronger new growth.

May 27, 1978 White Clover

Today I noticed the first open white clover flowers. The earliest I have seen this plant in bloom was May 16, 1977, and that was the year we had an unusually early spring.

White clover *(Trifolium repens)*, also known as white Dutch clover, is a profusely seeding perennial that establishes itself in pastures and along roadsides. It is a good lawn plant and holds its own with blue-grass very well. Clover flowers and leaves grow on separate stalks from stems that lie flat on the ground. Each leaf is made up of three leaflets, each with a pale "V" on it. Children often search areas of white clover to find four-leaf clovers, which are traditionally considered lucky. White clover is scattered throughout the United States, and occasional plants may be found wherever there is sufficient moisture to enable them to survive. However, they do not thrive in an acid soil as lime is necessary for their growth. An immigrant from Europe, it arrived with the early settlers.

White clover normally grows in association with grass. Even when it is seeded alone, grasses soon encroach and make a luxuriant growth indicating that its presence creates an ideal condition for grass growth. Clover plays a part in increasing nitrogen in the soil. Little swellings, which are called nodules or root tubercules, are found on the rootlets of all clover. These nodules contain a multitude of bacteria that are able to fix the free nitrogen of the air into nitrogenous compounds.

Besides being an important pasture and hay crop, white clover undoubtedly holds first place as a honey plant in North America. In favorable seasons over 200 pounds of white clover honey per colony is common. The best yields of nectar, which is used by honey bees to produce honey, come in seasons following a year of excessive rainfall when the conditions favor the rooting of thousands of new plants that are ready to produce a crop of nectar the following summer. Honey from white clover is the best quality. Mild-flavored and light-colored, it commands the highest prices in the markets. Most people prefer it to the somewhat more spicy flavors of alfalfa or sweet clover honey although they are similar in color.

White Clover & Honey Bee

The heads or flower clusters of white clover show that each one contains about fifty-five small florets, and each floret contains pollen and nectar. At first all the florets stand erect, but, as the marginal ones are pollinated, they cease to secrete nectar and bend backward and downward against the stem. This change in position is beneficial to both flowers and insects as it prevents useless visits of the insects. It is interesting to note, too, that most nectar is gathered on days when the temperature is between 80° and 90°F. The flowers are white when they open, but they often turn reddish and after pollination finally become brown.

The florets of a white clover head are too small to support the weight of a honey bee; the bee clings with its legs to several flowers, and only its head rests on the flower from which it is sucking nectar. Other insects can obtain nectar also as it is not deeply concealed. Bees never visit the flowers to gather the pollen alone, since the anthers are enclosed in a sac or keel formed by the two lower petals and emerge only when the bee's head is pushed into the flower. The value of white clover for its honey is much greater than for its pollen, and many home-coming bees enter their hives with empty pollen baskets. In the absence of bees, the flowers remain self-sterile and produce no seed.

May 28, 1974 Chirping Crickets

The chirp of the cricket is usually associated with the coming of autumn, but the careful listener may hear it in spring although the song is not so insistent as late in the summer. Around the time lilacs bloom, I listen for the first crickets, and this evening with the purple lilac in full bloom, I heard a field cricket chirping in our garden.

Field crickets are over one-half inch long with a black patent leather finish. Although the cricket is a good jumper, it most often escapes its enemies by running between grass blades. If we try to catch one, we realize how slippery it is as it efficiently slides through our fingers. The field crickets, which feed on plant material, are very common in pastures and meadows and along roadsides, sometimes also entering houses.

Crickets are among the most famous of the insect musicians. Their songs are produced by stridulation, that is, by rubbing one body part against another. When a field cricket sings, the chirps are created by rubbing a sharp edge (the scraper) at the base of one front wing along a file-like ridge (the file) on the bottom side of the other front wing.

Only the male crickets sing, and they do it to attract mates. There would be no use to chirp if other crickets could not hear. There is, therefore, an ear by the joint of the front leg, and crickets literally hear with their elbows. This ear is easily seen with the human eye as a little white disc-like spot. If a rival male is heard, the constant droning-like chirps are stopped, the wings are lifted to a higher angle, and the sound is resumed in a sharp and defiant manner. The field cricket I heard tonight was chirping in a constant steady manner, waiting for his ladylove.

May 29, 1974 Junebug

On warm May and June evenings we often hear low-pitched buzzing and banging noises as large brown beetles hit our screens. Occasionally they appear in April, and this year I observed the first single one on our front door screen at 9:15 p.m., April 25. Tonight I saw hundreds in our yard.

There are one hundred North American species of beetles in the group that is commonly known as junebugs, June beetles or even May beetles. They are usually brown and are seen around street or yard lights in the spring and early summer. The adults feed at night on foliage and flowers, and the larvae, known as white grubs, eat the roots of grasses and other plants. White grubs can be very destructive and damage pastures, lawns and crops like corn, small grains, potatoes and strawberries.

The life cycle of a May beetle usually requires three years to complete, and there are many obstacles to their living long. Birds and mammals, especially skunks, root out the white grubs to eat, and the adult beetles are preyed upon by birds, flying squirrels and many other animals.

May 30, 1979 Late Bloom of the Crabapples

Bobolinks singing from the tops of the crabapple trees added music to a setting of fragrance and visual beauty. The area apple trees are in full bloom, and the crabapples are at their peak. Even though the flowering is late this year, the profusion of color is excellent.

Many people ask how to tell an apple tree from a crabapple tree. The difference between a crabapple and an apple is somewhat questionable, and Dr. Donald Wyman, former horticulturist at the Arnold Arboretum (Harvard University), in his study of crabapples considered apple trees with fruit two inches or less in diameter to be crabapple trees.

Crabapples have many uses, both ornamental and economic. They are planted primarily for their beautiful five-petaled flowers that range in color from pure white to dark purplish-red, with many variations in between. Other assets of the crabapples are their fragrance and their beauty in the bud stage. In some cultivars, the color of the flower buds and flowers are identical, but often the pink, red or white buds may have white flowers.

Cultivars of crabapples that retain their bloom a long time and have small fruits adhering to the trees through the winter are the most desirable. The bright-colored fruits give these trees ornamental interest and provide excellent winter food for cedar waxwings and other wildlife. The fruits vary in size from one-quarter to two inches in diameter, and the colors range from dark red to yellow with a few having green apples. Although the trees are mainly ornamental, the fruits are often used for jelly-making and eating as they are. Two of the best for fresh eating are the Chestnut and the Whitney crabs.

Flowering crabapples are hardy throughout Minnesota. They are usually fast growing small trees and are not too particular about soil requirements, although good drainage is essential. They should be planted where they receive dull sunlight, and proper pruning will help insure many seasons of good bloom and fruit production. Over the years cultivars that are resistent to scab, fire blight and cedar-apple rust have been introduced. Dr. Snyder feels the ideal crabapple tree should be disease resistent, bloom over a long period and bear small colorful fruits that stay on trees into winter. Not many trees meet these standards, but I can recommend David, Red Splendor and Sparkler from my own experience.

May 31, 1973 Arboretum Azaleas

One of the highlights of the growing season at the Arboretum is the blooming of rhododendrons and azaleas. Various species and cultivars of these plants, which prefer light shade and acid soil, can be seen blooming from April into June.

The genus *Rhododendron* is a large one containing approximately one thousand known species that are native mainly in the Northern Hemisphere. In the moist mountain regions of the Himalayas and adjoining Asian countries, nearly nine hundred are indigenous to the area, but none grow naturally in Minnesota. The species with leather-like evergreen leaves are usually called rhododendrons, and those with deciduous leaves are usually called azaleas. Most rhodonden-drons have ten or more stamens, and most azaleas only have five.

An Arboretum visitor wanting to see large masses of colorful azalea shrubs should come when the bridal wreath spirea is in full bloom. At that time the mollis hybrids are at their peak with a spectacular display of flowers ranging from yellow to red.

Today raspberry plants are blooming in the garden, the first white clover heads are seen in the lawn, goat's-beard *(Tragopogon dubious)* started blooming along the roadsides, wild geranium is at bloom peak in the forest, and bridal wreath spirea and snowball shrubs *(Vivurnum opulus)* are covered with white flowers. Since I had correlated the bloom of these plants with that of the mollis hybrid azaleas, I knew the azaleas would be blooming, and a drive to the Arboretum confirmed this.

Spring, 1979

The Northern Lights azaleas are available through Minnesota nurseries for the first time this spring. These early Northern Lights *(mollis x roseum* hybrids) were developed by Albert G. Johnson, a former plant breeder at the Arboretum. Plants from his initial crosses made in 1957 have produced outstanding bloom every year for the past twenty years. Flower buds from Northern Lights hybrids can withstand winter temperatures of minus 45°F without injury. The six-to-seven-foot shrubs produce one and one-half inch fragrant flowers in clusters that range from light to deep pink. It is expected that these azalea hybrids will change the spring landscape of Minnesota in years to come.

Garden Roses

June 1, 1978 Tall Bearded Irises

The tall bearded irises, also called German irises, are at bloom peak here. One of my favorites is the common blue and purple iris *(Iris x germanica)*, which is widely planted in Minnesota gardens. It is a hybrid, involving a number of species in its development.

Although the exact origin of the tall bearded iris is not known, it was cultivated in ancient Japan, Babylonia and Egypt; the ancient Greeks, dazzled by the colors, used the word *iris* meaning the "eye of heaven," which was also their word for the rainbow. The flowers were a favorite in the royal gardens of Europe as early as the ninth century.

Irises continue to fascinate gardeners everywhere. The thousands of cultivars match every shade of the rainbow except bright green, and even that color may some day emerge among the hundreds of cultivars introduced each year. Tall bearded irises are prized as much for the beauty of their upright and drooping petal formations as for the colors that first attracted early gardeners. Each flower has six perianth parts (sepals and petals), three of which are reflexed and hanging and are called the falls, and three inner segments that are upright and called the standards. The tall bearded irises have prominent hairs or the beard at the base of each fall, and flower stems that grow from one and one-half to more than three feet tall.

June 2, 1979 Lake Waconia Lilacs

Our yard is filled with the songs of bobolinks and house wrens. On a quick walk around the house, I watched honey bees working the yellow pea-like flowers of the *Caragana arborescens* hedge, saw a monarch butterfly migrating toward the northeast and enjoyed the fragrance of lily-of-the-valley, crabapple and common purple lilac flowers. The lilacs are at their peak of bloom today; "peak" is when nearly all of the flowers on the plants are open but before any appreciable number have withered or dried up. This year the bloom has been unusually good but late appearing.

One of the reasons I record flowering dates is to show the peculiarities of any given season. Trees, shrubs, vines and other plants do not usually show their leaves or flowers at the same time each year. If one species flowers earlier or later than usual in a particular year, we can expect other species to be correspondingly early or late. If we know the sequences in which various plants burst into leaf or bloom, we may be able to predict by watching an indicator plant, such as the common purple lilac, when other events are likely to occur on the same plant or on other species, or even to predict events in the lives of insects or other animals. Throughout this book many correlations between phenological events will be pointed out.

The same phenological event doesn't usually happen each year on the same calendar date but is influenced by the weather. Common purple lilacs and other organisms are highly sensitive meteorological instruments that integrate weather factors, such as temperature, rainfall, humidity, wind and sunshine, and show by their growth or behavioral responses the cumulative effects of these factors. Temperature is usually the most important factor. For example, from year to year the first flowers on a particular common purple lilac shrub may open on dates as far apart as two to three weeks or more, depending largely on the accumulation of a certain number of temperature or heat units.

I am well aware of plotting phenological events by using daily solar radiation or growing degree days and keeping a record of the accumulation of them to determine flowering dates or other events. Some may wonder why the mathematical equations and resulting graphs are not included in this book. The answer is that my total daily entries are meant to give a description of the chronology of natural events for a year. I'm doing this in order that people can learn more about a few of the plants and animals that share the earth with us and also can learn to read the Upper Midwest landscape. I feel this can be accomplished better descriptively than mathematically.

Blooming Dates for the Common Purple Lilac *(Syringa vulgaris) on the northwest shore of Lake Waconia*

	First flower open on a cluster	*Peak of Bloom*	*End of bloom, at least 95 percent of the flowers have dried up*
1971	May 14	May 22	June 5
1972	May 18	May 23	May 30
1973	May 18	May 26	June 6
1974	May 16	May 28	June 6
1975	May 20	May 25	June 2
1976	May 9	May 17	May 28
1977	April 30	May 9	May 18
1978	May 17	May 24	May 29
1979	May 25	June 2	June 10
1980	May 4	May 17	May 27

1981	May 4	May 18	May 27
1982	May 14	May 20	May 30
1983	May 21	May 31	June 12

June 3, 1978 Tiger Swallowtail Butterflies

Insects are the largest single group of living organisms in the world, and in this group, butterflies and moths are scaly-winged insects that make up the order *Lepidoptera*. There are several ways to distinguish butterflies from their near relatives, the moths. Nearly all butterflies are diurnal; flying during the day, especially when the sun is shining brightly, but moths are mainly nocturnal in their habits. Another general difference is the attitude the adults assume when at rest. Most butterflies alight with their wings folded up over their backs while a majority of the moths settle with their wings in a horizontal position.

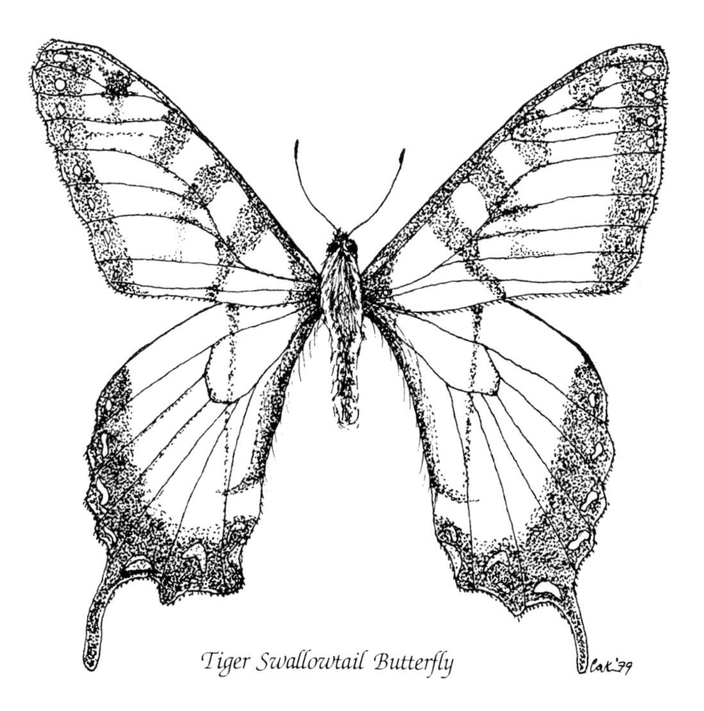

Tiger Swallowtail Butterfly

One final positive way to distinguish a butterfly is to observe the antennae (feelers). All butterflies have antennae with a club or swelling at the tip, and the antennae of moths resemble miniature feathers or are just thread-like filaments.

Of approximately 140 species of butterflies found in Minnesota, the eastern tiger swallowtail is one of the easiest to identify because of its large size and colorful wings. The four-inch wing span is highlighted by a striking pattern of yellow and black and a black tail-like projection on each hindwing.

Adult eastern tiger swallowtails appear on the wing during the month of May, and their numbers increase during June. This year I saw my first tiger swallowtail in this area on May 14, and last year it was May 7. Today I visited Itasca State Park where I saw many tiger swallowtails. I counted six along one short stretch of gravel road in three minutes of observation. Tiger swallowtails are fairly common in the Twin Cities area, but they are quite numerous in many parts of northern Minnesota. During the month of July there are fewer, but, with the emergence of the second brood in early August, they again become a familiar sight for the remainder of the month.

The green caterpillars of the eastern tiger swallowtail are generally found in the states east of the Rocky Mountains on leaves of ash and wild cherry trees. One thing I have noticed while studying these butterflies is that the females are dimorphic; that is, show two color forms. The more typical form is yellow and black with blue and orange markings like the male, but I have also seen females with dark brown scales in place of the striking yellow. Before looking at the wings carefully, I thought these melanic forms were the black swallowtail butterfly, another species.

June 4, 1974 A Day In June

A warm rain last evening and early this morning brought out the cedar-apple rust "fingers" on red cedar *(Juniperus virginiana)* trees, making them look orange from a distance. The cedar rust puts out spores in spring in the form of orange horns, an inch long or more, that are gelatinous in wet weather. A large gall covered with spore horns may look like a small orange, and a red cedar filled with them is often striking and beautiful. However, the spores are released from the spore horn as it dries and, unfortunately, are carried by wind to members of the apple family. To control cedar-apple rust, it's best to cut the galls off the cedars since the spores can be carried as far as a mile by the wind.

While working in the Arboretum today, I jotted down a few of my observations:

Black terns were circling Green Heron Pond and diving for fish.

About twenty-five cultivars of the shrubby cinquefoil *(Potentilla fruiticosa)* are now blooming.

Scotch pine and Japanese red pine are shedding pollen.
Tree roses are starting to bloom.

I saw more than one hundred monarch butterflies in the Arboretum today. Most of them were feeding on flowers of the Chinese lilac, with many more males than females. Although the females looked frayed, the males were much less faded, and some appeared to have recently emerged from their chrysalids. I wonder if the females may have made the trip to the wintering grounds in Mexico and back and if the males are from the new generation that developed this spring in states south of us.

June 5, 1978 Wild Grape Vines

The wild grape *(Vitis riparia)* is in full bloom and fragrant, to be followed in mid-August and into autumn by ripe fruit that is seedy but flavorful.

Other common names for the wild grape are frost grape and river bank grape. *Riparia* is a Latin word meaning "of river banks." It is a native grape that grows into trees, shrubs and other supports, attaching itself by twining and tendrils and often has a stem two or more inches in diameter. Wild grape leaves are broad and lobed, and the small green flowers grow in pyramid-like clusters. The grapes are bluish-black berries, about three-eights of an inch in diameter, good for making jelly and relished by wildlife.

The wild grape can be grown at home on a fence or as a climber on porches and pergolas. In the development of grape cultivars, plant breeders have used the wild grape as a hardy parent.

June 6, 1979 Tenspot Skimmer

Bird's-foot trefoil, a European legume, is blooming, and we see its showy yellow patches along roads and in fields where it has been planted to help control erosion. Jack pine and Swiss mountain pine are both shedding pollen, and new growth on the blue forms of Colorado spruce is out about three inches. While walking through the Arboretum iris collection where the tall bearded irises are blooming, I noticed the first tenspot skimmers that I have seen this year as they patrolled the nearby pond. They are large dragonflies that are common around ponds. They have a wing spread of three and one-half inches, the females have black spots on their wings, and the males have white spots between ten black spots on theirs. They are good fliers and use their aerial ability to catch other insects for food.

Dragonflies are relatively large and often beautifully colored insects that spend much time on the wing in darting and rapid flight. An expert hunter, the dragonfly has a streamlined body and glistening wings that carry it through the air at speeds of thirty miles per hour or more; each pair of wings strokes alternately, the front pair going up while the hind pair is going down, at a rate of thirty or forty strokes per second. Like hummingbirds, dragonflies can hover in the air or suddenly dart upward, downward or to one side. While sunning and resting, they extend both wings as if in flight. They can't sew up any part of the human body, and, in spite of common superstitious beliefs to the contrary, they do not sting as they do not have a stinging apparatus.

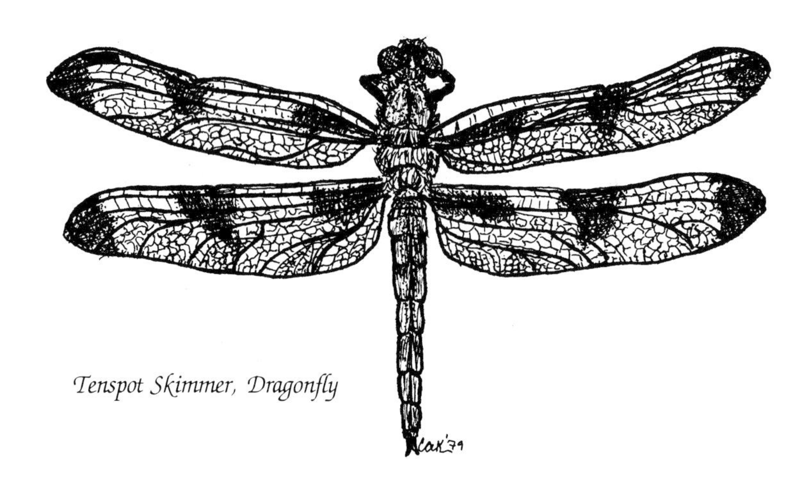

Tenspot Skimmer, Dragonfly

Nymphs of dragonflies are aquatic and live in ponds or streams where they feed on insects. The spiny legs of the adults form a sort of basket under the thorax for catching prey. The head swivels easily on the slender neck, and the huge compound eyes can see in nearly every direction, enabling the dragonfly to catch insects such as mosquitoes and gnats in the air.

Researchers who have marked individual adult dragonflies have found that many may live six to eight weeks. Most species will produce a single generation a year, with the eggs or nymphs overwintering, and a few of the larger darners are known to spend two or three years in the nymphal stage. Marking individuals has also revealed that some dragonfly territories are only as large as the average kitchen or living room.

June 7, 1978 Russian Olives

Hiking on the Arboretum bog boardwalk, I noticed that the pitcher plant, the tufted loosestrife and the blue flag *(Iris versicolor)* were all in bloom. In other habitats poison ivy is flowering along with the ox-eye daisy *(Chrsanthemum leucanthemum)*, which is the common white daisy of roadsides and old pastures. Today anyone who was near a Russian olive was in for a treat as the first open flowers exuded a superb scent, a blend of wild grape and narcissus fragrances.

The Russian olive *(Elaeagnus angustifolia)* is a deciduous shrub or small tree that may grow to twenty-five feet. It is a native of temperate Asia, naturalized in southern Europe and introduced into North America during colonial times. Because of its dense branches, extreme hardiness and resistance to drought, it has been extensively planted as a windbreak in prairie states. Russian olive trees can be striking when planted with evergreens or as a background tree in yards, and on windy days the silvery lower leaf surfaces make it especially attractive. The fruit is a food source for wildlife.

It's the three-eighths-inch flowers, from one to three of them at the base of the current year's leaves, that release an amazing fragrance and give the Russian olive special interest at this time of the year. Each flower has a bell-shaped tube and four spreading lobes about as long as the tube; it is silvery on the outside, like the bottom surface of the leaves, and yellow on the inside. This is a tree worth observing during its late spring blooming.

June 8, 1978 Our State Flower

When the peonies are blooming and the fragrant Russian olive flowers are opening, I look for the first blossoms of our state flower, the showy pink and white lady-slipper *(Cypripedium reginae)*. Minnesota's floral emblem is one of our most interesting wildflowers. Its Latin name has royal distinction. *Cypripedium* means "slipper of Venus" and *reginae* means "the queen." It is found growing wild in tamarack swamps and spruce bogs or moist woods in much of Minnesota except the southwestern one-third of the state.

The lady-slipper flower grows from the top of a leafy stem that may reach three feet. The deeply ribbed leaves, elliptical in shape, are from three to eight inches long. Sometimes two or more blossoms are found on a single stem. Petals and petal-like sepals are pure white and the two-inch long pouch is pink and white.

Most people do not realize the length of time it takes for a lady-slipper, which is the largest of our native orchids, to grow before it produces a blossom. One flower alone produces up to about 600,000 microscopic seeds, but only a few are fertile. Even when a seed germinates, the plant will not be larger than a pencil point when it is one year old, and a certain fungi must be present for growth to take place. The fungi, which lives in the roots of the orchid, delivers the elements of the soil to the plant as the orchid is without rootlets and cannot absorb food or water. These long-lived perennials require about fifteen years from seed germination until they first blossom, and pulling up one of the plants or breaking it off close to the ground will destroy fifteen or more years' growth, which is equivalent to cutting down a mature tree. The species has been protected by Minnesota law since 1925.

If you would like to see our state flower in bloom and can't visit it in its native haunts, come to the bog garden in the Arboretum when the peonies are in full bloom and the Russian olive has started flowering.

The showy pink and white lady-slipper began blooming in the Arboretum:

June 8, 1976	June 14, 1979	June 4, 1982
May 21, 1977	May 31, 1980	June 12, 1983
June 8, 1978	June 2, 1981	

Showy Pink and White Lady-slipper

June 9, 1975 Plant Plankton

Both fresh and salt water contain an enormous variety of living organisms. Plankton is a term applied to the minute forms of life which are suspended or floating in the water column. The plant plankton (phytoplankton) includes a vast array of single-celled, colonial and delicate filamentous algae, together with some bacteria and fungi. The animal plankton (zooplankton) includes protozoa and other minute animals.

Planktonic algae are the beginning of many food chains. Life in oceans and lakes depends on these tiny green plants that use sunlight to make food. The microscopic plants are eaten by progressively larger organisms including fish, which, in turn, may be eaten by man.

phytoplankton--→zooplankton--→small fish--→large fish--→man

The best fishing areas are those high in plankton. Planktonic algae are also important in helping to maintain the carbon dioxide-oxygen ratio of the atmosphere. It has been estimated that about 90 percent of photosynthesis occurs in the oceans, and most of this is accomplished by the phytoplankton. The green color seen in algae is chlorophyll, the green found in all plants. Plants can convert carbon dioxide to the sugars and starches they need, releasing oxygen as a waste product. The energy for this process comes from the sun through the chlorophyll.

Water covers over 70 percent of the earth's surface, but the freshwater habitat is a very limited one, with inland lakes covering some 1.8 percent of the world's surface and running water about 0.3 percent. A small part of the 1.8 percent is Lake Waconia, which has looked quite green the last couple days, so this morning I collected a sample of the plankton with a small mesh plankton net. I wanted to look at some individual algae to determine which species were most common. Using a microscope and looking at a drop from the collected sample, I found seven species of algae. It's like entering a new world when I peer through the microscope at these beautiful, minute, living organisms. They are identifiable by color and shape, and although they do not always look green, all algae possess the green pigment, chlorophyll. Strings of beads, spirals, stars, needles, round balls, long threads and vases are some of the shapes.

I took my water sample to Hibbert Hill, who lives on Lotus Lake, for further study. For about ten years he has been studying phytoplankton in Chanhassen area lakes, in an effort to learn more about freshwater communities, and he was able to identify several species for me. The identification of algae to species takes great technical skill, and I was glad to learn the identification of more of these miniature but important plants from him. Several days after talking to him, I read something in his collection of essays that referred to a lake not far from here that would also be true of other lakes.

"The life of Christmas Lake which one sees — the aquatic plants, the fish, the waterfowl — is vastly subordinate in numbers, and probably in total weight, to the life within the water which one cannot see except through a microscope."

June 10, 1979 Cottonwood Trees Shedding

Kentucky bluegrass is blooming along with pagoda dogwood and highbush cranberries. Eastern cottonwoods *(Populus deltoides)* are shedding innumerable seeds, which are being blown around by the wind on their cottony down. On May 1 as the cottonwoods were blooming, the large male trees shed large amounts of pollen. Now, as the seed pods of the female trees burst and the minute, silky-haired seeds fall, it reminds us of thistle and milkweed down.

Cottonwoods usually grow in moist lowlands near rivers and streams and along lake shores and other moist slopes. This tall tree species is widespread and important east of the Rocky Mountains. In Minnesota the majority of cottonwoods are found in the southern half of the state. Pioneers brought eastern cottonwoods to the treeless plains, and the species is still used as windbreaks and shade trees around farms on the prairies. Shade is provided by a broad crown filled with shiny green triangle-shaped leaves that rustle easily in the wind.

The cottonwood is a fast-growing tree, and in fifteen years could be sixty feet high, but at about 125 feet its limit of growth is reached. Its life span is short. At 75 years it is an old tree, subject to decay, and 125 years is exceptionally old for a cottonwood. The wood is light and soft, warps badly while drying, and is difficult to split, but it is, nevertheless, used for crates, packing material, paper pulp and firewood.

June 11, 1979 First Garden Strawberries

Although in the early spring of 1977 we had the first ripe garden strawberries on May 16, we had to wait until today to taste the mouth-watering fruit in this late spring. Strawberries are the most popular backyard garden fruit in America, requiring little room to grow and not much attention but producing a lot of fruit that is high in vitamin C.

It is not certain how the strawberry got its name. Some authorities think it's because straw was spread around the plants in gardens to keep down weeds and protect ripening fruit from the soil. But others think it got its name because the runners resemble straws or because of the old European practice of stringing wild strawberries on straws of grass. The Romans called it *fragaria* in reference to the perfume of the fruit.

Strawberries grow wild in many parts of the world. Modern plants probably originated from a chance crossing between North American and Chilean plants growing in the same garden. It belongs to the rose family, along with apples, pears, plums, raspberries and several other popular fruits. Botanically speaking, it is not a true berry but rather a pulpy receptacle with a surface covered with the true fruits (the seeds).

June 12, 1979 Alfalfa Hay

Hybrid tea roses are starting to bloom, and honey bees are foraging on the fragrant white and red flowers of the gasplant *(Dictamnus albus)*. I noticed that alfalfa plants have started blooming, and many Waconia area farmers are cutting alfalfa hay although it was on June 2 that the first area farmer was observed haying this year.

Alfalfa *(Medicago sativa)* is in the pea family, along with red clover, white clover, yellow sweet clover, black locust trees and the garden pea. Once established, a field of alfalfa continues to return valuable crops every year, and two to four cuttings are ready each growing season. Alfalfa, the "queen of livestock forages," is considered the best protein source among forage plants. Its taproot grows deep where it can absorb water from a great depth, so it is resistant to drought and can be grown in a wide variety of climates.

Since Alfalfa belongs to the pea family, it has the ability to extract free nitrogen from the air. Through bacteria in the root nodules, nitrogen gas from the air in the spaces among the soil particles is absorbed and is used in the manufacture of several nitrogen-containing substances, including amino acids from which the plants then make proteins. This process of utilizing nitrogen gas is called nitrogen fixation. Only plants like alfalfa that fix nitrogen have a high protein content.

Alfalfa is believed to be native to Iran, where seeds have been found in archeological deposits dating back to about 4,000 B.C., and Persians later raised it for their chariot horses about 500 B.C. When the Spaniards explored Central and South America, they brought alfalfa with them to feed their horses. It has contributed to the prosperity of farmers since its introduction to our country about 1791. In 1859 Wendelin Grimm purchased eighty acres southwest of Lake Minnetonka in what is now Carver Park Reserve and began developing a strain of alfalfa that would winter over in our cold climate. Grimm alfalfa, a significant forage crop, was the result.

Young tender leaves and flowering tops of alfalfa are excellent sources of quickly assimilated vitamins and minerals. Although some people eat the leaves and flowers and sprouts, most find them rather tasteless. This can be remedied by mixing them with other, more tasty greens in a tossed salad or by sprinkling the dried and powdered leaves into soups and stews.

From the standpoint of beekeepers, alfalfa is one of the most important honey plants, an attractive source of nectar for honey bees, which produce an alfalfa honey that has a pleasing, slightly minty flavor.

June 13, 1978 Blue Flag Blooming

Today I saw young mourning doves, catalpa trees about to bloom, and both reed canary and smooth brome grasses shedding pollen. Along the Arboretum bog boardwalk, I noticed the flowers of wild calla and tufted loosestrife and the one-half-inch wide elongated leaves of the narrow-leaved cattail. The tall, stiff plant consists of a yellowish, club-like spike, a gap and then a brownish cylinder made up of female flowers. The male flowers are now shedding their yellow pollen from the club-like spikes, and then later in the year the wind-borne seeds will rise on tufts of down from the cylinders.

Next to the boardwalk platform I stopped to admire the purplish-blue flowers of the blue flag. Naturalist Linda Sanford and gardener Mike Heger transplanted several clumps of the wild iris or blue flag *(Iris versicolor)* from a wetland in Cass County to this bog. Here the plants have flourished the last few years, and today there are close to 100 iris flowers. Each is three to four inches wide and stands on a sturdy stalk among the tall sword-like leaves. Blue flag is found over much of Minnesota in wet pastures, marshes, swamps and wet shores in full sun. The name flag is derived from the Middle English *flagge*, meaning "rush" or "reed."

Although no rain fell today, it is statistically the wettest day of the year.

June 14, 1979 Snapping Turtles

It's egg laying time for snapping turtles. Two days ago one dug a nest and laid eggs near the perennial flower border in the Arboretum. An entry in my field notebook for June 15, 1978, mentions that snapping turtles were laying eggs at this time last year, also.

The common snapper, one of eight turtle species found in Minnesota, often weighs thirty pounds as an adult. Some have been recorded as weighing forty to sixty pounds. It is more widely distributed in North America than any other turtle and is found in all states east of a line between North Dakota and Texas.

The snapping turtle has a thick, rough carapace with a heavy head, pointed snout and powerful jaws. The tail is much longer than that of any other Minnesota turtle and nearly as long as the carapace. It needs nothing more specific than permanent water and lives in sluggish

Blue Flag Iris

streams, ponds and lakes where vegetation is abundant. A study of feeding habits of snappers in Michigan showed their diets to be about one-third water plants, one-third game fish and one-third insects, crayfish, snails, clams, dead fish and other carrion.

Nests are excavated in a variety of locations from sandy shores to hilltops. The two main requirements for a nest appear to be a not too dry soil and a fairly open site where the sun can provide sufficient heat for successful incubation. The cavity is dug with the hind feet, the eggs are laid, and the nest is covered by raking movements of the hind feet. The average number of eggs laid is probably close to twenty-five, but one observer watched a female snapper lay fifty-two eggs at a rate of two per minute. The incubation period for the white spherical eggs, which are a bit more than an inch in diameter, is about eighty to one hundred days. Reports state that there are occasional nests where the eggs didn't hatch until the following spring.

When it is surprised on land, as can easily happen during the egg-laying season in June, the snapper opens its mouth, hisses loudly and strikes out with great speed and power. It is best to stay well beyond the reach of its powerful jaws, for a finger can be badly injured in their crushing grip.

June 15, 1978 Killdeer Nest

A pair of killdeers that chose the dwarf conifer collection in the Arboretum as their nesting site have made a depression in the wood chips and four eggs have been laid. They probably chose this spot because of the availability of suitable ground cover to provide camouflage for the eggs and the incubating bird. Although woodchips were used, it also could have been cinders, gravel or pebbles. The nest may be on gravelly bars and beaches, in pastures and cornfields, on playgrounds or driveways, between train rails, among stumps of a woodland clearing or even on a roof top. It is concealed by its very openness and the dark, blotched character of the eggs.

After the nest depression has been lined with pebbles, woodchips, grass or debris, four eggs are usually laid, and both sexes incubate them. They take about twenty-six days to hatch, and the chicks leave their nest as soon as they are dry after hatching.

The killdeer nests early. We have found a nest with eggs as early as April 12, and the pair here may be nesting a second time; the first eggs having been destroyed by predators or bad weather. They may also simply be starting their family late.

Stories of the parents' perfect imitation of a severe injury to themselves when the nest or young are threatened are well-known, even to people who have never seen a killdeer.

June 16, 1978 Yellow Sweet Clover and Honey Bees

Honey bees are attracted to yellow sweet clover, which is now at bloom peak and secreting nectar. These tall four-foot clover plants with their yellow flowers are prevalent along roadsides and other disturbed open areas. Yellow sweet clover was commonly grown for pasturage for dairy farms. It also made good hay and was used by many farmers to help restore the soil. A good growth of sweet clover plowed under in the spring will contain an average of 100 pounds of nitrogen per acre (the equivalent of 500 pounds of sulphate of ammonia). Since the 1930s alfalfa has replaced sweet clover as a pasture and hay plant.

The first yellow sweet clover florets are usually seen during the last week of May. These early blooming plants are those which grow on the protected south slopes. Here the sun's increasingly warmer rays stimulate photosynthesis and promote growth. The first sweet clover begins blooming heavily in June and usually provides one of the first

Killdeer

major honeyflows. When sweet clover was extensively grown, it was possible for beekeepers to get an average of 200 pounds of surplus sweet clover honey per colony.

Yellow Sweet Clover

June 17, 1978 Garden Roses

Both the old-fashioned and the garden roses (floribundas, grandifloras and hybrid teas) should reach their peak of bloom in a day or two here. Both groups are doing well this year and are extremely showy. Many of the roses have recurrent bloom, and we will enjoy them again later in the summer and fall. June, however, is rose month and, to see the greatest diversity and number of roses, the gardens should be visited now.

Interest in the rose, the queen of flowers, seems to gain momentum every year. I could hardly describe their history, development, culture and use in this short entry, but the Andersen Horticultural Library at the Arboretum has three shelves of books written entirely on the subject. They have an irresistible combination of elegance and charm, thorny vigor and lustrous delicacy, and they blossom in a fantastic variety of colors, sizes, shapes and fragrances. It is the sensuous appeal of roses that has made them the best-known and most popular ornamental plant in the world. Since many people want to "experience" the beauty of roses, the reason for this entry is to tell you when the greatest number of rose plants are at their peak of bloom here or in other places featuring rose collections.

Historical records show that wild roses were brought under cultivation in China about 5,000 years ago, and by the time of the Han dynasties just before the Christian Era, rose gardens had become so popular that huge parks were devoted to them. Although wild roses have single flowers of five petals, through cultivation, selection and hybridization some have evolved to the present day elaborate flowers. Close relatives of the rose include the strawberry, raspberry, hawthorn, peach, apple and apricot. The trait that connects them is the flowers, which have petals in sets of five. Many bear edible fruit, and the rose is not an exception; after a flower's petals fall, they leave behind a small, usually red, rose-apple called a rose hip, which is an excellent source of vitamin C. The chart shows that about a week or more after the peonies are at bloom peak and during the time when the catalpa trees bloom, roses are at their finest.

Date	*Arboretum old-fashioned roses over-all bloom peak*	*northern catalpa trees* (Catalpa speciosa) *at peak of bloom*	*Arboretum garden roses at June bloom peak*	*Arboretum peony collection over-all bloom peak*
1977	June 5	June 3	June 7	May 27
1978	June 18	June 21	June 19	June 12
1979	July 2	July 1	June 29	June 18
1980	—	June 13	June 16	June 10
1981	June 17	June 21	June 21	June 12
1982	June 17	June 29	June 23	June 14

June 18, 1979 Peony Collection

The single-flowered peonies at the Arboretum were at their peak of bloom June 12, and now the over-all collection, made up mostly of double-flowered types, is blooming profusely. Ants are the most common insects found on peonies and are crawling on the buds now, to the consternation or surprise of many viewers who wonder about the function of ants on the flowers. Ants do not help the flowers open, nor do they eat the buds but are only seeking the secreted sweet material.

For centuries the peony has been a standard perennial in gardens throughout the cooler regions of the world. The genus name *Paeonia* is said to commemorate the physician of the Greek gods, Paeon. Peonies are hardy, requiring very little attention, and when other flowers succumb to neglect, peonies continue to flourish. They are often seen in old, abandoned gardens, still blooming. They do not like to be disturbed and prefer to stay in the same place.

Peonies grow best in full sunlight and well-drained soil and should not be planted close to trees or shrubs where they will be shaded and

Double Peony

will have to compete with bigger plants for moisture and nutrients. Peonies may also fail to bloom for any, or all, of the following reasons; lack of moisture or phosphorous, crowded planting or being planted too deeply. A division containing three to five buds or eyes should be planted so that the buds will be just two inches below the soil surface. September is the best time to divide or plant them.

The peony plants are admired for their huge showy blooms, many of which have an impelling fragrance. Colors include white and many shades of pink to deep red. When used as cut flowers, peonies provide fairly long-lasting beauty, and because of their large size, the flowers are frequently used in church flower arrangements. No more than one-third of the flowers on a plant should be cut in order for it to bloom well the following year. Round wire supports will aid the heavy flowers in surviving rain and wind storms. After the plants have finished blooming, the foliage stays green and lustrous and is still attractive until it is killed by frost.

June 10, 1979. I have just received word that both lilacs and peonies are blooming at Lutsen along the North Shore of Lake Superior.

June 19, 1979 White Water Lilies

House wrens are feeding their offspring, and young gophers or thirteen-lined ground squirrels are out of their burrows busily playing, sunning and exploring. In the quiet backwaters of Lake Minnetonka the first white water lilies, double white flowers about six inches across, have appeared.

White water lilies *(Nymphaea tuberosa)* are dependent upon certain conditions in lakes, ponds and streams to live and cannot exist any place else. They must have quiet waters, not too deep, and a silt bottom. Every part of the plant relies on these conditions. The rootstock (rhizome) has only a few rootlets, and it lies buried in the muck as an anchor. Short branches sometimes break off and form new plants. Rising from the rootstalks are leaf and flower stalks, very strong and as pliable as rubber. The floating circular leaves of the white water lily are about one foot wide. The outside sepals and petals of the flowers are canoe-shaped and each help float the magnolia-like flowers that may or may not have a faint apple-like odor. The flowers open each morning for three or four successive days and close in the afternoons. After the blooming period, the flower stem coils in a spiral and takes the ripening seeds below the surface of the water. After several weeks the pod bursts and releases the seeds into the water.

June 20, 1978 Common Cattails Starting to Shed Pollen

Along the Arboretum bog boardwalk two kinds of cattails can be seen; the narrow-leaved cattails, near their pollen-shedding peak, and the common cattails, just starting to show yellow pollen. The upper half of the "cat's tail" contains the male flowers that become packed with ripe pollen during June and July.

The common cattail is similar to the narrow-leaved cattail but has wider sword-like leaves and no gap between the staminate (male) and pistillate (female) flowers on the spike. Every breeze causes the pollen to shower down on the cylinder of female flowers directly below, or over female flowers on neighboring cattail plants. Male flowers fade after the pollen is shed, leaving a bare stalk above the pistillate flowers that then develop into a brown, cylindrical seed mass that bursts into a downy cluster during the winter.

Forming dense stands in shallow water by its creeping rootstalks, the common cattail provides a favorable habitat for red-winged blackbirds and other marsh animals. It is a perennial that is widespread in shallow bays, marshes and springy places throughout the United States.

The common cattail is an extremely useful, edible native plant. In spring the young shoots, about four to sixteen inches long, can be easily pulled from the rootstalks, peeled to a tender white core and eaten raw or cooked like asparagus. When the flower spikes produce a heavy coat of bright yellow pollen, a surprising amount of this yellow dust can be collected by shaking the flowers in a bag. After being sifted, the pollen makes an excellent protein-rich flour when mixed half and half with wheat flour. Pancakes, cookies and muffins made with cattail pollen are famous. In the fall, winter or early spring the rootstalks are filled with starch and can be eaten raw, roasted, or dried and ground into flour.

Cattail leaves can be woven into mats and the spikes gathered for winter decorations, and, finally, the cattail down can be stripped off the spikes and used as stuffing in quilts and pillows and as a lining for diapers.

June 21, 1978 First Day of Summer

Today was the longest day of the year with fifteen hours and thirty-seven minutes of sunlight; but, even though the sun was at its highest today, it will take about five weeks until we get our warmest days. This is due to the lag of maximum ground radiation beyond the peak of solar radiation received by the earth. Ground radiation heats the atmosphere. As the sun travels south, its rays bring less and less heat here as the daylight period gets shorter. However, for some time the diminishing receipts still exceed the amounts of heat we are losing by the ground's radiation into the atmosphere and space. Summer does not reach its peak until the rate of heating is reduced to the rate of cooling, which makes July 26, statistically, our warmest day of the year.

On June 21 or 22 the earth is located in its orbit so that the north polar end of its axis leans at the full 23½° angle toward the sun. This is known as the summer solstice. The sun stands still in its northward motion and then starts heading south. The northern hemisphere is tipped toward the sun, and the southern hemisphere is tipped away. Thus, while all parts of the earth north of the Arctic Circle are having constant daylight, similar latitudes in the southern hemisphere are entirely without sunlight. Longer days, plus a greater angle of the sun's rays, result in a maximum receipt of solar energy in the northern hemisphere at this time. Summer, with its associated high temperatures, results north of the equator.

Many farmers in Minnesota and Wisconsin are busy today cutting or baling the first crop of alfalfa hay, and the first cutting will be nearly complete in the southern half of Minnesota within a few days. Twin Cities area catalpa trees are at bloom peak, the yellowish-green flower clusters on staghorn sumac shrubs are fragrant, and robins can be seen feeding on the ripe fruit of the red-berried elder. In the Arboretum the prickly pear cactus came into bloom, the first plants of the lily collection have a few flowers open, and the first Baltimore butterflies are on the wing.

June 22, 1978 Black-eyed Susans

One of my favorite roadside wildflowers, the black-eyed Susan, has come into bloom. The big, single, slender-stemmed blossom has ten to twenty long golden-yellow rays and a chocolate-colored central cone with disk-type flowers. Each flower head is about two to three inches wide and stands one to three feet high, with rough, hairy leaves and stem.

The black-eyed Susan *(Rudbeckia hirta)* is a "55 mile per hour plant," one which can be identified from a fast moving automobile. However, to appreciate its real beauty, a person should walk in a field, prairie, open forest or roadside ditch among hundreds of these bright blossoms.

June 23, 1977 Deer Flies

Horse flies and deer flies belong to the same insect family and can be included in a list of summer's most bothersome insects. They are now living up to this description.

The females are blood-sucking insects. Their mouth parts are developed for cutting the skin and sucking the blood that oozes from the wound, while the males feed chiefly on pollen and nectar and are often found on flowers. The larvae of most species are aquatic. Eggs are laid in masses on leaves and other objects that overhang the water in swamps or sluggish streams; and, after the maggots hatch, they drop into the water and stay in the bottom mud or sand where they feed on snails and other aquatic organisms.

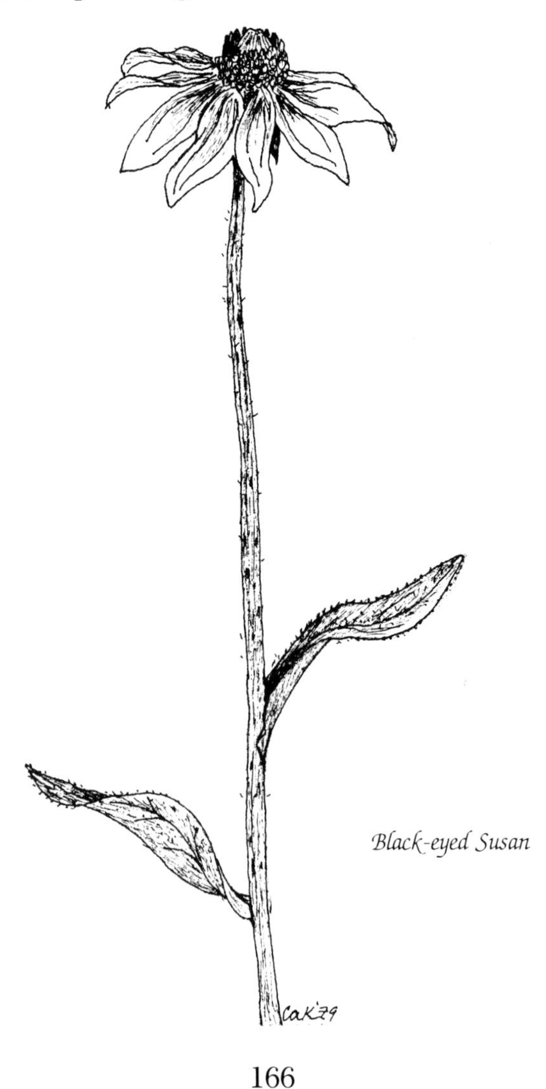

Black-eyed Susan

Humans, together with horses, cattle, hogs, deer and other wild and domesticated animals, are attacked by horse and deer flies that sometimes carry diseases. These insects are strong fliers, easily keeping up with a running horse.

The so-called greenhead, a horsefly that is about one-half inch long with green eyes and a yellowish-brown body, is often a serious pest on bathing beaches.

We usually encounter deer flies near marshes and streams where they buzz around our heads and get into our hair. Protection of arms, legs and any exposed skin is necessary for outdoor enjoyment when they are present. Deer flies, a little larger than horse flies, usually appear about the first week in June.

June 24, 1977 Early Summer

Our astronomical first day of summer arrived three days ago, but summer has been here since about May 21, according to plant development. On that date the Russian olive and the showy pink and white ladyslipper had just started blooming in the Arboretum, and alfalfa hay cutting was well under way in the southern part of the state.

Now we can hear the buzzing sounds of cicadas as we gather ripe blackcap raspberry fruit, garden onions and carrots. A friend from Cologne, Minnesota, reported that her family enjoyed eating their first garden-fresh sweet corn today. On the Arboretum prairie some blooming big bluestem grass stems are six feet high, the gray-headed coneflower just started blooming, and both the ox-eye and black-eyed Susans have many flowers.

I charted my observations that compare this very special growing season with the four that followed to point out just how early the summer of 1977 was. In July, 1977, Benton County Agent Burton Olson said: "We probably won't see another season this good for another generation. This has all the potential for a once-in-a-lifetime year." 1980 was another early year, with an early spring going into an early summer, but '77 was still the winner.

phenological happening in U of M Arboretum area	*1977*	*1978*	*1979*	*1980*	*1981*
first ripe garden raspberries	June 10	July 1	July 8	June 28	June 27
North Star pie cherries ripe	June 18	July 1	July 9	June 24	June 29
Arboretum clematis collection at overall bloom peak	June 20	July 7	July 9	July 1	July 2

basswood trees *(Tilia americana)* at bloom peak	June 21	July 8	July 16	July 3	July 5
male cicadas start singing (loud buzzing sound)	June 23	July 11	July 13	July 1	July 2
first meal of sweet corn out of garden	June 24	July 10	July 12	July 6	July 9
field corn starting to tassel	June 27	July 11	July 18	July 4	July 11
Canada thistle beginning to shed seeds on parachutes	July 3	July 11	July 19	July 1	July 6
first field corn silking	July 2	July 20	July 23	July 11	July 15
first katydid heard calling	July 1	July 16	July 25	July 18	July 9
Sungold and Moongold apricot fruit ripe	July 4	—	July 28	July 13	July 17

June 25, 1977 Blueberries

Botanically, the blueberry, like the currant, gooseberry, grape and tomato, is a true berry: a fleshy fruit usually containing many seeds. Blueberries have small, soft seeds, are juicy and sweet, and have a distinct and individual taste. Many American Indian tribes used them for food, both fresh and dried.

As we traveled to Lake George in Hubbard County just east of Itasca State Park today, I wondered if there would be any ripe blueberries yet as this is an early summer. Soon we were in the forest picking the bright blue fruits, as many as twenty-five from one shrub. During our week-long stay at Lake George we hope to enjoy many bowls of fresh blueberries for dessert and stacks of blueberry pancakes.

Blueberries belong to the heath family, along with cranberries, Labrador tea, wintergreen and azaleas, and to the genus *Vaccinium*, an ancient genus that became well established in North America following the glaciations of the Pleistocene time. In the northeastern United States including northern Wisconsin and northern Minnesota, the native species are the lowbush types that thrive in the wild wherever the terrain is suitable, forming dense, extensive colonies usually six to eighteen inches high. The fruit is generally gathered in July, August and September after the jug-shaped whitish-colored flowers have appeared in May and early June. Wild Minnesota blueberry plants grow in sandy, acid soil of dry, open forests and clearings and in rocky areas in the region of the coniferous forests, but less frequently in southeastern Minnesota.

A month later I returned to the Lake George jack pine forests and picked as many as seventy-seven ripe blueberries from one shrub. In the fall we visited the same forest again and this time were able to pick a few handfuls of blueberries, which still tasted good. At that time, September 27, the blueberry shrubs were at their peak of beautiful red fall color.

June 26, 1979 Luna Moth

Most of my students who are interested in insects are especially curious about the luna moth. Luna moths can be found east of the Rocky Mountains, from southern Canada to Texas and Florida. Although I have had several reports of luna moth sightings from various areas in Minnesota, I have seen the greatest number of these pale green moths, with their two flowing, ribbon-like tails, in the Itasca State Park area.

Four moths were seen early this morning at Lake George near Itasca State Park. Soon I found one that was spending the daylight hours at rest in a shady spot on the back of a cabin, with its wings spread out horizontally. I photographed it and watched it throughout the day. The moth stayed there until evening but flew off when it got dark.

The luna moth, also called moon moth, is light green and has a wingspread of about three and one-half inches. The forewings have a band of light purple or lavender across the frontal margin, and this color also extends over the back of the head. Each wing has a transparent eyespot. The long swallow tails of the hindwings give the moth a graceful shape and at the same time probably afford it some protection from observation. During the daytime the moth hangs, wings down, often beneath green leaves. The long projections of the hindwings resemble leaf petioles, making the insect resemble a pair of leaves.

The biggest and most striking moths are the giant silkworm moths: the cecropia, io, polyphemus and luna, which can be found in Minnesota in June. None of these beautiful creatures ever eats, but comes from the cocoon, flies about in the darkness, mates and then dies at the end of a few days. The females leave their eggs behind on the leaves of trees or other plants that provide food for the larvae.

The luna moth caterpillars feed on the foliage of oak, birch, aspen, walnut and hickory, and they also eat persimmon and sweetgum leaves in states that are south and east of Minnesota. The large greenish caterpillars normally spin cocoons among the leaves on the ground, with each pupa hibernating in the loosely fitting, papery cocoon. Adult lunas emerge the next year about the time the smooth wild rose produces its first flowers.

Looking over my field notes for June 26, I picked a few phenological events that may help to determine when to look for the luna moth adults. In some areas they are double-brooded, but I'm not sure of a second Minnesota brood. Lunas are common now in Hubbard County at the same time that the wild columbine is at bloom peak, together with the bridal-wreath spirea and highbush cranberry. Other phenological events that coincide with the luna's appearance are the flowering of the tall bearded irises and peonies and the end of the blooming of common purple lilacs.

I have seen many Eastern tiger swallowtail butterflies, but no banded purples have appeared yet.

June 27, 1973 Hummingbird Nest

Many people enjoy watching ruby-throated hummingbirds feeding from nectar-producing garden plants and backyard feeders containing water sweetened with honey or sugar, but very few have seen a hummingbird's nest. This afternoon I had the opportunity to see and photograph a ruby-throat on her nest that is on a horizontal limb of a large sugar maple in Marjorie Crosby's Lake Minnetonka area backyard.

During courtship the female ruby-throat sits quietly on a perch while the male displays in a pendulum dance. He flies in a wide arc and buzzes loudly with each dip, but the female shows no preference for a particular male until just prior to egg laying. Observers agree that the male takes no part in nesting activities and is even suspected of polygamy. Occasionally a male may be seen near the nest, but, after mating, he apparently becomes a free wanderer doing nothing but enjoying himself. He spends his time perched on a twig, resting and preening, while his mate chooses a nesting site, builds the nest and rears the brood.

When she is building a nest, she chooses a limb or twig, often sheltered by overshadowing leaves, and collects silky or downy fibers that are then held together with spider silk. The nest, two inches or less in diameter, is covered with bits of lichens. The time required to build it varies according to the weather but usually takes about a week, and when it is finished, it looks like a small knot covered with tree lichens.

The two white eggs, laid one day apart, are about the size of large peas. The female incubates the eggs, which hatch in fourteen days, and after birth the young remain in the nest for about twenty days. A variety of trees are used for nest sites, and the nests are generally built from ten to twenty feet above ground. The one I saw was fifteen feet up.

June 28, 1979 Catalpa Trees

The word *Catalpa* is a Cherokee Indian name adopted by early European settlers. The large heart-shaped leaves with seven to twelve-inch blades and long slender seed pods make the northern catalpa *(Catalpa speciosa)* easy to recognize. The trees are late bloomers in comparison with other ornamental trees in the area, but they now have great panicles of flowers that cover the trees and almost conceal the leaves. The catalpa and the horse chestnut share the distinction of bearing the most showy flowers of our ornamental trees. This year the catalpas are blooming a week later than normal because of the late spring.

A single catalpa flower is about two inches long and one and one-half inches wide. Although the general effect of the flower clusters is white, the individual flowers are spotted with purple and gold. The fruit, which ripens in autumn, is a bean-like, cylindrical capsule, ten to twenty inches long and one-half inch thick. The pods are green, then later turn brown and remain on the tree during the winter, but the leaves turn black and fall after the first hard frost. Toward spring the pods split in half, freeing the flat, winged seeds.

We have a northern catalpa in our backyard, which I expect to reach a height of about fifty feet. The natural range for this catalpa is from southern Illinois and Indiana to western Tennessee and northern Arkansas. It attains its maximum size of about 120 feet along the rich bottomlands of the Ohio River basin.

June 29, 1971 Canada Thistle

Common elderberry shrubs have started blooming, together with the common mullein with its tall, torch-like flower stalks, the common milkweed with its cluster of light purple, fragrant flowers and an equally common plant, the Canada thistle.

The Canada thistle *(Cirsium arvense)* is not a native of Canada but was introduced from Eurasia. After being naturalized, it has become a troublesome weed (a plant out of place) throughout the northern half of the United States and north into Canada from Quebec to British

Columbia. This species is listed as a weed of twenty-seven crops in thirty-seven countries and constitutes the worst thistle problem for warm as well as cool temperate regions. In pastures it reduces forage consumption as cattle will not graze near either tall or spreading plants because of the sharp spines on the leaves.

Creeping thistle, the name given to the plant in England, is descriptive and exact. Rootstocks of the Canada thistle are perennial, invading gardens and meadows and creeping in all directions, just deep enough to be sure of moisture. A single seed can develop into a large colony of plants one to four feet high if left unmolested for a few years, while rootstocks send up shoots from the broken parts if severed by a blow.

It's hard for most people to find a single virtue of the Canada thistle, and it may, perhaps, be the worst weed of the United States. Still, just looking at the thistle, we must acknowledge it to be a beautiful green plant with an artistic form. It also shares its seeds with goldfinches, and the strongly honey-scented flowers are visited by many kinds of insects including honey bees. They are attracted to the rose-purple flowers and then produce a light honey of good quality. In connection with an account of the Toronto Convention of the North American Beekeepers' Association in 1883, A. I. Root wrote about Canada thistle honey:

> "One of the funny surprises was to find tons upon tons of the most beautiful white honey, both comb and extracted, that it has ever been my good fortune to taste, all made from Canada thistle. . . . For whiteness, transparency and beauty of flavor, I have never met anything anywhere like it."

"American Honey Plants" by
Frank C. Pellett, published by
American Bee Journal, Hamilton,
Illinois, 1923.

June 30, 1977 Lilium

Plants called tawny daylilies, calla lilies and trout lilies produce beautiful flowers, but they are not true lilies. True lilies, members of the genus *Lilium*, are perennial plants growing from bulbs. The bulbs are made up of fleshy scales and are not enclosed in a protective outer coat as, for example, tulips are. True lilies produce leafy stems from a few inches to several feet tall, topped by a terminal flower or cluster of flowers. Although completely varied in size, shape and color, lily flowers always have six anthers and six perianth parts (three petals and three sepals), and in popular writing the six perianth parts would be called the six petals.

The Andersen Horticultural Library at the Arboretum has twenty-five books dealing entirely with the genus *Lilium*. In addition to those, there are hundreds of books and periodicals with sections on true lilies. The lilies are at bloom peak today. We had an early spring, followed by an early summer, so the over-all peak of bloom is a week or so early.

Species lilies are wild lilies such as turk's-cap lily and wood lily, two Minnesota natives. Lily species grow wild over the temperate regions of both hemispheres, the greatest number being found in eastern Asia. Most species grow in a particular type of soil in a limited

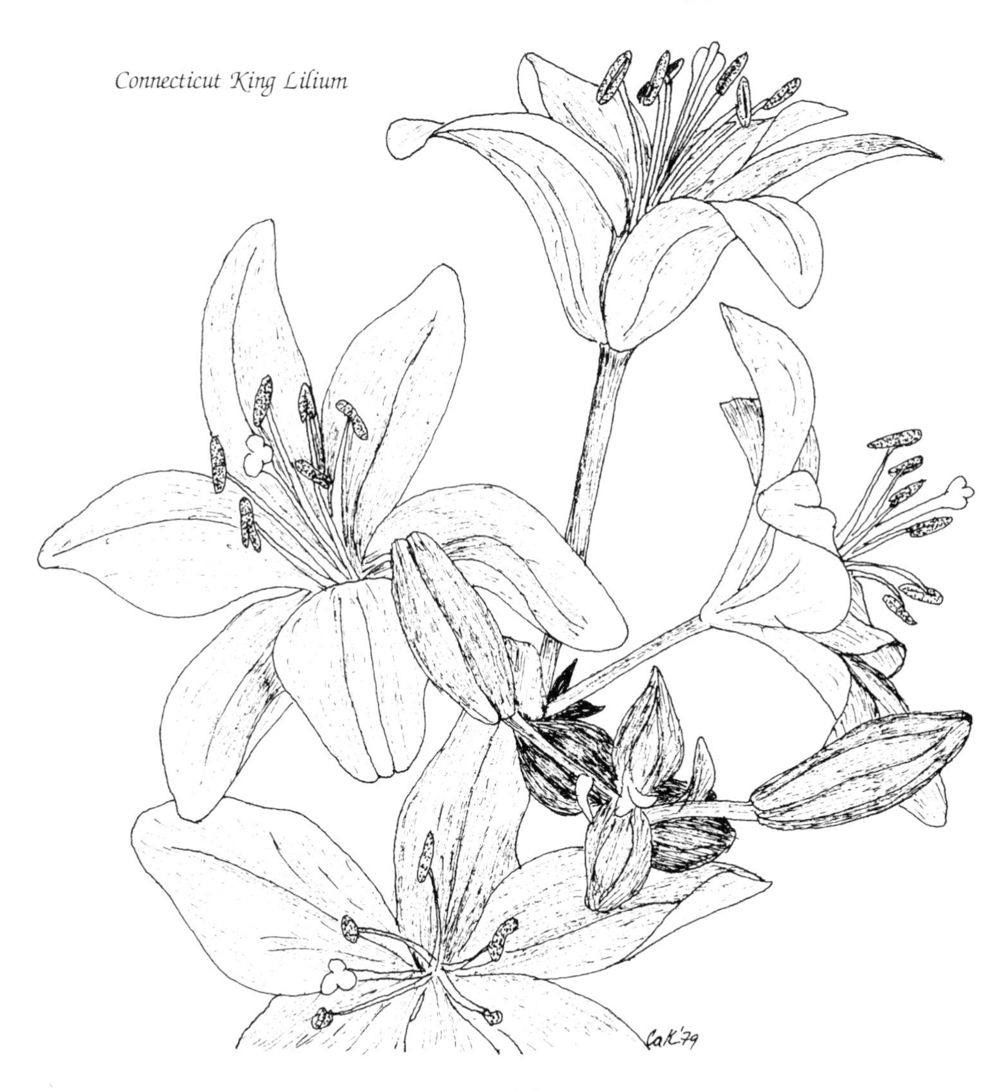

Connecticut King Lilium

geographic area, and unless a garden can provide these conditions of soil, temperature and moisture, the flowers will gradually die. The hybrid lilies are more popular than the species because by selection they combine the best characteristics of several species that go into their breeding. They are then capable of growing and thriving in a variety of soils and in different climates. These hybrids are sold as named cultivars like Tobasco, Enchantment, Jamboree and Connecticut King.

Most lilies require well-drained soil and bloom best in full sunlight. They mix well with most garden flowers, perennials as well as annuals. The slender stems take up little room, and the colorful flowers grow above low companion plants. Lily bulbs are usually planted in early October so that roots can form before the ground freezes. By selecting species and cultivars with different flowering dates, a gardener can plan for lilies to bloom from early June into September.

Arboretum lily collection at over-all bloom peak:

July 6, 1971	June 30, 1977	July 15, 1979
July 7, 1972	July 12, 1978	July 10, 1980

JUNE

June is the month of rains. Temperatures above 95°F may occur on any date over most of Minnesota, and yet frost is always possible in low areas and in the north on any date.

97

White-tailed deer are in their red-brown summer coats. **(97)** Female wood ducks can be seen with their young. **(98)** Black locust trees **(99)** and the smooth wild rose **(100)** both begin flowering in early June.

98

99

100

101

When the goat's-beard **(101)** is blooming, farmers are busy cutting, **(102)** raking **(103)** and baling **(104)** the first crop of alfalfa hay.

102

103

104

In June: Irises bloom. **(105)** Peonies flower nicely. **(106 & 107)** We look for the pink and white lady-slipper, the Minnesota state flower. **(108)**

105

106

107

108

109

110

Honey bees feed on white clover **(109)** and yellow sweet clover. **(110)** Female soft-shelled turtles dig nest cavities and lay eggs. **(111)** Young 13-lined ground squirrels venture above ground. **(112)**

111

112

113

White water lilies **(113)** and yellow water lilies bloom. **(114)** Indian paint brushes are showy **(115)** as is the wildflower called balsam regwort. **(116)**

114

115

116

117

118

119

Eastern tiger swallowtails can be seen sunning **(117)** and drinking from wet sand. **(118)** Banded purple butterflies **(119)** and luna moths **(120)** are on the wing in June.

120

The northern maidenhair fern is seen in hardwood forests. **(121)** Along roadsides and in old pastures, the ox-eye daisy is seen in patches. **(122)** Staghorn sumac shrubs **(123)** and catalpa trees bloom. **(124)**

123

124

125

126

Purple martins keep busy feeding their young. **(125)** The red-berried elder has ripe fruit available to catbirds and robins. **(126)** Wild gooseberry fruit is green and tart. **(127)** The first ripe blueberries can be found at the end of June in Minnesota's jack pine forests. **(128)**

127

128

July
Clematus
Jackmanii

July 1, 1978 Great Spangled Fritillary

While I was picking the first ripe raspberries today, an orange-brown butterfly went zigzagging by, close enough for me to see the black lines and dots on the wings and the silver-colored spots on the under surfaces of the hindwings. After checking an identification book and my reference insect collection, I was sure that the erratic flier was a great spangled fritillary. They are quite common throughout the state, and I have seen them numerous times before. This butterfly with its three-inch wing span is one of the best known of the fritillaries.

Great Spangled Fritillary

An observer will often see flowering milkweeds, surrounded by a throng of insects that are sucking the nectar from the blossoms, and one of the most conspicuous insects is likely to be the great spangled fritillary. This species haunts forests, fields and marshy areas, appearing wherever violets, the larval food plants, grow.

Females begin the life cycle by laying their eggs late in summer on the leaves of a variety of violets or on nearby grasses or twigs. Having deposited the eggs, the mother butterflies soon die. It would seem natural if these eggs remained unhatched until the following spring, but the fact is that the eggs hatch quickly into very small caterpillars. The young larvae eat their empty shells from which they have just emerged and then wander off to find winter sleeping quarters. The following spring the larvae feed on tender new violet leaves and grow rapidly. By early June they are nearly two inches long and are spiny and predominantly black. The full-grown caterpillar then changes to a chrysalis that breaks open about two weeks later as a fully developed butterfly that waits quietly while its wings expand and tissues harden. Those which emerge in late June or early July may survive until early September, which is a comparatively long life for a butterfly that does not hibernate as an adult.

July 2, 1978 Garden Raspberries

Pie cherries including the North Star are ripe now, and the raspberries are ready for picking, with the peak to come during the middle two weeks of July.

Since almost everyone likes the taste of fresh raspberries, they are, luckily, one of the easiest fruits to grow. They produce abundantly, and one grower figures that each foot of a row produces a pint of berries during the season. They blossom late and are seldom bothered by frost. Raspberries can usually be grown without spraying, take a minimum amount of care and are easy to pick without bending over. In addition to these desirable features, there are many varieties and cultivars suitable for almost every section of the country. The raspberry is a nearly perfect fruit.

The English name raspberry comes from the thorny canes of the shrubs. The plant grows wild from the arctic to the equator wherever there is enough moisture, and because it grows in so many places, people in different regions have given it different names. As far back as Roman times it was called *rubus*, meaning something like "red berry." This Latin name lives on in the scientific name of the raspberry genus, *Rubus*. Like the blackberry to which it is closely related, the raspberry belongs to the rose family, and the blossoms of a raspberry plant resemble miniature wild roses.

Raspberry fruit is an aggregate fruit; that is, each of the little bumps in the berry is a tiny fruit itself, complete with a seed and fleshy covering. The berries should be picked as soon as they will slip off the core without breaking the texture of the berry. The patches should be picked thoroughly every day, and all berries that will slip from the core removed. If the picker overlooks a berry that is ready to be picked, it will be overripe the next day.

There are raspberry plants called ever-bearing that produce both a fall and a summer crop. Fallred and Fallgold produce a crop of fruits near the top of the new canes, beginning in late summer. On the summer-bearing types the canes remain vegetative the first year, but the second year both produce a crop on the second-year canes. After they fruit, these canes die and should be removed.

July 3, 1978 Basswood Tree Flowers

There is a progression of flowers, ripe fruit and seeds as the summer season advances. At the present time reed canary grass has ripe seeds, tartarian honeysuckle shrubs have either bright red or orange fruit, and basswood trees *(Tilia americana)* are blooming.

The basswood, also called the American linden, is common in deciduous woods throughout the Upper Midwest. It's easy to recognize the large, smooth, heart-shaped leaves that are four to six inches long, dark green above and light green below, and edged with coarse teeth. The basswood forms a handsome, compact, symmetrical tree that grows from fifty to one hundred feet high, occasionally even higher.

At this time of the year a basswood tree can actually be located and identified by sound and smell. The blooming trees soon will be loaded with clusters of fragrant, creamy white flowers that perfume the neighborhoods and attract the honey bees that gather by the thousands to harvest the nectar. On a calm day the buzzing of their wings makes a humming noise that can be heard from a great distance. The honey bees and the insects will pollinize the flowers and the basswood will then bear fruit, each about the size of a pea.

The basswood blooms for about two weeks, and it can be an excellent source of honey. Honeyflows are irregular, however, and can only be depended upon about one year out of two. When the flows are good, there are enormous yields of honey with a rather strong flavor.

I have read that the wood of basswood, valued for its light weight and good working qualities, is often used in building beekeeping supplies. The wood is also used in the manufacture of furniture and other woodenware articles as well as pulp for paper.

Basswood trees beginning to bloom in the Arboretum area:

June 29, 1973	July 9, 1979
June 20, 1976	June 28, 1980
June 9, 1977	June 28, 1981
July 2, 1978	July 4, 1982

July 4, 1978 Knee High

On this date a year ago I wrote in my journal, "Much of the field corn in the Waconia area is up six to eight feet and has started shedding pollen. How about that for the 4th!" A farmer from the Delavan area in Faribault County had a corn stalk over thirteen feet high that day. These are examples of the remarkable growth that was the result of the early spring followed by an early summer in 1977.

This summer we are in an average growing season, and yet much of the field corn in Carver County is three to four feet high and some even higher. The corn is a foot or two above our knees today. In another week the first tassels will appear, and by July 20 field corn will be silking.

The corn ear is the female flowering structure. Each potential kernel has a long slender tube called the silk that receives pollen from the male flowering structure, the tassel. On a well-developed corn ear there are 750 to 1,000 kernels arranged in an even number of rows around the cob. In normal corn belt hybrids there are sixteen, eighteen or twenty rows of potential kernels per ear, with about fifty kernels per row and 750 to 1,000 silks per ear.

The tassel normally emerges a week or ten days before the silks, but pollen shedding is delayed until two or three days before the silks emerge from the ear husks. Pollen shedding usually continues for five to eight days. Pollen grains fall on the silk and are held by minute hairs and a sticky surface. They germinate and send a pollen tube down the silk to the ovule where the pollen nucleus fertilizes the egg, and the new kernel begins to develop. Under favorable growing conditions all silks will emerge and be ready for pollination within three to five days, so there is usually time for all silks to be pollinated before the tassel stops shedding pollen. Yet despite this overlap in the timing of pollen shed and silking, the pollen of a given plant rarely fertilizes the silks of the same plant. About 97 percent or more of the kernels produced by each plant are pollinated by other plants in the field. The pollen itself is light and is often carried a considerable distance by the wind, but most of it settles within twenty to fifty feet.

The corn plant is one of nature's most amazing energy-storing devices. From a seed which weighs little more than one-hundredth of an ounce, a plant seven to ten feet tall develops, and this plant in turn produces hundreds of seeds similar to the one from which it started.

July 5, 1979 Young Purple Martins

Today Millard Skarp and I enjoyed the gurgling chatter of purple martins as they perched in their multi-roomed houses that are set on poles about fifteen feet above ground, and we watched their aerial displays high above Lake Minnetonka. Millard lives on Browns Bay, and every day from April to September he studies and enjoys the behavior of the purple martins that return each year to his yard. He provides apartments, thoughtfully placed and maintained, for them, and in return these largest members of the swallow family give him pleasure with their aerial displays and songs during the spring and summer months.

Today both male and female martins were busy feeding their young. We watched them bringing in dragonflies that the young snatched and swallowed, often with difficulty. The diet of the purple martin could almost be covered by one word — insects, but this is not literally true as they eat a few spiders also. Their food is generally procured on the wing and in the usual swallow fashion of darting, swooping and wheeling in streamlined flight. Martins do not usually fly at a great speed, but they can, if necessary, when they are catching swift insects like dragonflies. The great variety of insects they consume includes some moths and butterflies and many species of beetles, bugs and flies. At times martins may also resort to ground feeding where they find ants and other insects. Sometimes, too, they can be seen flying close to the surfaces of lakes or rivers, dipping down for drinks.

Only one brood of young is raised each summer by martins in the Upper Midwest. I have read that the dark steel-blue males establish territories, and each female, similar in coloring but light-bellied, selects a male-nestbox combination, but not one or the other. The nest is started about a month before the eggs are laid, with both sexes building it. Usually four or five eggs are laid, and incubation apparently is performed by the female only. The eggs hatch in about fifteen days and the young remain in the nest for nearly a month, but often heat and parasites may cause many deaths. Once the young leave the nest, many will return night after night for about a week.

After the nesting season has ended each summer, martins gather into assembly groups before leaving the area. The early migration of martins comes to a peak the second half of August in Minnesota as the birds leave for their winter home in Brazil. While they are there, they feed on insects in the air as before, but they do not nest. Their homing instincts are strong, and many will return to the same nesting area the following spring.

July 6, 1978 What's Blooming in the Arboretum?

Many flowers are blooming profusely as we approach the middle of summer. Adam's needle *(Yucca filamentosa)*, a hardy yucca that is suitable for northern gardens, is at bloom peak now, extremely showy with its five-foot tall spikes of creamy-white flowers and long, narrow evergreen leaves.

Also nearing bloom peak is the clematis collection, which attracts many Arboretum visitors each summer. The trellis is nearly covered with climbing plants, most of the sixty species and cultivars overlayed with large flowers. Clematis is ideal for covering fences, arbors, trellises, porches and walls and can also be used informally over rock slopes and tree stumps and on pillars and lamp posts. Some of my favorites that are blooming now are Duchess of Albany with its two and one-half inch bell-shaped, pinkish-red flowers; Victoria with five-inch purple blossoms; Mme. Edward Andre, a massive flowering maroon introduction from France; and the most popular of all, Jackman with violet-purple flowers.

Blooming wild flowers on the restored prairie include ox-eye, butterfly-weed, stiff coreopsis and showy tick-trefoil, together with the leadplant and gray-headed coneflowers that just started to bloom the last few days. Near them the common milkweed plants are loaded with fragrant flower clusters.

Along the bog boardwalk common cattails are shedding pollen, and swamp milkweed, tall meadow-rue and marsh skullcap are blooming.

Honey bees are busy on the flowers of white sweet clover, bird's-foot trefoil, many of the stonecrops and the basswood tree blossoms, while the yellow pea-like flowers of genista are being visited by bumble bees.

Black-eyed Susans, common elderberry shrubs, the swamp azalea *(Rhododendron viscosa)* and lilies also add color to the landscape. I have mentioned only a few of the blooming plants of this area, which is rich in floral beauty.

July 7, 1978 Blue Vervain

Look for blue vervain, a summer perennial wildflower that is never really in full bloom, in roadside ditches, marshes, swamps, wet meadows and, in fact, any moist soil. Only a ring of tiny blossoms, each about one-sixth of an inch across, is open at any time. However, in spite of having only a few small flowers open, the bright violet-blue color is so intense that the plants make a handsome show. The flowers are nectar-bearing, and honey bees and other insects forage on them. It is a native of wet places, grows about three to five feet tall, and has the scientific name *Verbena hastata*. The name *Verbena* is the Latin for any sacred herb. Plants in this genus, according to old herbal writings, were a general cure-all.

Possibly there is some chemical compound in blue vervain plants that could be helpful, but we don't regard it as a medicinal plant at this time. In researching the source of the common name, I found that the word vervain is derived from two Celtic words, *fer*, meaning "drive away," and *faen*, meaning "stone," an allusion to its supposed ability to cure or drive away kidney stones.

Blue vervain is a slender, leafy plant with a square, grooved stem that branches at the top into many narrow flower spikes. The small five-petaled flowers begin blooming at the bottom of the spikes with the result that by mid-summer each flower spike bears ripening seeds

Blue Vervain

below, a few blue blossoms midway and buds in many stages at the top. A group of plants beside a running stream or other wetland is attractive and beautiful. The plants have just started blooming now, and they will continue to flower into September. For this reason some people who see the flowers at this time of the year are reminded of fall and think of them as a sign of autumn, another example of how one season slides into another.

July 8, 1979 Lightning Bugs

After the sun goes down and it becomes dark, flashing of the lightning bugs or fireflies can be seen if one is in or near their habitat. I usually see their tiny lights over meadows and grassy ditches not far from woodlands, usually from late May until early summer. The flashing is a recognition signal enabling the sexes to find each other. Each firefly species has a characteristic flashing rhythm, and an expert observer can identify species by the length of the flashes and the interval between flashes.

Fireflies or lightningbugs are soft-bodied beetles that have segments near the ends of their abdomens that enable them to produce light. The light is unique in being cold, and nearly 100 percent of the energy given off appears as light. It is produced by the oxidation of a substance called luciferin that is manufactured in the cells of the light-producing organ. Since they can take in air through tiny openings in their abdomens, the fireflies control their blinking yellow lights by controlling the air supply. When air is admitted, the luciferin in the presence of an enzyme called luciferinase is almost instantly oxidized, releasing the energy as light.

July 9, 1973 Summer Snack

A group of junior high students came to the Arboretum to learn about edible wild plants. I had only an hour to spend with them, so we went out on the grounds for a first-hand experience. After we stopped under a large basswood tree that was loaded with fragrant flowers, I picked and ate a flower. In this era of the supermarket few people take advantage of the great store of edible wild plants available, and very few have developed the skills necessary to identify such plants. Since the students trusted my ability, especially after I ate a couple of blossoms, soon they, too, enjoyed the mild-tasting flowers of the American basswood.

Then we reached a thicket of the blackcap raspberry, and without hesitancy they enjoyed the mouth-watering fruit there. Our next stop was the old-fashioned rose garden area where we gathered the clover-like leaflets of wood-sorrel and the paddle-shaped purslane leaves. Purslane leaves are rich in iron, taste mildly acid and are mucilaginous. The students ate both but preferred the sour wood-sorrel leaflets.

We finished our hike by eating tree-ripened apricots, which have a sweet, sprightly flavor, and along with them, some red currants. Although these last two snacks were from cultivated plants, I needed to make the point that nature's free harvest alone cannot adequately feed our large population. Even around small towns the wild edible plants would soon be depleted if everyone depended on them for survival.

Knowledge of what can and cannot be eaten in the wild is of great value. When canoeing or hiking into the back country, one can travel more lightly and can vary a diet with edible plants that have a different taste and frequently a higher vitamin content than commercially grown vegetables. If lost or separated from a store of provisions, one need not starve; even a bit of knowledge about edible wild plants will get a person out alive and even healthy.

The hour hike was too short for the students to get that bit of knowledge, but hopefully the experience will spark their interest. Many excellent field guides in small book form are available for people to study at their leisure and to slip into their backpacks before a trip.

July 10, 1978 Common Milkweed at Bloom Peak

If you enjoy the perfume of flowers, this is the time to get close to the fragrant flower clusters of the common milkweed *(Asclepias syriaca)*. About thirty to sixty individual flowers are found in drooping dull-purple clusters that are rich in nectar and attract many insects. A native perennial plant growing three to four feet tall, the common milkweed is also the most familiar milkweed plant. It can be found in meadows, fields, roadsides and waste areas, always in full sun.

When researching the popular literature concerning the common milkweed, I came across some interesting information. These are a few things I found:

> The genus *Asclepias* was named in honor of Aesculapius, Greek god of medicine, undoubtedly because in the past some species have been used to treat a variety of ailments. Carolus Linnaeus used the species name *syriaca* for our common milkweed, thinking that

the plant came from Syria; hence the misnomer, which the rules of nomenclature do not permit us to change.

The plant is found from New Brunswick to Saskatchewan and southward to Georgia, Tennessee and Kansas.

The flowers contain nectar, and some American Indians sweetened wild strawberries with the dew from the blossoms.

A striking peculiarity of the plant is the large amount of milky-white sticky juice that pours out of the slightest wound to a stem, flower or leaf. This milky juice is not the sap of the plant. It is a special secretion and quite distasteful, which is the reason grazing animals avoid the milkweed. It served some early European settlers as glue.

Early settlers also used the long silky threads on the seeds to stuff pillows and mattresses, and during World War I, children were paid a penny a pound for the milkweed silk, which was used to stuff life preservers.

Common Milkweed

Young stems, leaves, pods and flower buds have sometimes been cooked like asparagus. Although the milky juice is bitter and mildly toxic, both of these properties can be eliminated by boiling, using several changes of water.

Only bees seem able to pollinate the flowers, even though flies, butterflies and other insects are attracted to the flowers. The pollination is extremely intricate. If one observes and compares the number of blossoms on a milkweed stem with the number of pods it bears, it becomes apparent that only a few of the flowers become fertilized.

Common milkweed plants spread vigorously by means of creeping subterranean rhizomes as well as by seeds. As a result, we may sometimes find a solitary stem, but more often two to five plants sustain and support one another. The plants have thick, oblong, gray-green opposite leaves in summer or open pods in fall or winter.

July 11, 1978 Ripe Currants

The elegant garden lilies are almost at bloom peak. I saw the first field corn tasseling and the first Canada thistles shedding seeds on their parachutes, and I heard the first cicada buzzing this afternoon. I also enjoyed eating ripe red berries from the Red Lake and the Cascade currant bushes. These are outstanding varieties that were developed and introduced by the University of Minnesota Horticultural Research Center. Both are wonderful for eating off the plants or made into delicious sauce or sparkling red jelly. They are ready for picking now as they are fully colored, and since they produce their flowers and fruits in drooping clusters which hang down like clusters of grapes, harvesting is easy.

Although fresh currants are sold in Europe at grocery stores and fruit stands, they are seldom seen on the fresh fruit counters of our supermarkets. People who enjoy the pleasant, tart but mild flavor should consider growing a few shrubs in their gardens. They begin bearing when they are about three years old and have a productive life of many years. A good yield is about two to three quarts of fruit per mature bush.

Currant shrubs should be planted in early spring in a sunny location, in almost any soil with good drainage except light sandy soils that become hot and dry during the summer. If the plants are set about an inch deeper than they were in the nursery, new shoots will be forced to rise from below the soil level forming a bush rather than a single stem. The plants require little care except for weed control and pruning, which consists only of the removal of the oldest stems at ground level in early spring before growth starts. Such pruning will keep the shrubs young and fruitful for many years.

Currants have few insect and disease problems, but most currants and gooseberries, which are close relatives of currants, are susceptible to white pine blister rust. Rust spots develop on the undersurfaces of the leaves, and hair-like projections hang down from these spots. The disease does little harm to the currents and gooseberries, but it can be fatal to the white pine trees to which the spores can be carried. First a few limbs will die and then, finally, the whole tree. The disease does not spread from one white pine to another but must always come from one of the host plants. Laws in many states require that all currant and gooseberry plants must be planted at least 900 feet from white pines. A permit is needed to grow them in certain northern Minnesota counties where white pine is an important tree crop.

Currants are cold-weather plants and not likely to grow well in the warmer parts of the country. They are native to the cooler parts of North America, Europe and Asia, and for centuries have added their tart flavor to the often dull diet of northern European lands. The name currant originally meant a kind of dried grape raised in the region of Corinth, Greece, and shipped from there to the rest of Europe where they were used in cookies and cakes. In England the name "Corinth" became corrupted into "currant," and, perhaps because the small berries of the currant bush looked a bit like the dried Corinth grapes, the name of the imported fruit was given to them.

July 12, 1979 Lunch with the Gophers

Our three-year-old son Christian and I enjoyed a hike in the Arboretum and a picnic lunch there. Eight gophers, four blue jays and several common grackles and red-wings joined us. They certainly liked our food as we shared a few potato chips and bits of bread in exchange for the chance to watch them at very close range. We were fascinated by the actions of the birds and gophers. It is surprising to see these animals set aside their fear of us as they give in to their desire for a free meal. The birds could escape on the wing in a second if alarmed, but the gophers had many feet to travel on their short legs before reaching the safety of their burrows on the grassy hillside.

Our so-called Minnesota gophers are also known as thirteen-lined ground squirrels. They are animals of the Great Plains and prairie regions of central United States and south central Canada. Land that has been cleared for farming has opened new territory for gophers, and their range has expanded, especially eastward, during the last century. Where they are abundant, thirteen-lined ground squirrels may number from five to twenty per acre. Soil type, which determines the kind of vegetation and the ease of burrowing, affects their number and distribution.

I have been criticized occasionally for admitting that I like them, but over the past ten years I have been intrigued by their behavior as I continue to study them informally. I like to hear their bird-like, high-pitched, trilling alarm calls that are sounded frequently over the grasslands as they keep a sharp watch for enemies. They stand upright, forelegs pressed against their bodies, hind legs and tails forming tripods to support their backs, and in this position survey the area around their homes for several minutes at a time. Then, whenever they are startled, they run into the safety of their burrows.

Grasshoppers are a favorite prey of gophers, and they pursue them with swift, cat-like leaps. About half the diet of gophers consists of insects like grasshoppers, crickets, caterpillars, beetles and others. Plant materials like grass seeds are also relished, and during the summer they take many cheek-pouch loads of food into burrows for storage. Most of the damage they inflict on newly planted seeds and sprouting crops occurs in springtime when few insects are available, but they seldom venture far out into cultivated fields. Their fondness for insects prevents grasshoppers and other insects from multiplying into hordes.

July 13, 1973 Prairie Bloom

A prairie is defined generally as a natural grassland composed of native perennial grasses and herbaceous plants. This primeval vegetation that occupied the land for thousands of years has been destroyed and the land planted with man's crops.

Before European settlers arrived on the plains of the Midwest and West, prairie grasses and wildflowers stretched as far as people could see. In Minnesota more than one-third of the state or about 19 million acres were covered with prairie vegetation. Hundreds of thousands of square miles in the United States are known today as farmland but were at one time the prairie.

Remnant prairies still exist. It has been through the initiative of a relatively few individuals and conservation groups such as the Nature Conservancy that these have been saved, but in spite of their efforts, remnant prairies are still being destroyed. Some are plowed up and planted to crops; others are sprayed with herbicides or ruined by over-grazing or continuous mowing. These remnants must be guarded since they are our remaining link to a world that lived 10,000 years ago. Prairies are too few to make prairie plants common, but the remaining plants and the animal life they support need our protection.

Most prairie plants are long-lived perennials. Each autumn the upper parts die back to ground level, but the roots remain alive. There is evidence that many prairie plants live for decades, even centuries, like large trees in a forest. In order to carry out meaningful research with regard to our changing environment, we need natural landscapes, such as virgin prairies, forests and bogs, to serve as standards against which to evaluate the changes that have occurred throughout our country and the effects of those changes on people and other biological organisms. In addition to being aesthetically appealing, prairies are a gene pool for organisms that may serve us in the future.

This morning I joined part of the Arboretum staff on a trip to the Schaefer Prairie, a 160-acre prairie relic in McLeod County. Dr. Snyder, the Arboretum director, and Al Johnson, the Arboretum taxonomist, helped us identify some of the plants we were not familiar with. We could easily see why so many early travelers described prairies as garden-like, for more than 200 plant species have been recorded on the Schaefer Prairie where we saw several dozen in bloom today.

One of the plants we saw was the butterfly-weed, one of the brightest and most conspicuous of the northern wildflowers. It was topped with blazing orange flowers, and, unlike other milkweeds, this plant has no milky juice. Both purple prairie clover and white prairie clover were in bloom. The leadplant had flowers in dense violet spikes and compound gray leaves with soft hairs, giving the plant both its lead color and its name. Prairie phlox, prairie larkspur and the stiff sunflower had showy flowers. We walked through big bluestem and prairie cordgrass, and as we did, I thought how man has changed the face of the prairie lands as he has changed the face of the earth. However, although most of the prairie is gone, its accumulated productivity now supplies food for many hungry people of the world.

July 14, 1979 Cicada Buzzing

On this date in 1936 a high temperature of 108°F was recorded in Minneapolis. According to consulting meteorologist Bruce Watson, that is the highest temperature recorded for the Twin Cities as a principal feeder weather station since records were first kept at Fort Snelling in August, 1819. Today's high temperatures were only in the mid-80s, but the male cicadas sang loudly and shrilly. I wonder what they sounded like on this date in 1936 since their powerful, sometimes pulsating buzzing intensifies with warmth. But possibly 108°F was even too warm for cicadas.

Cicadas are common insects, more often heard than seen since the majority are arboreal. The sounds are produced by the males, with each species having a characteristic song. To some uninformed people this sound is often attributed to telephone wires vibrating on hot days. Their sound-producing mechanism is complex, but to explain it simply, the sound is made by vibrating membranes stretched over a pair of sound chambers situated one on each side of the abdomen. Whatever the mechanism, I love to hear the buzzing sounds on a warm day.

There are over seventy-five species of cicadas in North America. Most are large, black insects, one and one-half to two inches long, with green markings and clear wings. Their broad, blunt heads have widely separated, prominent compound eyes. For most, their life cycle is completed in two to five years, with some adults appearing each summer.

The periodical cicadas have a life cycle of thirteen to seventeen years, and adults are present in a given area only in certain years. Female cicadas cut slits in young twigs and deposit eggs there, and as the wingless young hatch, they drop to the ground, burrow in and stay there for the prescribed number of years as nymphs, living on juices sucked from roots. When full-grown, the nymph emerges from the soil and climbs a tree trunk, the skin splits down the back, and the adult comes forth.

First cicada heard:

June 23, 1977	July 1, 1980
July 11, 1978	July 2, 1981
July 13, 1979	July 3, 1982

July 15, 1979 Gray-headed Coneflower

While out on the prairie in the Arboretum, I noticed that the gray-headed coneflower *(Ratibida pinnata)*, also called the prairie coneflower, had come into bloom. Each flowering head is gray in the center with bright yellow petals (ray flowers) about two inches long that droop down almost parallel to the stem. These plants grow three to five feet tall and have slender hairy stems and deeply cut leaves. The cylindrical gray cones of the flower heads exude an anise scent if bruised. Gray-headed coneflowers are sometimes encountered along roads and railways now, but since these perennials are palatable to livestock, they are not often seen on rangelands, only on the remnant prairies.

We are able to enjoy seeing hundreds of coneflowers waving in the wind along with thousands of other individual prairie plants of many species because Albert Johnson, former Arboretum taxonomist, took the initiative to reestablish a prairie in the Arboretum on former farmland.

Grey-headed Coneflower

July 16, 1979 Blackcap Raspberries

The blackcap raspberry *(Rubus occidentalis)* is native between Quebec and Minnesota and south to Arkansas and Georgia. It is found in thickets, ravines and edges of forests and is also cultivated as a horticultural plant. It is a plant with strong arched canes containing hooked spines.

Today I checked a patch of this wild raspberry and found, to my delight, ripe dark-purple berries. Eating wild fruits that are firm, sweet, juicy, and have outstanding flavor is a rare pleasure, and I'll be back again in a few days as much more fruit is ripening.

Although I prefer to eat them fresh as I pick them, the berries can be used in jam, jellies, juice, sherbet and ice cream, or they can be canned, frozen, or dried.

July 17, 1979 Migrating Shore Birds

In the middle of July the fall season seems far away, but the bird migrations have begun already. Ann Sigford, naturalist at the Wood Lake Nature Center in Richfield, reported seeing a greater yellowlegs there today, and three days ago observers in Meeker and Stevens counties saw yellowlegs, stilt sandpipers, least sandpipers, semipalmated sandpipers and semipalmated plovers.

These birds and about twenty-five other species are shore birds that can be observed in the Twin Cities area, some for only a few days each year as they migrate through. They are highly migratory and are water birds in the sense that they spend a large part of their lives about the shores of lakes, streams or seacoasts. They typically have pointed wings and slender, fairly long bills, which are suitable for searching in shallow water or probing in mud for food. Their long legs and partially webbed feet are adapted for wading and their plumage is waterproof.

The early migration that is taking place now is related to the shore birds' nesting habits. Most nest in the far north, arriving on the tundra usually in May while snow still covers about two-thirds of the ground. As soon as the snow melts in the arctic and the dark ground is exposed to the warming sun, vegetation breaks out and great swarms of insects appear. The major obstacle to life in the far north is the brevity of the summer season, which causes the nearly explosive blooming of the flowering plants, the hurried development of insects and the short nesting period of the shore birds. Almost all northern birds are primarily insect predators, and the insect swarms in the arctic are their food. The hatching of millions of shore bird chicks is, no doubt, synchronized with the peak of the insect cycle.

Nearly all shore birds nest on the ground, and the usual clutch size of four large eggs seems to be the maximum number successfully incubated. The young are precocial, covered with down and able to leave the nest the same hour they hatch. All adult birds leave the far north before or as soon as the young begin to fly, but before they are able to follow their parents. Some biologists think this may be an adaptive trait designed to lower the population size and reduce competition for food. The young are left to fend for themselves after their parents leave, and they migrate south later. How they find their way southward, many traveling as far as Argentina, is a migration mystery.

By mid-July the migration of several species through Minnesota is well under way, reaching a peak in mid-August. A second peak occurs again in September when the young birds follow the migratory paths of their parents. The early return of small numbers of adults to our area now is probably correlated with the abandonment of their nests during severe weather in the arctic. Mud flats along the edges of water are places to look for migrating shore birds as they fly through the Twin Cities.

July 18, 1979 Dry Lawns

Our lawn grasses are dry and turning brown. That's not surprising since about one inch of water per week is needed to maintain a green lawn, and we have received very little rain so far in July. Maintaining a green lawn all summer usually requires some watering by homeowners.

On anything larger than a tiny lawn, however, watering is probably a waste of our water resources. This becomes apparent when we remember what happened during past dry spells. Lawns became dormant during dry periods but recovered after the rains returned. The only reason to water our yards is to keep them green. If one has a limited amount of water, it is best to use the water for evergreens, young shade trees, flower gardens, fruits and vegetables to keep them alive and growing, according to Dr. Snyder.

These warm, sunny days are ripening the fields of oats, the field corn is growing fast and has just started tasseling, and white sweet clover plants are at bloom peak along roadsides. Long-horned meadow grasshoppers calling from grassy spots add to our summer idyll.

July 19, 1979 Choke Cherry Fruit

Clusters of red to dark purple choke cherries are ripening in the Arboretum area. This is a bitter fruit about the size of a pea that can be found on the edges of forests and fields, in thickets, on stream banks and along fence rows. Your outdoor education has been neglected if you have never picked the berries from the bushes and eaten them!

The choke cherry is a large shrub or small tree, seldom reaching over twenty feet in height, with two noteworthy characteristics: First, it is reported to be the most widespread species of tree in North America, growing from Alaska and Canada, throughout the states and into Mexico. Second, the fruit makes one of the most tart, refreshing jellies ever tried on fresh corn bread. I also make an unusual-tasting and invigorating hot weather drink by mashing the fresh choke cherry fruit, draining the juice and adding water and sugar to it.

July 20, 1978 Ripe Apricots

Apricot trees blossom before the other fruit trees in our yard. This year they bloomed on May 5, with plums on May 12 and apples on May 18. Because they bloom early, blossoms are sometimes injured by frost, and pollination can be a problem because of cold, wet weather. But even without a crop of fruit each year, the trees are attractive ornamentals, especially in spring when the light pink flowers cover the trees and again in fall when the leaves turn golden-yellow.

Sungold and Moongold are two varieties developed at the University of Minnesota Horticultural Research Center especially for this area. Both have the Manchurian apricot in their breeding, and one of each must be planted for cross pollination.

Today I picked and ate several tree-ripened apricot fruits. Not everyone likes the slightly different taste of the apricot, but to me the sweet flavor resembles the peach although the fruit is drier. Many people have never eaten a fresh, tree-ripened apricot since most of the commercially grown apricots are raised on the west coast where they are then dried, canned or shipped to the rest of the country before fully ripened.

The apricot is one of the oldest fruits raised by man and seems to have originated in China where it was being cultivated more than 4,000 years ago. In the fourth century B.C., Alexander the Great is said to have tasted an apricot in Persia or Armenia and was so pleased with it that he arranged to have apricot trees planted in Greece, his native land. From there they spread throughout the Mediterranean region before the beginning of the Christian era. At the present time the Soviet Union is the world's leading apricot producer.

July 21, 1979 Common Prickly-pear

The prickly-pear, a native Minnesota cactus, started blooming on June 29 and has now finished flowering. As hundreds of people have stopped to look at the three-inch yellow flowers that last only one day each, they have also noticed another characteristic: its distinctive fragrance. Now we wait for the fruit to ripen. With the skin and seeds removed, the berries can be eaten raw, or after the fruit ripens they can be used to make cactus candy.

The prickly-pear cactus is a handsome plant that grows in Minnesota in open, usually rocky places, in the southern and western parts of the state. Growing close to the ground, it is seldom over a foot high. The sprawling green jointed stem is made up of flat sections called pads, which in turn are armed with spines. The large spines are a nuisance, but the minute, reddish-brown, barbed bristles are more to be feared as they penetrate and work their way into the skin, causing trouble for days.

June 22, 1978 Monarch Notes

Swamp milkweed flowers seem to be the chief source of nectar for the Arboretum's present population of monarch butterflies. I noticed these plants and the feeding monarchs next to the bog boardwalk and in damp, sunny spots on the prairie today.

The monarch is probably one of our most familiar insects. It can easily be seen because of its colors and large size; in addition, no butterfly is more widely distributed throughout the United States. It is bright orange and black and has a four-inch wing span. At the end of summer the species gather in flocks and fly south with a few returning the following spring.

During March and April monarchs migrate north into Texas from Mexico. Females oviposit on milkweeds, and their progeny appear in April or May. We see many dull-colored monarchs in Minnesota during May and June that have returned from the overwintering area, together with a few newly emerged, bright specimens from new generations that were produced in southern states. By July, however, all of the older migrants will have died in the northern states with only their offspring remaining.

Monarchs can make their home wherever the milkweed flourishes. We can see an example of this in Hawaii where the monarch became established only after milkweed was introduced there. The larvae of this butterfly dine on milkweed and will die of starvation among acres of lush green leaves if some of those leaves do not belong to the milkweed family or the closely related dogbane family.

Dr. Fred Urquhart from the University of Toronto has been investigating their migrations for more than twenty-five years. As a result of his work and through the cooperation of volunteer research associates who have tagged thousands of migrating monarchs, we now know that the monarchs from the eastern part of the United States and Canada spend the winter months in a small area in the mountains of central Mexico.

I had casually observed them for more than ten years, but in 1973 I began tagging them, which intensified my interest and observations. I have seen that each year monarchs usually appear about May 20 and are gone by October 20. During the last of May and the first few days of June they can be seen feeding on the nectar of blooming lilacs, and throughout the summer they sip nectar from many more plants species. The best area in which to see them is the restored prairie of the Arboretum. Here, during peak periods when thousands of plants are in bloom from mid-summer to late-summer, fifty or more monarchs can be seen along the trail. They are especially numerous in August and the beginning of September when they feed on the flowers of blazing-star *(Liatris)*.

July 23, 1979 Daylily Collection

The scientific name for daylily, *Hemerocallis* (hem-er-o-KAL-is), comes from the Greek words *hemera*, meaning day, and *kallos*, meaning beauty; an apt description since each lovely flower lasts only one day although the plants produce a succession of blooms for several weeks. The funnel-shaped lily flowers range in color from yellow and orange to red and maroon, but regardless of their principal color they have yellow, orange or green throats. Each flower also has six stamens, three petals and three petal-like sepals. The plants require hot days to put on their best show.

Forty years ago the daylily was almost a rare flower in gardens of the United States, and the chief kinds were the tawny roadside and the lemon yellow. Now the number of cultivars is in the thousands with about 125 in the Arboretum. The homeland of *Hemerocallis* is China, Japan and some off-shore islands. Their use by the ancient Chinese people began before the development of written language, and the earliest records report the use of the plant for food. The flower buds are digestible and nutritious, and when cooked or eaten raw they taste almost like green beans.

The daylily is one of the sturdiest and most interesting herbaceous perennials that has been introduced to American gardens. Grown for their attractive sword-like leaves and conspicuous flowers rising on tall leafless stalks, they also have a superior ability to compete with weeds, withstand drought and remain vigorous in the face of neglect. The plants, which grow two to four feet tall, are especially attractive in a mixed flower border. They are sun-loving and grow best in well-drained soil that may be light or heavy but should have plenty of humus.

Although they may be planted anytime the ground is not frozen, mid-September is the planting deadline to be safe. They should have time to form new roots and begin to anchor themselves before winter.

Daylily

A mulch for winter protection is needed on all plants newly set in the fall.

Overall bloom peak for the daylily collection in the Arboretum:

July 20, 1970	July 20, 1975	July 20, 1980
July 20, 1971	July 18, 1976	July 20, 1981
July 20, 1972	July 11, 1977	July 20, 1982
July 20, 1973	July 20, 1978	
July 20, 1974	July 23, 1979	

July 24, 1978 Grand Marais Peonies

A friend visited the North Shore of Lake Superior the past couple of days, and taking a side trip along the Gunflint Trail, he made a list of wildflowers in bloom. Some of them include fireweed, pearly everlasting, Canada hawkweed, Joe-Pye weed, fringed loosestrife and cow-parsnip. He mentioned that the blueberries are just getting ripe, wild red raspberry fruit is abundant, and in Grand Marais the peonies are in bloom. Spring and summer arrive late there in comparison to the Twin Cities where peonies were blooming well on June 15.

Meteorologist Bruce Watson calls Grand Marais Minnesota's weather refuge. He says that while the rest of us freeze in winter and bake in the summer, the people of Grand Marais bask in mild temperatures where 80°F is hot and 0°F is very cold.

July 25, 1978 Red Mulberry Fruit

Today I had a special treat — I ate my first red mulberries *(Morus rubra)* this summer. Although some people think the berries are too sweet and others that they are too acid, the birds and I love the taste. Each one-inch-long berry is actually a compound fruit of many drupes (a drupe is a fruit with a soft, fleshy part covered by a skinlike outer layer and containing an inner seed), resembling a blackberry or raspberry. It is first red as it ripens and then turns dark purple.

The red mulberry is a native tree of eastern North America. It seldom grows wild in the Upper Midwest, but it may occasionally be seen in rich forests in the southern parts of the area and has been found in the Mississippi River Valley as far north as Hennepin County.

When it is grown in Minnesota, it reaches a height of about twenty feet and is sometimes planted by gardeners as an ornamental tree. It is also planted by birdwatchers as a source of food for birds such as cardinals, catbirds, rose-breasted grosbeaks, blue jays, northern orioles, American robins, brown thrashers, cedar waxwings and red-bellied woodpeckers. The tree that I ate from today is the Illinois Everbearing Mulberry, which will continue to produce ripe fruit through August.

July 26, 1975 Bog Botanizing

A botanist is a student of plants. To go botanizing one would go out in the field to investigate the plant life. One doesn't have to be a professional botanist to go into the field to study plants. Anyone with an eye for nature and an inquisitive mind, armed with a field guide to plant identification, can enjoy countless hours in the field and make some very interesting observations.

At the Arboretum there is a boardwalk going over a wetland area that allows people to get near such aquatic plants as lesser duckweed, common cattails, tamarack trees and pussy willows. I have walked slowly across this boardwalk hundreds of times the last seven years, and each time, while enjoying the beauty of the plants, I have learned something new. It has opened up a whole new world to me.

Today the swamp milkweed and purple loosestrife are in full bloom. I ate some fruit from the swamp red currant and watched honey bees forage on the flowers of spotted touch-me-not. The meadowsweet shrubs are displaying panicles of white flowers, and the red-osier dogwood had both ripe fruit (white berries) and clusters of white flowers. Boneset and flat-topped white asters are starting to bloom and give the boardwalk an autumn look. A swamp sparrow was busy feeding its young, and I also saw a yellowthroat, a catbird, a rose-breasted grosbeak, an American goldfinch and a song sparrow, along with two common pond dragonflies: the white-tailed skimmer and tenspot skimmer.

These animals and many more are found along the boardwalk because of the plants. No plants, no animals; that sounds like a simple fact. It may be a simple statement, but the relationships between the plants and animals and their environment, called ecology, is as complex as it is interesting. One who enjoys botanizing is very likely to become a student of ecology.

July 27, 1976 Warm Lake Water

I love to swim, and we usually begin swimming in Lake Waconia toward the end of May and continue into September. The cut-off temperature for me is about 65°F. When the water surface temperature is below 65°F in the spring, I wait to begin the swimming season, and I end it in September when the water temperature drops again.

The surface temperature of our lakes usually peaks during the last few days of July. Yesterday 79°F was recorded at the surface and 50°F in the deeps of Lake Minnetonka, and today I recorded 83°F on the surface of Lake Waconia. That, no doubt, will be our high for the summer and means perfect swimming for everyone who likes this form of relaxation and exercise.

July 28, 1978 Bumble Bees

As I took a quick look around today, I saw that common burdock, red clover and Joe-Pye weed are among the many flowering plants being visited by foraging bumble bees that have only two energy sources, flower nectar and flower pollen.

There are two groups of social bees in North America: the native bumble bee and the honey bee. Even though there are many species of bumble bees, the most common kind can usually be recognized by their robust shape, hairy bodies and black and yellow markings, with a few having orange markings. Relatively large bees, most of them are three-fourths of an inch long or longer. As social bees, bumble bee colonies contain three castes: queens, drones (males) and workers. Unlike honey bees, a colony of bumble bees does not live through the winter. Only the young queens remain alive, hibernate underground and emerge in the spring to search for a new nesting site. Most nest in the ground, usually in a deserted mouse nest or burrow of some animal.

The first brood raised by the queen consists of workers, and once the workers appear they take over the duties of the colony except the egg laying. They enlarge the nest, collect food and store it in little sack-like honey pots and care for the young. Actually, all of the eggs in the bumble bee nest in the spring and early summer develop into workers. Later in the summer drones and queens are produced, and all but the queens die in the fall. Like the honey bees, the drones are mates for the queens.

On observing bumble bees in flight, people are surprised that these burly giants can actually make progress through the air on such small wings. Antoine Magnan, a French zoologist, made some very careful studies of bumble bee flight in 1934 and came to the conclusion that due to their size they should not be able to fly at all. Fortunately, the bumble bees never heard this and so are still flying as usual.

Bumble bees, which collect both pollen and nectar at the same time and are, therefore, very good pollinators, are the busiest of all bees. They are said to visit twice as many flowers in an equal amount of time as other bees. It's during these infinite trips to flowers that bumble bees transfer pollen on their bodies from the male flower parts to the female flower parts where fertilization takes place. Before a plant can produce fruit or seeds, the flowers must be pollinated, and although many important plants such as grasses are pollinated by wind, many others depend upon the insects. Every year we have a multi-billion dollar job performed for us, virtually free of charge, when this pollination job is done by bees and other insects. We have fruits and vegetables because insects carry pollen.

The stinging equipment of bees and wasps is a modification of the egg-laying apparatus, so it is not possible for the male to sting. Unlike honey bees, bumble bees have no barbs on their stinging probe, and a female bumble bee does not lose her weapon when she uses it. She can sting repeatedly, as you may have discovered. No one should fear bumble bees or any other stinging insects but should maintain a healthy respect for them. This, together with sensible precautions when around them, will help to alleviate fear. These insects are important, and we can live side-by-side with them without trouble if we remember a few things. I have listed tips on how to avoid being stung:

Be careful when you're mowing the lawn, cutting vines or pulling weeds. Wear a hat, gloves, long sleeves and pants. Since bright colors attract insects, khaki is an ideal outdoor clothing fabric as it's pale in color and has a tightly woven texture which is not readily penetrated by an insect's sting.

Perfumes, scented lotions, hair spray and food smells attract stinging and biting insects.

If a bee or wasp flies into the car, stop slowly and open all windows. A stopped or slow-moving vehicle will give the insect an opportunity to leave.

If you are in a field and are attacked by several bees from a disturbed nest, if possible, run through a wooded area where the leaves and branches will hinder their direct, speedy pursuit.

Some people are much more sensitive to stings than others. If you are with someone who is stung and has a strong reaction, do not underestimate the seriousness of the situation. Get medical help as soon as possible. A special stinging insect emergency kit equipped with an injection of adrenaline and antihistamine tablets and carried on the allergic person is a necessity.

July 29, 1972 Roadside Ditches and Wildflowers

It has been said that travel is an enriching experience, and this enriching experience can be broken down into many small enjoyments and encounters. One part of each automobile trip that I enjoy, across the state or perhaps just to and from work, is the chance to catch quick glimpses of the plant life in roadside ditches where there is a wealth of material to observe.

At the present time tansy, black-eyed Susans and some early blooming goldenrods are yellow, wild bergamot has lavender flowers, and wild cucumber has clusters of white blossoms. Although I know these wildflowers well enough to spot them while cruising at fifty miles per hour, they could be enjoyed more if one slowed down or stopped to look at them. Stopping to look, together with a good field guide to wildflowers, is a good way to begin learning about and delighting in this very special resource, roadside plants.

July 30, 1980 Zinnias

The signs of summer can be seen as Mantet and Oriole apples are being picked and sold at the University of Minnesota Horticultural Research Center. In addition, about twenty types of chrysanthemums are blooming in the Arboretum collection, gladiolus flowers can be seen in area gardens, and the showy zinnias are at their peak. Zinnias like hot weather, and when temperatures are cool they simply stand still.

Zinnias, popular annuals grown in gardens throughout the world, thrive best in well-drained, rich soil in a sunny location. They can be put into gardens as small plants after the danger of frost has passed or be seeded directly into the earth when night temperatures remain above 50°F. Coming in a great variety of forms and sizes, the colors range from yellow through orange, scarlet, purple, rose, salmon and even green, with multicolored and striped varieties also available. Gardeners like zinnias because they are easy to grow, their flowers are attractive, and they are decorative in borders and mixed flower beds as they add color to late summer gardens.

The majority of the zinnias are natives of Mexico where they were cultivated at a very early date. The horticultural art of the Aztecs was highly developed, and at the time of the Spanish invasion in 1520, the gardens of Montezuma equalled, if not surpassed, anything in Europe. Besides zinnias, these gardens contained flowers like the dahlia, sunflower and morning glory. Apparently zinnias were overlooked as plants to be sent back to Europe until the eighteenth century. At that

Zinnias in Arboretum Tea Room

Zinnia 'Firecracker'

time Dr. Johann Gottfried Zinn, a German professor of botany, is reported to have been sent zinnia seeds from his friend, the German ambassador to Mexico, although evidence points to others in Europe also receiving zinnia seeds from Mexico at that time. The word zinnia commemorates him, but the garden plants we now enjoy, the result of years of hybridization and selection, are quite unlike the early plants.

July 31, 1980 Purple Loosestrife

Purple loosestrife, also called lythrum, grows to about four feet and is loaded with rich reddish-purple flowers on spikes one foot long. At the Gray Freshwater Biological Institute marsh near Lake Minnetonka, thousands of these plants, now near bloom peak, provide a truly spectacular sight. This showy perennial is beautiful, but it is also an aggressive species that tends to crowd out native aquatic plants that are valuable to waterfowl and other wildlife.

Purple loosestrife *(Lythrum salicaria)* usually begins blooming in the Lake Minnetonka area toward the end of June, but there are still some flowers in September. A person traveling from New England to the Upper Midwest in July and August can see wetlands along the highway covered with tall purple flower spikes and recognize the purple loosestrife.

It was introduced to the United States from Europe, a fairly recent immigrant that has become naturalized. The species was first recorded in New York in 1843, but in the book, *Northland Wild Flowers* (University of Minnesota, 1977), John Moyle says that it has been abundant in the marshes around Lake Minnetonka only since 1940. A few years ago I saw some blooming in a ditch in the northern part of the state near Waubon, west of Itasca State Park, but it is found more generally around the Twin Cities.

The purple loosestrife became established in marshes, on shores, on the edges of streams and in wet ditches after first being started as a common garden plant. It's a good honey bee plant as it supplies nectar and pollen in large quantities, and the honey produced is dark with a distinctive flavor. Possibly an ecologist, after making a careful study of the plant in the near future, will be able to give us some answers concerning the threat this species poses to other wetland plants and animals. We have nothing in wet areas among our native flora to compare with purple loosestrife because it will establish itself easily and tenaciously in spite of sedges and cattails, and it is very difficult to eradicate.

Banded Purple, Viceroy & Cabbage Butterflies

JULY

July is our warmest and sunniest month of the year. The peak of summer occurs around July 26.

129 130 131 132

Cumulus clouds build into a thunderstorm on a hot July day. **(129)** Basswood trees bloom. **(130)** Field corn should be knee high (or taller) by the 4th. **(131)** Prickly pear, a native Minnesota cactus, blooms. **(132)**

133

134

Delphinium and garden lilies bloom. **(133 & 134)** Raspberries **(135)** and currants are ripe. **(136)**

135

136

Daylilies reach their bloom peak in July. **(137)** Young raccoons play. **(138)** Baltimore butterflies are on the wing. **(139)** Black-eyed susans are showy along roadsides. **(140)**

137

138

139

140

We can enjoy tree ripened apricots. **(141)** Fields of oats become ripe. **(142)** The first sweet corn is ready to eat. **(143)** Beekeepers begin extracting honey in late July. **(144)**

141

142

143

144

AUGUST

August is the month of light winds and usually lacks the extreme heat of July. It is a sunny month, thanks to the domination of the Atlantic high pressure system.

145

146

147

148

August is the month of beautiful gardens. **(145)** Choke cherry fruit is ripe. **(146)** Gopher young have grown up. **(147)** Cicadas buzz on hot days. **(148)**

149

The bull thistle blooms. **(149)**
Swallows line up on wires in preparation for migration. **(150)**
American lotus blooms. **(151)**
Farmers cut their second or third crop of hay. **(152)**

150

151

152

153

154

155

156

Fields of sunflowers bloom. **(153)**
Goldenrods become showy. **(154)**
We eat our first ripe apples. **(155)**
Monarch butterflies cluster on trees. **(156)**

157

Dahlias come into bloom. **(157)** Spider orb-webs glisten on dewy mornings. **(158)** Prairies are filled with blooming grasses and wildflowers such as the gray-headed coneflower. **(159)** The first backyard plums are ripe in late August. **(160)**

158

159

160

August 1, 1979 Ducks and Geese

In the Twin Cities area the Canada geese, mallards and wood ducks that lost their flight feathers early in the summer are now flying again. All ducks, geese and swans of North America shed their flight feathers and spend time as flightless birds, and although there is a variation in the times this occurs, in general it would be safe to say that it is between June and into August. Ducks, swans and geese individually shed all their flight feathers simultaneously once a year rendering them unable to fly until they are replaced. Ducks moult all their other feathers two times a year while swans and geese have one annual moult during which the entire plumage is renewed.

Indian pipe *(Monotropa uniflora)*, a remarkable forest wildflower, is blooming in our area forests. It's a non-green plant, so it does not carry on photosynthesis but obtains its nourishment from decayed organic material through a fungal relationship (mycorrhiza) associated with the roots. All parts of the plant, the three-to-nine inch stem, the scale-like leaves and even the pipe-shaped flowers, look as if they were molded from white wax, but they turn black as the fruit ripens or the plants are picked.

Mud-dauber wasps are busy building nests of mud that are commonly found on walls and ceilings of old buildings. They consist of a number of cells, each about an inch long, placed side by side and provisioned with spiders for the newly hatched young wasps to feed on.

There are some lovely signs of summer. Choke cherry fruit is ripe, black walnut fruit is full-size but green, and winter squash and pumpkins are well formed on their vines. Cattails look like brown sausages, and common burdock, the biennial plant of neglected farmlands that is known for its large rhubarb-like leaves, just started blooming. Common burdock flowers are tiny, but together they form a purple head on top of a globular collection of hooked bracts. Later the hooked seed pods attach easily to animal fur or clothing, providing an excellent mechanism for seed dispersal. It has been noted that the inventor of a mechanical fastener got his idea from these hooked pods.

August 2, 1978 Buffalo Berry

I just stopped by the Arboretum's colored foliage collection to see the buffalo berry fruit, which is at its peak of ripeness and providing good eating. It is found at forest edges, in ravines, along streams and low meadows in western Minnesota, North and South Dakota and the Rocky Mountains. Buffalo berry (*Shepherdia argentea*) is a thorny, branched plant with silver and green leaves that grows as a shrub or small tree up to twenty feet tall and often forms thickets. Part of the trees in the group produce fruits and some bear only pollen. At the end of April the yellow flowers of the staminate (male) trees are small, about one-eighth of an inch, and colorful, but the pistillate (female) flowers are inconspicuous.

The fruiting trees produce large quantities of ovoid red berries, about one-fourth inch in diameter, that are mature in late July or early August. They were gathered by Indians and eaten raw, cooked in a sauce that was used to flavor buffalo meat (hence the common name), or dried for winter use. The buffalo berry is popular now for making jelly, but those who enjoy picking and eating the berries fresh find the fruit tart and pleasant. Each berry has a single seed that is fairly large and can be readily chewed.

August 3, 1979 Wild Cucumber

The wild cucumber *(Echinocystis lobata)*, a native annual vine, is blooming on area trees, shrubs and fences. The long clusters of white male flowers are sometimes nearly a foot tall and often have more than 100 flowers in each cluster. They are shaped like six-pointed stars about one-half inch wide. In contrast, the female flowers, which produce the fruit, are small and green and usually solitary or in small clusters below the long stalk bearing the male flowers.

By the use of branched tendrils, wild cucumbers with their five-lobed maple-like leaves can climb up trees into the sunlight. As the common name suggests, each ovoid two-inch fruit, which is covered with weak prickles, resembles a cucumber but is not edible. Eventually four large dark seeds are released through a hold in the lower end of the fruit leaving behind an empty, papery shell.

Butternut trees in the area have their first yellow leaflets, a normal occurrence as they drop their leaves early after showing fall color. Virginia creeper vines and the sumacs have some red on their foliage.

August 4, 1972 Ripe Mountain Ash Fruit

The European mountain ash is cultivated for its white spring flowers and its colorful fruit. The flowers are small yet conspicuous as they bloom in large, flat-topped clusters about six inches wide. Over eighty species of mountain ash trees are known and are so closely related that some botanical authors think they could be considered to be one circumpolar species with geographic varieties. All species prefer cool, moist soil and grow best in the northern part of Minnesota where two native species are found. I especially remember the abundant bright red fruit clusters on small native mountain ash trees along the North Shore of Lake Superior. The European mountain ash is the most commonly planted of all mountain ash species because it will tolerate city conditions and its size is suited to yards.

While in the Arboretum mountain ash collection today, I noticed the European mountain ash trees are loaded with big clusters of orange fruit, which the robins were busy eating. The fruit, a little over one-fourth inch in diameter, is also eaten by the catbirds, pine grosbeaks, northern orioles, brown thrashers, cedar and Bohemian waxwings and others. The fruit is rich in vitamin C and makes a delicious jelly while in some European countries the berries are dried and ground into flour.

The European mountain ash (*Sorbus aucuparia*), a Eurasian tree, was first introduced to America in colonial times. It has since become naturalized even in Alaska where it is the only naturalized tree. After being introduced in the southeastern part of Alaska, it has escaped into areas near towns. In the Twin Cities area it is often planted as a medium-sized lawn tree that can be grown in partial shade but does better and makes a more colorful display in the sun. It grows to a height of thirty to forty-five feet with branches about three-fourths as wide as the height of the tree and attractive green pinnate leaves that turn reddish in the autumn. In areas with large bird populations the ripe apple-like fruits do not last long.

August 5, 1978 Ragweed

Ragweeds are by far the most important hay fever plants in North America. When the allergenic toxicity of pollen was tested with pollen-sensitive individuals, ragweeds proved to have a high toxicity. The common and great ragweeds that are now blooming in the Twin Cities area are annuals that originated in America.

Giant ragweed (*Ambrosia trifida*) is a tall plant, three to ten feet high, with rough stems and broad, three-lobed leaves. The tiny nodding green flowers on spikes several inches long produce great quantities of pollen that is shed and carried through the air. People who are sensitive to this pollen and come in contact with it then develop symptoms of hay fever.

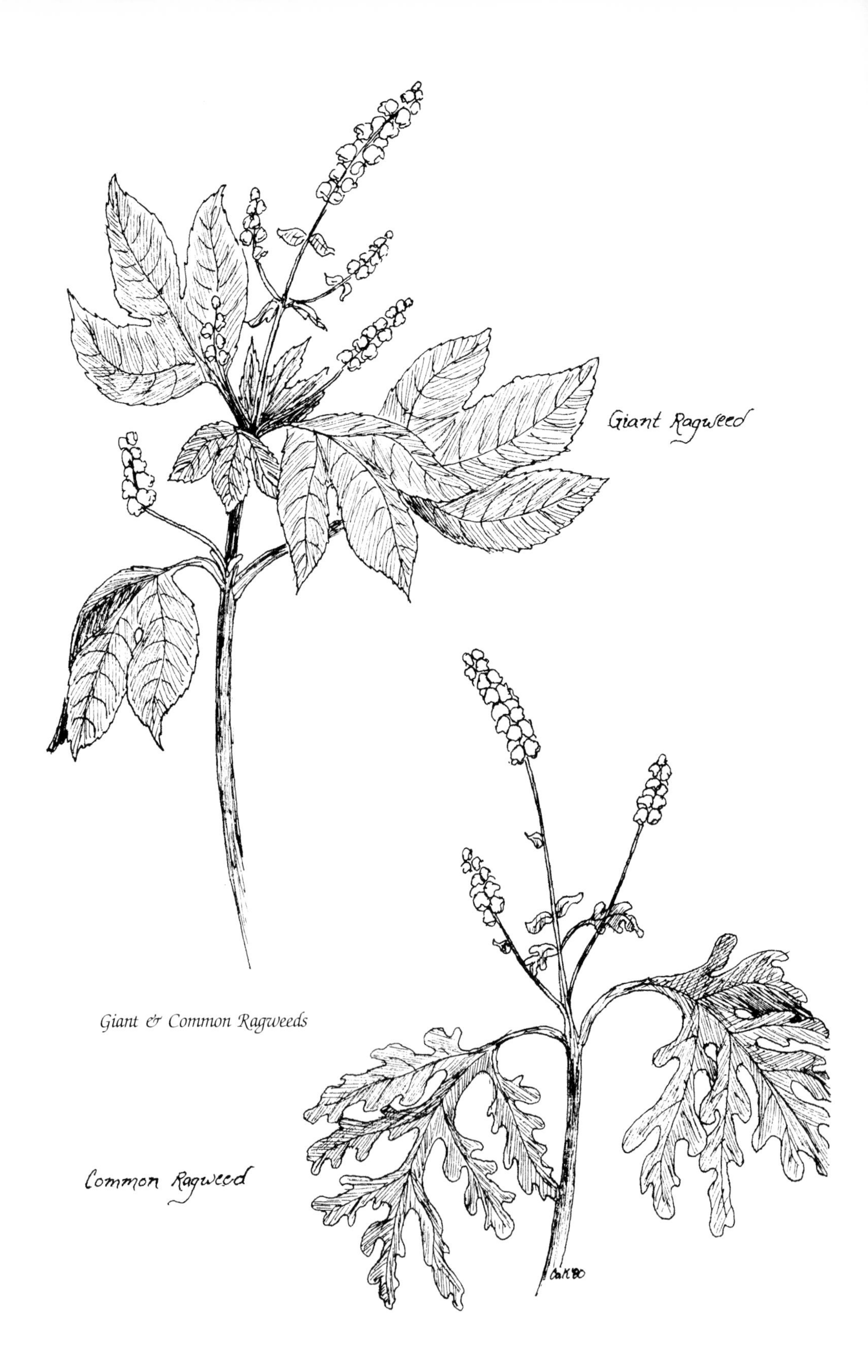

Giant & Common Ragweeds

The more numerous plants of common ragweed *(Ambrosia artemisiifolia)* are also shedding pollen now. They have finer more dissected leaves, and the plants grow only one to four feet tall. Together these two ragweed species cause more hay fever than all other plants put together.

Common ragweed flowers and sheds pollen from early August to late September throughout most of its range, the exact time depending upon latitude. In the northern part of its range the plants come into flower several weeks earlier than in the southern part. The great ragweed flowers about the same time, but it generally starts a few days earlier. They are pioneer plants and invade soil that has been disturbed. The plants are found along banks of streams, on flood plains, in roadside ditches and fields and on vacant lots.

Some goldenrods are now in bloom also. Most goldenrod pollen is carried by insects with small amounts getting into the air but always in much smaller quantities than the pollen of ragweeds and grasses. It is also felt among researchers that imperfectly insect-pollinated plants such as sunflowers, goldenrods and dahlias must be given some consideration in hay fever studies.

Great ragweed starting to shed pollen in the Twin Cities area	Common ragweed starting to shed pollen in the Twin Cities area
August 5, 1976	August 12, 1976
August 1, 1978	August 2, 1978
July 28, 1979	August 4, 1979
July 31, 1980	August 5, 1980
July 28, 1982	July 28, 1982

August 6, 1980 Annual Garden Flowers

If you ask people who grow annual flowers in their gardens why they grow them, they may give you a dozen different reasons. Some gardeners like them for cut flowers, others for the colors they add to the garden, and some because they are easy to grow. Annual flowers make it possible to have a new garden each year with different species and cultivars, and there is great enjoyment in starting with a tiny seed that becomes a full-grown plant in a single season. An added bonus is that once annuals start to bloom, they keep on continuously throughout the summer.

Unlike perennials, which store up energy in their roots and grow from those roots again, annuals live and die in one season. To perpetuate their kind, they produce seeds in great quantities, and in order to do that they must produce many flowers. If the flowers are cut before the seeds can form, the plant tries again and again in an effort to make up the loss. The more you cut flowers from an annual plant, the more it blooms; it's like having your cake and eating it too. In late summer a botanist once counted 300 blossoms and buds on a single petunia plant that had been started from a seed in spring. California poppies, cosmos, zinnias, petunias, snapdragons and marigolds are just a few of the annuals in bloom now.

Today I tasted a great apple called the State Fair. Spot picking of this bright red, early-season apple that usually ripens between the middle and end of August has just started at the University of Minnesota Horticultural Research Center. It was developed by the University of Minnesota and first released to the public in 1978. The fruit is characterized by crisp, juicy, moderately acid white flesh and pleasing flavor, and it has better durability and storage characteristics than other early apples. It can be eaten fresh, cooked as sauce, or baked in pies.

August 7, 1978 Honey Bee Navigation

Today as I watched honey bees on the garden roses and the curly mint and wooly thyme blossoms in the herb garden and on an early blooming goldenrod, I wondered, as I have before, how they manage to find these flowers. The closest hives are half a mile away, and some bees might come from an even greater distance. After several hours of reading about honey bee behavior in five good references at the Arboretum Andersen Horticultural Library, I found that many other people have wondered about honey bee navigation also, and several scientists have made some fascinating discoveries.

Unlike humans, honey bees can navigate and communicate without prior experience as these abilities are instinctive. At every stage in their behavior, however, learning is also essential; but bees are not unique in this as both instinct and learning are crucial to most insects. Among things that a foraging honey bee must learn is that the sun moves, how flowers look and smell, what the hive looks like, and many other things.

More than 2,000 years ago Aristotle noticed that, on any particular foraging flight, a bee will gather food from a single kind of flower and will bypass other flowers. The bee has learned to distinguish one species of flowers from all others, which is an advantage to the plant, for it tends to ensure cross pollination far more than if the bee were to visit a variety of flowers.

Early in this century Karl van Frisch challenged the prevalent belief that bees were colorblind — to believe this, he reasoned, would be to believe that the bright colors of flowers pollinated by bees had no biological significance. He was able to show with a series of experiments that they are able to perceive colors. Thinking that the odors of flowers probably evolved as alluring signals for them, von Frisch was also able to show that bees can distinguish one floral odor from among about 700 others.

Later it was discovered that they learn the color of a flower only during the final two seconds before landing on it, the odor while actually on the flower, and the landmarks around it as they fly away after feeding. They learn to associate a time of day with a particular food source, and since many flowers produce nectar only during specific times of the day, bees would waste a great deal of time and energy if they did not learn this.

On their return trip to the hive, honey bees depend on their unique navigation systems and use the sun's position to get close to the hive as they are too myopic to find the tiny hive entrance directly. For an insect whose vision is so fuzzy that a daisy more than three feet away is a formless blur and the distance to an object can be judged only if it is no farther than six inches away, there is no choice but to depend on large landmarks near the hive. Since the appearance of the hive may change with, for example, the addition of a new super, and the nearby vegetation changes with the season, honey bees are programmed to relearn what the hive and the surrounding area look like on the first flight out each day. A colony can be moved many miles overnight without causing any difficulty for the bees, but moving it only a few feet during midday produces swarms of frenzied foragers searching in the old location even though they had flown out only a few minutes earlier from the new position.

Honey bees orient themselves with respect to the hive after locating a group of flowers with a good nectar flow and rely on the position of the sun and their own sense of direction, distance and time. Back at the hive, a forager will translate this knowledge to other bees and direct them back to the site without accompanying them. The translation is done with a dance that will "tell" the other bees the distance and direction of the newly discovered food. Willing recruits attend these dances, then use the information gained to find the new food source as they pick up the scent of the flower from the returning bee.

August 8, 1977 Monarch Life Cycle

Driving to Itasca State Park, I was amazed to see so many monarch butterflies that were attracted to the blooming plants in the roadside ditches. When I reached there, I checked common milkweed plants and found several monarch caterpillars. Since each female monarch

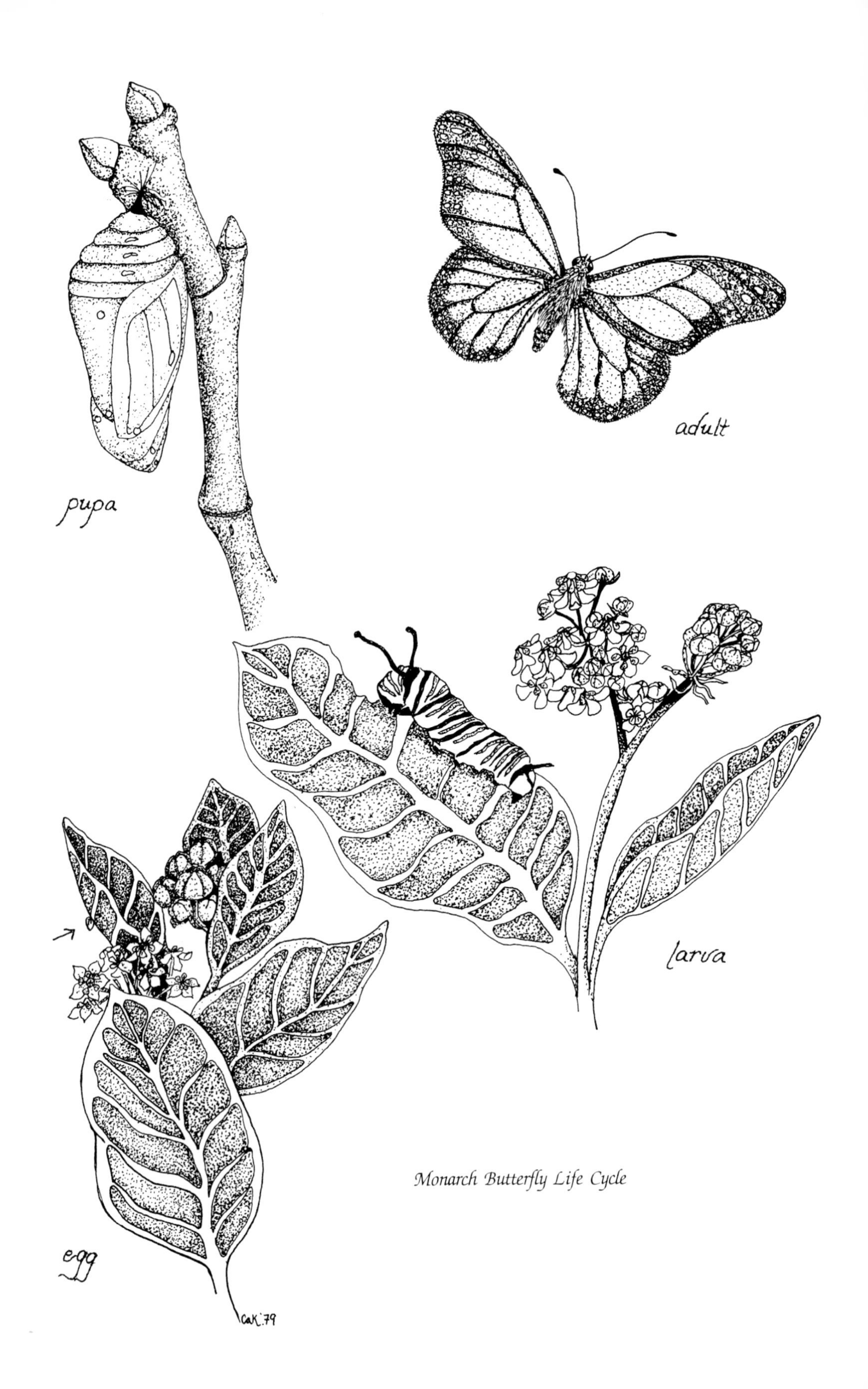

Monarch Butterfly Life Cycle

can lay a possible 700 eggs, and we expect two or three generations per summer, we will be seeing the Minnesota monarch population at its peak during the next couple of weeks.

Their life cycle is extremely interesting, taking about five weeks to progress from egg to adult in four stages:

Egg — The life cycle begins on the underside of a milkweed leaf when the female deposits an egg no larger than the head of a pin.

Larva (caterpillar) — The striped caterpillar, its body circled with black and yellow bands, emerges from the egg in three to twelve days depending upon the air temperature, and it immediately eats the egg shell and then starts to feed on the milkweed leaf. Within two weeks the larva will have multiplied its original weight 2,700 times and shed its skin five times; a six-pound human baby that grew at the same rate would weigh eight tons.

Pupa (chrysalis) — The final shedding of the larva occurs after the fully developed caterpillar has stopped eating and has located a sheltered perch, such as a small tree branch or a leaning fence post. Here the larva weaves a dense mat of silk, then grips the fiber while violently dislodging its last larval skin to reveal the pupa. The green chrysalis is studded with gold spots that control the color in the developing wings.

Adult (winged stage) — The pupa turns transparent in about two weeks, exposing the features of a grown butterfly. Cracks then spread across the chrysalis wall, and the adult emerges pumping body fluid into its limp wings. After the wings dry, the new butterfly sails away to feed on nectar from various flowers. Some monarchs fly south in the fall and may even return to their summer breeding grounds the following spring, but none ever survives longer than a year.

August 9, 1979 Eating from the Garden

Area gardeners are still picking a few ripe raspberries and gooseberries. Zucchini squash are coming fast, potatoes are being dug, and green beans are being picked. In addition, gardeners are harvesting tomatoes, broccoli, cabbage, cauliflower, sweet corn, beets, carrots, green peppers and celery.

The cultivation of fruits and vegetables in the home garden is a pleasurable and profitable activity. Freshly gathered produce can be superior to that usually found in the markets. The home gardener can grow varieties of the best quality and flavor, which may not be grown commercially because they do not ship or keep well. Fruits and vegetables can be picked at their peak stages; and a garden that is a few steps from the kitchen, which some people can have, is a convenience. But the satisfaction of cultivating fruits and vegetables at home is an intangible thing that can't be measured in money.

This is a busy time of year outdoors with many phenological events to report. I'll just mention a few from the Twin Cities area:

Beekeepers have started extracting honey.

Bur oak acorns are nearly full-size but still green. Squirrels have been busy gathering them.

Catalpa seed pods are now about one foot long.

The first snowy tree crickets have started chirping.

The cardinal flower is full of brilliant red flowers on elongated clusters.

August 10, 1976 Wild Grapes and Elderberries

On this hot day I refreshed myself with a couple of handfuls of wild fruit taken from wild grape *(Vitis riparia)* vines and common elderberry *(Sambucus canadensis)* shrubs.

A grape vine is a climbing, woody perennial best recognized by its alternate simple leaves that are lobed and toothed and by its purple, seeded berries that grow in bunches. There is danger in confusing wild grape vines with a Virginia creeper vine, which has poisonous fruits that resemble grapes in size and color. I have seen both vines growing up on the same tree, but the Virginia creeper, unlike the grape, has palmately compound leaves and the branches holding the purple fruit clusters are conspicuously red.

Wild grapes are found in thickets, edges of forests and along streams, and the fruit becomes ripe in August and September. They can be used for any recipe that calls for grapes, but since they are tart, they generally need more sweetening than cultivated grapes when they are made into juice, jelly and syrup.

Common elderberry shrubs are usually about five to ten feet tall and grow wild in damp, rich soil along streambanks and in roadside ditches and thickets. The large, flat-topped clusters of dark-purple berries make delicious jelly when mixed with the juice of one or more tart fruits such as crabapples. Elderberry juice can be chilled and used as a cold drink, and the berries can also be successfully sun dried. Drying removes the mildly unpleasant taste, and when reconstituted in boiling water, the berries add a delicious flavor to muffins or can be used in fruit stews or made into pie filling. The fruit is rich in vitamin C and also contains vitamin A, calcium, iron and potassium.

August 11, 1979 Butterfly Watching

The thermometer in our weather hutch near the northwest side of Lake Waconia read 50°F for a low this morning, and as I walked in the dewy grass, the air was cool. I heard on WCCO Radio that 28°F and frost were recorded at Embarrass, Minnesota, and about thirty-five miles east of that coldest spot in the nation, the Environmental Learning Center near Isabella also reported frost with a low of 30°F.

With sunny skies the air temperature was up close to 70°F by mid-morning, and the butterflies were extremely active. Our eight-year-old son Andrew and I went for a ten-mile bike trek around the lake at that time and observed a dozen species of butterflies including sulphurs, alfalfas, cabbages and monarchs. The air was calm, so we could see these flying beauties very well as they drifted by us in search of nectar and other fluids. I also spotted a second generation tiger swallowtail in perfect condition, and second generation red-spotted purples and banded purples together with Milbert's tortoise shells and pearl crescent-spots. The painted lady, red admiral and viceroy were the most elusive butterflies, and we saw only one of each.

August 12, 1979 Sunflowers

Although bees are the most common visitors to sunflowers, many other insects such as the monarch butterfly also find them attractive. Dr. Basil Furgala from the University of Minnesota says that research shows sunflower yields increase 35 to 100 percent if farmers don't spray their plants with insecticides because insects are needed to pollinate sunflowers completely. He states that any farmer who wants to be a serious sunflower grower should have honey bees in the area.

The flower heads of the sunflower are a perfect example of an adaptation for insect pollination, as the crowding of many flowers ensures conspicuousness and the consequent pollination of a maximum number of flowers in a single visit. Sunflowers are related to the daisies, asters, marigolds, chrysanthemums and dandelions, all of which are members of the family of plants known as the Compositae. An important characteristic that holds these plants together as a family group is that one flower is not a single flower but a whole bouquet. Examining a sunflower closely, we can find many, sometimes hundreds or thousands of small flowers are packed together in a structure known as a head. The outside yellow flowers are called the ray flowers, and although flowers normally serve to produce seeds, the ray flowers (banner flowers) of the sunflower are sterile and apparently their only function is to attract insects. The flowers in the center of the head, called disk flowers, are inconspicuous and small but attend to pollination and production of seed.

Sunflowers have become the fourth largest field crop in Minnesota. Fields of these flowers, many of which are now in bloom, are spectacular. The huge flower heads with their bright yellow ray flowers all face east, and those that have finished blooming have drying flower heads all bent down to the earth. It is probable that most people believe that sunflowers twist their stems so that their blossoms face the sun all day, but as Anna Comstock wrote in her *Handbook of Nature Study* in the early 1900s, (reprinted by Cornell University Press, 1957):

> "This belief shows the utter contentment of most people with a pretty theory. If you believe it, you had best ask the first sunflower you see if it is true, and she will answer you if you ask the question morning, noon, and night."

Green plants are phototropic and respond by growing toward the source of light. Many plants, particularly in early stages of growth, bend toward the east in the morning and toward the west in the evening, and the common sunflower shows this tendency also. But once the flower head opens, it no longer turns toward the source of light, and the heads of the common sunflowers end up facing east the whole day.

There are more than sixty kinds or species of sunflowers, some of them with many varieties. Most species grow wild in North America. The sunflowers are known scientifically by the genus name *Helianthus* from the Greek *helios* meaning sun, and *anthos* meaning flower. The best known sunflower around the world is *Helianthus annuus*, the common sunflower. Each plant lives a single season, hence it is called *annuus* for annual. It grows as a native plant on prairies and dry places from Minnesota to Missouri and west to Washington and California. As a wild plant, it has a branching form with many flowers three to six inches across and grows three to ten feet high, but the unbranched forms with massive flower heads are cultivated for their oily seeds. There are also cultivars of the common sunflower with red or double flowers that are grown for their ornammental value.

Early European explorers found American Indians gathering wild sunflower seeds for food, and plants being cultivated along with corn and beans in some regions. The common sunflower was used by the Indians for bread flour, which was made from its ground seeds, and for oil used to season food and to anoint the hair.

Many people think that the common sunflower originated in Russia, probably because one of the best known varieties is the Mammoth Russian or Russian Giant. The sunflower, which was grown by American Indians, went to Europe from America, eventually reached Russia and then was reintroduced as a cultivated plant into the Americas from Russia. It was not until the 1880s that the Mammoth Russian sunflower began to be sold by seed companies in this country.

The sunflower has gradually developed from a minor crop into one of the world's most important suppliers of vegetable oil, and in 1970 it ranked second only to the soybean. The Soviet Union is the sunflower capital of the world, and by the early 1970s 12 million acres were being devoted to the cultivation of sunflowers there. Starting with varieties having an oil content around 28 percent in the 1920s, the Russian plant breeders increased this to 49 percent in 1955. Sunflower crops of significance are produced in Argentina, some parts of Africa, Romania and other parts of Europe, while Canada has increased its acreage also. Until recently the sunflower has been a minor crop plant in the United States, grown chiefly for bird seed and snacks for people, but now it has become an important oil crop, also.

Sunflowers were found to be well-adapted to the Red River Valley area of Minnesota and were grown there experimentally for oil production in 1947. They have characteristics that make them particularly adaptable to the kind of land found there. Sunflowers are drought resistant, and they thrive in heavy clay soils but also do well in light sandy soils; they survive flooding better than many farm crops; they have good resistance to frost; and they require less fertilizer than most crops. In 1967 only 96,300 acres were used for sunflower production in the U.S. but by 1979 in four states alone — North Daktoa, South Dakota, Minnesota and Texas — farmers planted 5.3 million acres of sunflowers.

Sunflower leaves and stems make good livestock food, and the seeds have been used for food for poultry. The stems have also been used as a source of fiber for the manufacture of fabrics and paper in some countries, and seed hulls are used in the manufacture of ethyl alcohol, for lining plywood and in growing yeast. Research is going on in the United States to find new ways to use the oil and other parts of the plant; at the same time work is being done to increase yields. At the present time the oil, which is high in polyunsaturates and low in cholesterol, is a basic ingredient in some margarine, cooking and salad oils. Most of the crop grown in the United States is exported to Europe, where the seeds are crushed and the oil is extracted for use as salad and vegetable oil. Many people, particularly the Russians, are fond of the seeds for snacks.

My reason for devoting so much space to this entry is to emphasize the importance of a native plant that has come to be of great value to people now. It is interesting to speculate about plant species we presently encounter in our visits to natural upland and wetlands that might someday have a profound influence on the human population.

Much of my information on the sunflower comes from the book, *The*

Sunflower, by Charles B. Heiser, Jr. (University of Oklahoma Press, 1976).

August 13, 1979 Arboretum Prairie

I think of zigzag Canada goldenrods and white snakeroot, all now blooming, as autumn flowering plants even though they begin in summer. In the Arboretum perennial gardens the common rosemallow is very colorful, the garden roses are fragrant, and about one-third of the mum varieties have their first flowers.

I joined a group led by Al Johnson, the Arboretum taxonomist, on a tour of the prairie this afternoon. He began work on the restored Arboretum prairie in 1963. Seeds, sod, hay and individual plants were brought to the site, largely from other prairie relics in the area. The idea is that the plants that have been set out will find their places on the newly restored prairie and crowd out unwanted ones. Kentucky bluegrass, red clover and white sweet clover are plants out of place on the prairie and so are considered weeds. Al's planning and work have paid off; the restored prairie now covers about ten acres and has really come into its own — it looks like a prairie.

As we hiked through tall grasses, we saw big bluestem and Indian grass in bloom. The compass plant, a typical prairie perennial and among the tallest of the nonwoody plants, was eight feet tall and showing off its four-inch sunflower-like blossoms and large, deeply cut lower leaves. The leaves stand on edge, and in open dry places they orient themselves in a north-south direction giving the plant its name. Al pointed to Missouri goldenrod, a low-growing, early-flowering goldenrod of the prairies that had just come into bloom, and he also showed us purple prairie clover, Canada tick trefoil and Culver's root, all still blooming.

The prairie restoration is an exciting project. Few people have had the opportunity to see and learn about prairies, one of America's endangered natural systems, but these few acres have become an outdoor classroom as well as a beautiful place.

August 14, 1979 Monarch Butterfly Aggregations

An aggregation is defined as making a union into a mass, or as a collection. Four days ago the first obvious aggregation of monarchs was seen, as observers in Chaska and Wayzata noticed that they were gathering by the hundreds to roost at night in trees. During the last few days, people from Orono, Mound, Edina, Lester Prairie, Brownton, Hutchinson, Kimball, Collegeville and other locations have also reported observing clusters of monarch butterflies. Some observed thousands gathered on trees.

About 7:30 last evening I noticed monarchs starting to gather in our next-door neighbor's yard. They were flying along and over Lake Waconia and came to roost on the lower branches of a big Norway spruce and a green ash about 100 feet from the shore, the largest cluster made up of about thirty butterflies. All settled on the east side of the trees for the night, and after warming up in the sun's rays this morning, they left. Last year I first observed the clustering on our neighbor's trees on August 28.

We have been seeing the beginning of the monarch migration that eventually leads them to Mexico for the winter. After seeing the clustering, I called Dr. William Herman, University of Minnesota endocrinologist who has studied monarch butterflies for years. He had been out in a field near Osceola, Wisconsin, this morning and had collected 315 monarchs that were all in diapause — no egg production. The first generation, produced from eggs laid by returning migrating monarchs, was on the wing in July, and now the butterflies we see in aggregations are, no doubt, the second generation. Their egg production probably will be delayed until next year when they leave the wintering site in Mexico. Dr. Herman mentioned that we normally see the monarch aggregations, probably of the third generation, during the last week in August.

He said that several thousand monarchs have collected near Osceola in an oak grove next to an open field of red clover where they feed. He believes that if the weather stays nice they will roost during the night in the grove and stay in the area of the food supply, but some of them may have begun flying south already.

Later this evening I checked the monarch roosting site next door. Only three monarchs had gathered, and that means the fall flight is underway.

August 15, 1974 Minnesota's Lotus Lily

American lotus, lotus lily, water chinquapin, yellow nelumbo, pondnuts, wonkapin and yellow water lily are all common names for this member of the water lily family Nymphaeaceae. Over the years many plants in many lands have been called lotus and along with the others our *Nelumbo lutea* has no special right to the name either, for it is not the lotus of Homer or of ancient Egypt.

The American lotus is distinguished from other aquatic flowering plants by the peculiar, inverted cone in the middle of the flower. The cone has several holes in its flat upper surface and within each hole a pistil that gives rise to an acorn-like seed. The fragrant, pale yellow flowers are six or eight inches across with both the flowers and the bowl-shaped one-to-two foot leaves usually rising a foot or more above the water's surface. After the flowers fade, the nut-like fruits ripen in the pockets on the flattened top of the cone-shaped seed holder that eventually breaks off and acts as a boat to carry the seeds away from the parent plant.

The American lotus plant may be found in the shallow water of ponds and lakes and slow-moving streams from New England to Ontario and Minnesota and southward to Florida and Texas, but the plant is also very local in distribution. While it is common in some areas where it grows, it is only found in relatively isolated places.

Conway MacMillan in his book, *Minnesota Plant Life*, published in 1899, referred to this native water lily as the Indian lotus. He stated that the plant is not very common in Minnesota and is confined to only a few localities. On his botanical surveys he saw it in the Mississippi River at Mendota, Red Wing and LaCrosse and in Lake Pepin and in Halsteads Bay, Lake Minnetonka. Some plants can now also be found in Lotus Lake and Lake Susan, both near Chanhassen. This year the plants in Lake Minnetonka began blooming about July 25 and are still flowering.

American Indians used the lotus for food, and white settlers who tried the plant in various ways were enthusiastic about it. The rootstocks, often up to fifty feet long, bear tuberous enlargements that are filled with starch in autumn. These tubers and the growing tips of the branches of the rootstocks can be baked and are said to have a pleasant mealy quality, suggestive of sweet potatoes. Half-ripe seeds are said to be delicious either raw or cooked, with a flavor somewhat like chestnuts.

Caution: The American lotus is a protected species in Minnesota. Plants in the North are extremely rare, which makes it inadvisable to gather the lotus for food. However, further south in the United States where the plants are abundant, little harm will be done unless hundreds of people develop a taste for American lotus. Since the rootstocks are beyond the reach of all but the most enthusiastic foragers, this is unlikely.

The related oriental lotus is extensively cultivated in China for its seeds and rootstocks, which our own native species could also provide under cultivation.

August 16, 1978 Ripe Beacon Apples

The juicy Beacon apples are ripe, and the first ones are a special treat. I enjoy the slightly acid flavor, and every summer I look forward to eating these apples.

Beacon is an early-maturing apple that was introduced in 1936 by the University of Minnesota Horticultural Research Center and is suitable for culture throughout the state. Its medium-sized fruit, about three inches in diameter, is evenly distributed throughout the tree and does not cluster, the skin is thick and tough, and the fruit does not bruise easily. Beacon apples will keep for about one to one and one-half months in cool storage. They are attractive red fruits with firm flesh and are good for fresh eating, pies and sauce.

The first blossoms were open on Beacon apple tree near Lake Waconia:	I ate the first ripe apples from the same tree:
May 7, 1976	August 5, 1976
April 29, 1977	July 27, 1977
May 16, 1978	August 15, 1978
May 26, 1979	August 22, 1979
May 3, 1980	August 4, 1980
May 4, 1981	August 6, 1981

August 17, 1976 Chimney Swifts

The sun set in a partly cloudy sky at 8:12 p.m., CDT, tonight, while we were out on the playground at the Prairie Farm Elementary School looking up toward the school's chimney. There were three of us: my five-year-old son Andrew, his ten-year-old cousin Beth and me. We were in Prairie Farm, Wisconsin, located in the west central part of the state, next to the school Beth attends. Above us 130 chimney swifts were gathered, all flying in the same direction around and around the chimney and uttering sharp chirping notes. At this time in many other locations in the Upper Midwest, people could have availed themselves of the same opportunity to see chimney swifts as they gathered at sunset above their roosting sites. But I'm afraid few people did.

We watched the first two swifts drop into the chimney at 8:20. The rest of the flock followed in a thin stream with most of them going in between 8:30 and 8:33. At 8:35 as I counted, 129 birds had dropped into the chimney, and then one more appeared. We stayed for a few minutes and listened to the birds chattering from the roosting site, and later one lone, last swift came and entered the chimney at 8:44. Soon it was quiet.

The chimney swifts are here to feed on flying insects and to nest. Their fall migration is beginning and will reach its peak in late August and early September as they head for South America, although occasionally I have seen a few in our area during late September and early October. One observer in Pennsylvania reported seeing about 10,000 enter a large chimney within thirty-seven minutes during their migration in September. The sight must have been like a column of smoke going back into the chimney. Others report that inside a chimney roost the swifts cling with their sharp nails to the sooty walls in rows and clusters, overlapping like shingles on a roof.

Nesting of chimney swifts takes place in May through June and may be in chimneys, airshafts, barns, silos, open wells or hollow trees. Nests are made of twigs broken off by their feet while in flight and then cemented together and attached to the nesting site with glutinous saliva. Both sexes incubate the eggs, which hatch in about twenty days, and the young first fly when they are about thirty days old. To find enough food for their young, the adults sometimes fly at night gathering insects.

The entry for April 29 contains more information on chimney swifts.

August 18, 1978 The Value of Honey Bees

I am not a beekeeper, but I am a bee observer. In a cursory way this growing season, I have been watching honey bees and the flowers they visit. I have seen them on about one hundred different kinds of plants, and I wonder how many more plants I would have noted if I had taken more time to observe them. Today the bees are foraging on purple loosestrife, boneset, goldenrods, sunflowers and other flowering plants. They are so busy that a person can get within a few inches to watch them.

There are about 3,000 beekeepers in Minnesota, according to Dave Noetzel, extension entomologist at the University of Minnesota. Only about 200 make their living exclusively from the production of their honey bees while the rest keep bees to supplement their incomes or as a hobby.

Mervin Eisel, education director at the Arboretum, has ten colonies or hives of honey bees on the edge of the Arboretum. On most days during the growing season, more than 600,000 of his bees are out gathering nectar and pollen for their colonies, and as they do, they help to pollinate hundreds of different kinds of plants in the Arboretum.

The main honey harvest in Minnesota began last week. There are about 175,000 colonies of honey bees in the state, which yield almost 15 million pounds of honey each year for a total crop value of about 6

White-lined Sphinx Moth hovering

million dollars. The value of bees to Minnesota agriculture is actually thirty to fifty times higher than that amount because bees are responsible for pollinating many important crops. Recent studies indicate that about ninety crops in the United States depend at least partly upon bees for pollination. Honey bees carry reproductive pollen from one plant to another for about 80 percent of the raspberries, strawberries, apples, sunflowers, alfalfa, clover and soybeans in Minnesota, according to Dave. Here in the Arboretum, wildflowers, serviceberries, ornamental crabapples and honeysuckles are a few of the plants pollinated by the honey bees. Hundreds of other noncrop plants in the state are bee pollinated; in fact, the whole complex is so involved in nature's web that an estimate of their value is nearly impossible.

August 19, 1974 White-lined Sphinx Moth

Most insects including butterflies and moths lead dangerous lives. Birds and dragonflies capture them in the air, rodents consume them

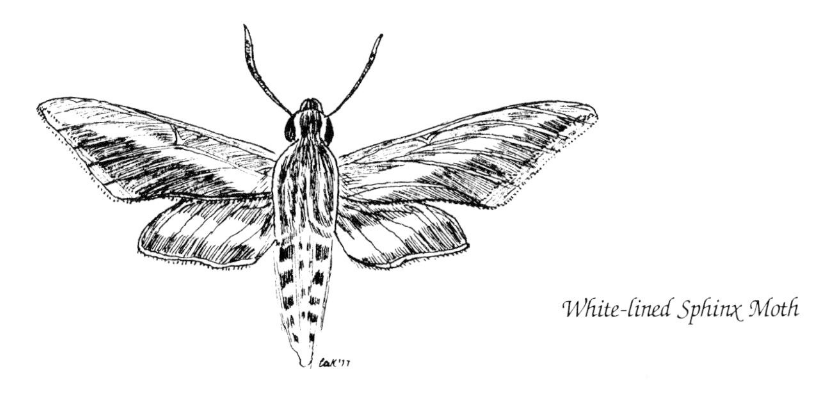

White-lined Sphinx Moth

on the ground, spiders catch them in webs, and many humans destroy them with insecticides and attracting-devices. Insects devour our food and spread disease, so we try to control them, but the good they accomplish also makes them important. Only a little more than 1 percent harm people, and many of the other 99 percent are useful.

Some people say that they would like to live in a world without insects, but an earth without insects would be a drab and colorless place. With no insects, there would be almost no flowers since they would not be pollinated; there would be no natural silk, no honey, and few if any song birds because without insects for food and seeds from insect-pollinated plants, most birds would starve. Whole natural communities like freshwater streams where fish depend upon insects for food would be greatly influenced, and life for the surviving living organisms would be altered.

Around lilac blooming time in the spring and again in August and September, I get many questions from people concerning a hummingbird-like animal that hovers in front of flowers and extends a straw-like tube into them. In most cases it's the white-lined sphinx moth, the most common sphinx moth, that people have seen. One visited our white petunia flowers this evening about forty-five minutes after sunset, but at other times we have seem them flying in bright sunlight. They are found in areas from southern Canada to Central America.

Sphinx moths, hummingbird moths, hawk moths and hornworns are all names for the same family of moths. These moths have spindle-shaped bodies that are large enough to accommodate the powerful wing muscles, and each is important as a pollinator with its long proboscis. It has a wingspread of about three inches, the forewings are long, narrow and pointed, and the hind wings are relatively small. The moth is brown with white lines on head, thorax and wings, and a rosy-colored band across the middle of each hind wing.

Linnaeus gave the name sphinx to these moths probably because of the habit their caterpillars have of resting, or sometimes threatening, with their heads drawn in and the front segments of their bodies elevated in a way to resemble an Egyptian sphinx.

Another interesting name for this group of insects is hornworm, which refers to the thick-bodied caterpillars that have a conspicuous horn or spine-like protuberance on the rear of their bodies.

White-lined sphinx caterpillars are generally recognized by their green bodies with yellow spots. They are leaf-eaters consuming leaves of portulaca, chickweed, purslane, azalea, elm, grapes and some field crops. If we are going to have white-lined sphinx moths to pollinate flowers, to thrill us with their antics in front of a deep-throated flower, or to amaze us with their hummingbird-like actions, we have to pay the price by allowing some holes in the foliage food of the caterpillars.

August 20, 1978 Orioles and Jelly

I enjoyed several ripe, flavorful Whitney crabapples that were ready for eating today. Robins and gray squirrels have been helping themselves to the ripening mountain ash fruit while northern orioles have been eating grape jelly that has been set out for them.

Al and Esther Zander from the Glen Lake area of Minnetonka have been putting grape jelly out for orioles since the birds first arrived on May 4. Now the birds are consuming six pounds of grape jelly per day. Al has counted as many as thirty orioles at one time, and as an observer of oriole behavior for many years, he has noticed that they always increase their grape jelly consumption, as they are doing now, the last two weeks before going south. Esther mixes grape jelly half-and-half with water, using an egg beater to get twelve pounds of a mixture with good pouring consistency that they use to fill small glass jars in the oriole feeders, sometimes refilling them several times a day.

Orioles glean caterpillars from trees and shrubbery. They also eat beetles, ants, bugs, grasshoppers, aphids and many more insects. They like fruits such as wild cherries and juneberries, and they probe flowers for nectar. The Zanders' yard is a bird haven where the orioles hunt for their natural food along with dessert stops at the grape jelly feeders.

August 21, 1978 Wetland Plants

Since many people equate wildflowers with the spring scene, they don't take the time to visit forests, meadows and wetlands to discover the joys of the wild blossoms of summer and fall.

I took a hike across the Arboretum bog boardwalk today and made several plant notations. The first thing I noticed was that ruby-throated hummingbirds are visiting the pendant golden-orange flowers of the spotted touch-me-not. Purple-stemmed aster, flat-topped white aster and Joe-Pye weed are all in bloom, and boneset plants are topped with flat clusters of dull-white flowers that are being visited by honey bees.

An unusual feature of boneset is the way the hairy stem seems to grow through the leaves that are united at their bases. Herb doctors took this as a "signature," and leaves of the plant were wrapped into the splint or bandage for a broken bone in the belief that they helped set it as the common name suggests.

Broad-leaved arrowhead has many flowers, each with three white petals and large arrowhead-shaped leaf blades. In the bottom muck in which this plant grows, the perennial rhizomes produce edible starchy tubers known as duck potatoes, an inch or more in diameter, and utilized by muskrats and perhaps ducks. It was once dried for winter food by the American Indians.

Turtlehead with its spikes of white flowers, each two-lipped and resembling a turtle head, was the next wildflower that caught my attention. I watched small bumble bees crawl into the long flowers, no doubt for a drink of nectar.

Gray dogwood fruit is turning from whitish-green to almost a metallic blue, winterberry fruit is now about one-third red, red-osier dogwood has some foliage showing fall colors of purple, red and yellow, and there is some red on the highbush cranberry leaves. The bur-marigolds just started blooming, and cattail leaves are turning brown with about one-third already dry. Although fall is coming, there are still several weeks to hunt for wildflowers in the wetland habitats.

August 22, 1979 Franklin's Gulls Arrive

Franklin's gulls have returned to Lake Waconia for the fall season. Today I saw about twenty-five soaring and circling overhead as they were hawking for insects. These birds, also called prairie doves, are animals of rare beauty and graceful actions and are of great economic value to the farmers in the areas where they live.

Adult Franklin's gulls weigh more than one-half pound and have a three-foot wingspread, black heads and gray backs and wings. The black wing tip is separated from the gray by a white band. After the nesting season is over, their heads turn white with dusky patches on the tops. Franklin's gulls nest in prairie marshes from southern Canada to South Dakota and western Minnesota, but they winter south of the United States. Their food includes grasshoppers, crickets and other insects from the air, soil and wetlands. They also eat small fish and have been known to eat mice and other small land animals.

Some lakes in southern Minnesota become assembling places for large numbers of these birds during the months of September, October and November. Hundreds and even thousands gather, making the middle of a particular lake their roosting place each night. As evening approaches, the gulls return to the lakes in great undulating lines or V-shaped formations. They usually glide for a great distance as they approach the shoreline and then fly very low over the water's surface until they reach the gathering spot. Their evening flight is one of the most fascinating sights of fall bird life in southern Minnesota and continues for about two hours. The horizon yields flock after flock until darkness descends, but even after dark, straggling, far-traveling gulls can be seen approaching the lake. At sunrise the Franklin's gulls leave their lake roosts in shimmering, whirling flocks to forage for miles over the surrounding country and often follow farmers in the fields to get the unearthed cutworms and grubs behind the farmer's plow.

Last year most of the Franklin's gulls had left Lake Waconia a few days before or by November 16 for their wintering range. The last ones departed November 19. This year more than 1,000 still came during the evening of November 18, but by November 25 their numbers had dwindled to a few dozen.

August 23, 1979 Minnesota Apples

Ordinarily this would be the peak of Beacon apple picking, but the season is about ten days late and only a few are ripe.

The apple variety called State Fair has a great many ripe apples now, and some trees could be picked clean. There will soon be ripe Red Baron and Wealthy apples, followed by such favorites as McIntosh, Sweet Sixteen, Haralson and Regent. Apple connoisseurs now begin to take notice of the many varieties of Minnesota-grown apples available, each with its own special flavor and texture.

The apple can be classified as a nutritious snack providing a sweet touch that is also healthful and does not hurt the teeth. A medium-sized apple that is two and one-half inches in diameter, besides being 85 percent water, has about seventy food energy calories, twenty grams of carbohydrate and traces of many vitamins and minerals. In addition, the mild acid of the apple is effective in cleaning tooth surfaces and leaving a pleasant taste in one's mouth.

Scientists believe that the earliest apples to be cultivated grew wild first in the mountains of southwestern Asia, probably in the area between the Black Sea and Caspian Sea. The first Minnesota full-sized apple variety to withstand cold winters, bear fruit regularly and have good keeping qualities and flavor was developed in the 1860s by Peter Gideon. He lived near the south shore of Lake Minnetonka after he had moved from Illinois in 1853 to take up a 160-acre claim. A self-educated horticulturist, he is said to have brought with him a bushel of apple seeds, and for the next forty-five years he worked to develop apples that could withstand the cold northern climate. Peter Gideon's famous apple named Wealthy, after Wealthy Hull, his wife, was introduced into general culture in Minnesota in 1873. The Wealthy, an early apple ripening in late August, is still widely grown throughout Minnesota. This variety is good for fresh eating, pies, sauces, freezing and baking.

Since then he and other horiticulturists in Minnesota have developed many varieties of apples suitable to our climate and the taste of apple users. Lists of fruits for Minnesota put out by the University of Minnesota Agricultural Extension Service in the 1970s include about twenty-five recommended apple varieties; some for early season, some for mid-season, and some that become ripe in late season. Although some apples on the list originally came from other states, most were developed at the University of Minnesota Horticultural Research Center. Checking nursery catalogs and books on apples, an interested grower can obtain a list of more than 100 apple varieties that could be grown in Minnesota orchards now, but not all of them would be grown in all parts of the state because they are not hardy enough.

Snappy, crisp, juicy, sweet, spicy, mildly acid, tangy, tart, aromatic; all are words used to describe the fruit of various apple varieties, in addition to which each has its own special flavor making it fun to taste many varieties. If you are interested in planting one apple tree or a small orchard or a large one, this is the time of the year to begin sampling apples and noting characteristics. By October you will have quite a list of apple varieties that you will think are good, and if you only have space for one tree, it may be a difficult decision to choose the best one. The decision on which one to plant, however, can be delayed until early spring as soon as the soil can be worked as that is the best time to plant it.

In Minnesota there are about 125 commercial orchards. Their total of 5,000 acres is minuscule compared with the acreages of corn, soybeans or sunflowers, but it puts Minnesota twenty-seventh in the nation in apple growing. Minnesota produces about 600,000 bushels of apples compared with a national total of 175,000,000.

Fun facts: There are about forty-two pounds of apples or about 100 apples in a bushel. It takes about ten apples to make one apple pie.

August 24, 1978 Swenson Red and Edelweiss Grapes

Eating some delicious cultivated grapes and at the same time being able to visit with the person who was instrumental in their development was my privilege when I met Elmer Swenson, their developer. The berries are from two varieties of grape vines, Swenson Red and Edelweiss, both introduced by the University of Minnesota Horticultural Research Center in 1977.

Elmer, who is a gardener at the Horticultural Research Center, is a grape and apple specialist who loves to work with fruit of all kinds. He began hybridizing grapes in the early 1940s on his dairy farm near Osceola, Wisconsin, and in 1968 he took some of his hybrids to the

Research Center. When his expertise was discovered, he was hired to work at the Center, and cultivating grapes became a part of his job. Each weekend he returns to his Wisconsin farm to work in his own vineyard. In looking for good flavor and texture in grapes for this region, Elmer had three main problems to solve. He wanted to develop grapes that were winter hardy, were resistant to disease and produced early-maturing fruit.

Two of Elmer Swenson's grape varieties have been named, and more will be introduced in the future. The quality of the Swenson varieties and their suitability for the northern region are creating great excitement among grape fanciers. Since the list of suitable grapes recommended for Minnesota growers is short, two more varieties are a valuable addition.

The first grape variety I tasted was Swenson Red. Elmer had suggested Norvin for a name, a contraction of Northern and Vinifera, but the University of Minnesota named it after him. Every grape on the cluster was ripe and delectable, and each beautiful red berry was delicious. He said that this variety was from a cross he made in the early 1960s, and the first fruit was harvested in 1967. He uses Concords, wild grapes and French hybrids in his hybridizing program, and Swenson Red has one-eighth "wild blood," he said. The one-half inch or larger berries are firm and should keep until mid-winter at 34°F in plastic containers. Swenson Red is particularly valuable in northern states because of its early maturity (full maturity is normally in early September in the Twin Cities area), high sugar content (20 to 22 percent), and fine dessert quality. It has survived minus 25° to minus 30°F without protection, but it is not considered hardy enough to grow well without cover at temperatures lower than that.

Edelweiss was the second table grape that I tasted fresh from the Horticultural Research Center vineyard. This so-called white grape has medium-sized green fruit that is sweet with a pleasant flavor. In breeding and selecting Edelweiss, a grape was developed that is suitable for planting in the northern states where, again, early maturity and hardiness are important. The vines are productive, vigorous and disease resistant and are considered even hardier than Swenson Red. Edelweiss fruit reaches its peak of maturity a few days before Swenson Red.

August 25, 1976 Migration of Common Nighthawks

It's common nighthawk migrating time. In a few minutes just before sundown tonight, I watched forty birds over our Lake Waconia yard. Only four or five of these dark birds with long pointed wings and white patches on each outer wing were visible at any one moment.

They were gliding, diving and circling, feeding on insects in the air and definitely headed south. Having been residents throughout the state since May, they are on their way to winter in South America.

The name common nighthawk is inappropriate since they are not strictly nocturnal — they are often seen flying in sunlight; they are not hawks either, although they do "hawk" or catch flying insects on the wing. The word common describes them because this species summers over towns, cities, suburbs, open plains and mountains of most of North America from northern Canada south into Mexico. I had thought originally of common nighthawks as city birds as I often saw them over towns and cities and learned about their nesting sites on gravel and tarred flat roofs. Later I found that they are numerous in wild habitats, nesting on open barren rocks, beaches and openings in forests, but they do not make a nest and eggs are laid in an exposed spot chosen by the female.

Nighthawks consume great quantities of insects taken out of the air with their large mouths. We see them hunting near the ground or high in the air over tree tops and buildings, meadows and forests. An analysis of their stomach contents has shown that in a single day one nighthawk captured over 500 mosquitoes and another ate 2,175 flying ants. Drinks of water are taken in flight by skimming surfaces of lakes and streams.

August 26, 1979 Ripe American Plums

This year there is a good crop of red and yellow fruit on the American wild plum trees *(Prunus americana)*, which I have been enjoying. The plums can be eaten raw, cooked as sauce or made into a jam or jelly. They were used extensively by American Indians who often dried them for winter by cutting them open, removing the center stones and spreading them out in the sun.

Thickets of wild plum are common throughout the Arboretum area where the trees grow to a height of about fifteen feet and have white flowers that began to bloom on May 21 this year. American wild plum is native from Massachusetts to Manitoba and south to Florida and New Mexico. This species is the origin of many cultivated plums grown in Minnesota and other areas, in some cases directly by selection and others by hybridization with other species.

August 27, 1971 Late August Bounty

Today I saw many signs that summer was drawing to a close. The berries on the common elderberry shrubs are ripe, and the edible golden-yellow fruits of the mayapple are ready to be picked. Prickly ash seeds are dropping, while clusters of bright red berries appear in place of each spadix on the Jack-in-the-pulpit plants. Goldenrods and asters are blooming, the Jerusalem artichoke, a native perennial sunflower, is at bloom peak, and dahlia flowers are spectacular. Best of all, the deer flies and mosquitoes aren't as bothersome as a few weeks ago so that a hike anywhere on the Arboretum grounds is much more enjoyable.

Out on the prairie the white flowers of rattlesnake master, the yellow flowers of prairie dock and the tall spikes of rose-purple blossoms on the blazing star are blooming profusely, attracting the monarch butterflies. Ruby-throated hummingbirds continue to feed on spotted touch-me-not flowers in wetland areas, and bumble bees hover over the big bull thistle flowers and red clover blossoms. Hostas are blooming, dozens of birds can be observed, and red mulberries are ripe and ready to be sampled.

The Arboretum is here for the enjoyment of those who wish to become acquainted with new plants and animals, learn more about already familiar ones or observe the aesthetics of nature and gardening together, in a setting that changes moods every hour.

August 28, 1975 Common Reed Grass

The Arboretum's reed marsh, a roughly circular area of about six acres between the entrance road and State Highway 5, is a southward extension of the basin of Lake Minnewashta and contains a dense stand of common reed grass *(Phragmites communis)*. It is spectacular to see now as each eight or nine-foot tall plant is topped with a big plumy inflorescence. Blackbirds of several species use this area for a nightly roost in summer and fall.

Growing in about two feet of water in the northeast part of the main basin of Lake Minnewashta is a thinner and small emergent stand of reed grass. I wonder if the reed grass got started in this area in the 1930s when the lake level was down. Reed grass is the tallest of our native grasses. Besides growing in shallow, marshy waters, it can also flourish on muddy shores and riverbanks. It tends to form continuous patches, sometimes extending over wide areas by the outward growth of its rhizomes. Distributed almost worldwide, it is found across southern Canada, in much of the United States, and south through Mexico to Chile and Argentina. It is found widely in Europe, even in Norway beyond the Arctic Circle and up into the Swiss Alps. This tall grass with stiff wide leaves and coarse hollow stems is also found on the other side of the world in Japan, Egypt and Australia.

The common reed grass was named *Phragmites*, a Greek word meaning "growing in hedges," apparently because of its growth in ditches in arid lands. *Communis*, the species name, means "growing in colonies."

Pens and styluses made from reed grass were used in ancient Egypt and Western Asia to record the social and political events. In addition to using reed grass for writing tools, the ancient people of these areas used it for food, medicine, sandals, well-insulated houses, sleeping mats, fuel, boats and brooms. In some parts of Europe where it is abundant, common reed grass has long been used for thatch and matting purposes and, more recently, for construction board; while in the Soviet Union it is an important crop of cellulose for paper manufacture. Calligraphy is often done with hand-made pens cut from the stems of our common reed grass today.

Donald B. Lawrence, writing in the University of Minnesota publication, *1972 Landscape Arboretum Annual Report*, gave a good account of the role that reed grass has played in the transmission of knowledge from the ancient past to the present day. He felt that the Arboretum's six-acre reed marsh, one of the finest and most accessible stands of this beautiful large aquatic grass in the state, deserves preservation. Reed grass has played an important part in our cultural heritage, and the quality of this particular stand should be preserved.

August 29, 1979 Butternuts and Bur Oak Acorns Falling

Orb webs showed their unusual patterns along the roadsides this dewy morning. Orb webs, intricate and beautiful in design, are most often placed vertically because they are then more likely to be in the path of flying insects, the food of the orb web weavers. The number of radii or spokes in the orb webs differs with the different species of spiders, but they are usually fastened to a silken framework that, in turn, is fastened by guylines to surrounding objects. At this time of year, the busy season for insect trapping, a spider may construct a new web every twenty-four hours. While the spiders are busy catching their food in webs, the squirrels are busy gathering the falling butternuts and bur oak acorns.

Butternut trees are native from New Brunswick to Georgia and west to the Dakotas and Arkansas. In Minnesota the trees grow in rich forests and on the lower slopes of hills in the valleys of the Mississippi and St. Croix rivers. The tree grows to a height of about forty-five feet and has pinnately compound leaves. It is planted for its shade and edible nuts but is hardy only in southern Minnesota. The oblong, sticky fruits should be gathered when they fall to the ground. The

Bur Oak leaf & tree

green outer husk of the nut, which was once used for dyeing cloth yellow or orange, is difficult to remove. It can be taken off with a hammer or by running a heavy object such as a car over it. After removing the husk, nuts should be dried for several months before cracking them, but they are worth this unusual amount of trouble to obtain as they have a fine quality and distinctive flavor.

Bur oaks are found throughout most of Minnesota and are common in our area also. Their acorns, which are distinguished by their deeply fringed caps, are now dropping and keeping the local squirrels active. Although the acorns of bur oaks *(Quercus macrocarpa)* are edible, a person wishing to forage for acorns should do some careful reading and studying before heading out to gather his lunch.

August 30, 1978 The First Fall Colors

We can always count on seeing splotches of fall color now, about the time a few fall warblers start migrating through the Arboretum area. Fields of Canada goldenrods with their arching plumes of golden-yellow flowers are brilliant, and there are tinges of red on some road-side sugar maples. Virginia creeper vines are showing some red leaflets, sumac shrubs have red, orange and yellow leaflets along with the less prominent but more common green foliage, and our large native basswoods are showing off scattered yellow leaves.

I hate to see another summer draw to a close, but these sprinklings of autumn are enough to make us all look forward to the next episode in our "theater of seasons."

August 31, 1977 Heavy Rain

From last evening until this morning, 7.65 inches of rain fell on the Arboretum while someone in Edina recorded 8.3 inches in his rain gauge. We received 6.1 inches on the shore of Lake Waconia, and the official total recorded at the Minneapolis-St. Paul International Airport was 7.38 inches. In LeSueur only .15 inches of rain fell, and very little fell south of the Twin Cities, so it was a storm of limited size. Seven inches of rain from one storm is what we expect only about every 200 years in any one area in Minnesota, which is fortunate as it flooded basements and roads and closed the airport for two hours. It did, however, effectively end the dry spell, and lakes and ponds, which were at a low level, rose seven inches or more in a very short time.

We are beginning to have a very good fall mushroom season. Rod Kuehn, our local mushroom expert, brought in two giant puffballs, each about fifteen inches across, ready to be eaten and looking like two big white loaves of bread. He also found honey mushrooms and inky caps, which can be eaten but with caution as some people have become ill from eating them after only a small alcoholic drink. I, too, spotted several meadow mushrooms ready to be picked, but although I enjoy eating mushrooms, I would rather look at and photograph all kinds, edible and poisonous. I seldom eat any wild mushrooms with the exception of the few that I am absolutely certain of. Poisonous mushrooms are known to be poisonous because someone ate them and became sick or died; edible mushrooms are known to be edible because many people have eaten them regularly, sometimes in large quantities, with no ill effects. Some kinds are difficult for even an expert to identify, but others can be identified by a beginner with a good guide book and help from a knowledgeable teacher.

Virginia Creeper

September 1, 1976 Spotted Touch-me-not

Honey bees, bumble bees and ruby-throated hummingbirds are regular visitors at the spotted touch-me-not *(Impatiens capensis)*. When touched even lightly, its mature seed pods burst open into curling segments and scatter the seeds, and it is this action that gives the plant the common name of touch-me-not. The orange-yellow, one-inch long blossoms splotched with reddish-brown hang from their slender stalks like pendant jewels, which may be the reason for an alternative common name, the spotted jewelweed, or perhaps the plant is also known as jewelweed because its leaves are unwettable, causing rain drops to stand on the leaves in spherical drops.

Touch-me-not may be found near streams or in other damp and well-shaded areas, but does not like open sunny places unless the places are very damp. It is an annual wildflower with surface-spreading roots and hollow, succulent, translucent stems which would not be able to reach a height of two to four feet if the plants did not grow in a community, with each plant helping to support another one.

At the end of each touch-me-not flower there is a twist or pointed spur, a nectary, that is very sweet. A butterfly with its long, flexible sucking tube that can curl around and probe to the bottom is successful in securing the nectar, but hummingbirds and bees also avail themselves of the contents of the nectary and become pollinators.

Euell Gibbons, a well-known edible-plant enthusiast and writer, mentioned in one of his books that he had gathered young sprouts of touch-me-not in the spring when they were no more than four to six inches high, cut the tender stems into short lengths, and cooked them like green beans. After draining the cooking water and seasoning the sprouts with butter, salt and a little black pepper, Euell reported that they were delicious.

I have never eaten touch-me-not but have used it as a poison ivy lotion. The stems can be squeezed, and the watery juice applied to relieve the itching from poison ivy. A better way, probably, is to gather some plants, cover them with water, and after boiling them down until the liquid is about half its original volume, strain the juice. The concentrated juice seems to be effective both in preventing the rash after exposure to poison ivy and in treating the rash after it has developed. The liquid will keep only a few days in a refrigerator, so putting the strained juice into ice cube trays and freezing it is a good way to preserve it. When it is needed, either as a preventive or as a

Spotted Touch-me-not

treatment, rub the area with one of the touch-me-not ice cubes or melt them and use the liquid. The juice has been used to treat athlete's foot, and recently scientific analysis confirmed that it has fungicidal agents.

September 2, 1978 Fall Warblers

At least 80 percent of Minnesota's bird species fly south through the Mississippi flyway, according to Dr. Harrison Tordoff, director of the University of Minnesota Bell Museum of Natural History. Sandpipers, warblers, wrens, vireos, thrushes and swallows make the trip. Migration for some birds began as early as July. Many millions improve their health by leaving Minnesota for the winter season each year.

Much has been written about the origin of migration, but Dr. Tordoff believes the reason for the evolution of migration is not hard to understand. If you have animals that are mobile with a seasonal food supply that fluctuates, the natural result is migration. It's as true today as it was long ago that the birds that move in the right direction survive.

Most temperate zone birds begin their migrations because of the change in the length of daylight, and others get their signal from the shrinking food supply. Since individual birds have a tendency to return to the same place because they are familiar with the food supply, available shelter and predators, we often question how they know which way to travel. Bird navigation is interesting and complex. Landmarks and compass directions taken from the sun, stars and invisible lines of the earth's magnetic field all help guide various bird species.

Waves of migrating birds — warblers, vireos and flycatchers — are moving through today. Because the warblers represent so many species and are small and very active, they can be hard to identify. To make autumn warbler identification even more difficult, most adults are less brilliantly colored in fall than in spring. Immature warblers with dull plumage generally outnumber adults, and during migration the birds gather in mixed flocks to add to the confusion. It's not surprising that Roger Tory Peterson in his book, *A Field Guide to the Birds*, (Houghton Mifflin, 1947) has a section on these confusing fall warblers alone. Even with a good field guide book, quality binoculars and plenty of spare time, an observant and experienced birder will find a study of the fall migrating warblers a challenge.

September 3, 1974 Early Frost

The earliest statewide frost on record struck large parts of Minnesota early this morning, damaging vegetable crops and cutting into corn and soybean yields that already have been decimated by summer drought. Frost occurred in low spots around the Twin Cities on September 1, but this morning the effects of a general frost could be seen over a large area. A low temperature of 30°F was recorded at International Airport between 6 and 7 a.m., the earliest freeze since records began to be kept in 1819. On the average, the first frost occurs on October 13 in Minneapolis.

Frost covered our house roof and much of our yard on the shore of Lake Waconia at the same time that the lake was steaming in the cold air. Later in the day I checked some neighborhood gardens and saw that cucumber and muskmelon vines and tomato plants had been killed, and the snapbean plants had dead leaves. A few gardens located in higher, protected spots escaped frost damage. In local wetland areas I noticed spotted touch-me-not and sensitive fern plants that had been killed by the frost, but both the bull and Canada thistles continue to bloom and to shed seeds.

This afternoon when the temperature warmed up to 62°F, painted turtles were out sunning, and snowy tree crickets were calling.

September 4, 1975 Native Asters and Goldenrods

The landscape in rural and natural areas is broken by glowing, golden-yellow patches of blooming goldenrods and by rich lavender-blue, bright purplish-blue or white rays on aster flowerheads that are clustered at the ends of the stems. The several species of both native asters and native goldenrods, all members of the composite or daisy family, help complete the autumn scene.

Among the showiest of the goldenrods at the present time is the stiff goldenrod *(Solidage rigida)*, a common perennial of prairies and dry thickets. I have noticed that the migrating monarch butterflies, hungry for nectar, have switched their attention from the flowers of blazing stars to the dark yellow blossoms of the stiff goldenrod. This goldenrod with rigid leaves and flat-topped flower clusters several inches wide is also visited by honey bees, wild bees and Milbert's tortoise shell butterflies.

Mount Royal plums are ripe now and delicious for fresh eating and making jam. There are still a few ripe fruits left on the wild plum trees also, and we still enjoy the great flavor of Beacon apples eaten fresh off the tree.

Canada Goldenrod

September 5, 1979 Fallgold and Fallred Raspberries

An Arboretum worker brought us some ripe groundcherries explaining that the fruit falls to the ground when ripe and has been falling for about a month in her garden. Groundcherries have a distinctive flavor and an unusual golden color with a tan, papery outer covering.

One of the Arboretum gardeners who has been harvesting his first fall crop of radishes and broccoli reports that cucumbers are still ripening, tomatoes are past their peak now, and both Fallgold and Fallred raspberry plants are bearing ripe fruit. These raspberry varieties produce a good crop of berries in July on the over-wintered canes (branches), and then from mid-August until it freezes, they bear fruit on canes from the current season's growth.

American goldfinches have been feeding from bull thistle seedheads. In the Young America area southwest of the Arboretum about 500 white pelicans stopped by to do some fishing on local lakes where they scoop up the fish while swimming. I enjoy watching these huge white birds with a nine-foot wingspread, black primary wing feathers and great orange-yellow bills as they fly in lines and sometimes circle high overhead.

September 6, 1958 Dedication of the Arboretum

The University of Minnesota Landscape Arboretum was formally dedicated this afternoon at a program sponsored jointly by the University of Minnesota and the Minnesota State Horticultural Society with 400 people present. Dr. Leon C. Snyder, head of the Department of Horticulture at the University of Minnesota, is the new director of the Arboretum, which will be devoted to research in testing and developing hardy ornamentals for landscaping in Minnesota. The Arboretum will give people an opportunity to see plant materials in natural landscape groupings as well as the variety of plants available for use. It will be a place of forests, meadows, wetlands and plantings that gardeners, wildflower enthusiasts, birders, entomologists, hikers and picnickers will enjoy.

Dr. Donald Wyman, horticulturist for the Harvard University Arnold Arboretum, was the principal speaker. He said that the Arboretum is unequaled because it is situated in a colder area than any other arboretum or botanical garden in the United States, and research here will benefit many people in the northern areas of the country. "Minnesota's Arboretum will be of national significance," he predicted. "Although there are over 100 arboretums in the United States, this one is unique. It will be watched by nurserymen and amateur gardeners alike. If plants grow here, they should grow in less rugged climates." Dr. Wyman defined an arboretum as "a living museum of woody plants, each properly identified and labeled."

Tours of the grounds via tractor and hay rack were conducted following the formal dedication. Dr. Snyder has already begun development of the 160 acres with university students and fruit farm staff as the workers. A road has been constructed through the property, a small headquarters building established, trees and shrubs labeled, and planting begun.

September 7, 1979 Departure of Northern Orioles

Northern (Baltimore) orioles have a strong homing instinct and often return year after year to nest in the same yard and often the same tree. It is the bird's custom to build a new nest each year, even though the old nest may appear well-preserved for two or three years after being built. The olive and yellow females are the architects and nest builders. Bird nests are only used for rearing young, and the nests are not used after about July 1. After today these gray pendulous bags of expertly woven plant fibers, bark and string that have been secured and suspended from the ends of branches will remain as symbols, with the promise that many of the orioles will return next May. There is a banding record from Fargo, North Dakota, of a northern oriole retrapped and released at the same place seven years after it was banded.

The bright orange and sharply contrasting black plumage of the male Baltimore oriole makes it very conspicuous as it searches for food. These colors must have caught the attention of early European settlers in Maryland because the bird was named in honor of Lord Baltimore, an early colonizer there, who had chosen orange and black as his family colors. Orioles also attract attention with their loud, clear voices. The absence of this small bird's cheerful whistles and chattering is a sure sign of the retreat of summer.

Northern orioles winter on land from southern Mexico to northern South America. Occasionally I hear about orioles attempting to winter over in Minnesota and other northern states, but most of these birds probably die in early winter. Observers in Central America report that the first northern orioles arrive there during the second week of September, but the large influx does not come until the end of the month. There is almost no other winter visitant so widely and uniformly distributed throughout its wintering range.

It's an adaptable bird that makes itself at home almost anywhere that trees and shrubs provide fruit and insects. Northern orioles winter in arid areas or rain-forests, on mountain sides and plantations. Females and young males may predominate, but the mature males in their bright orange and black plumage are most noticeable and have few rivals in beauty, even among the most brilliant native birds. They are usually seen singly or in small groups, and their clear whistles can be heard during the first few weeks following their arrival in fall and again for a month or so before their departure for the north in April.

The dates that follow contain a few highlights of northern oriole observations made by Al Zander in the Glen Lake area of Minnetonka for 1979. More observations on oriole behavior can be found in the August 20 entry.

1979 Northern Oriole Phenology

May 5	— First oriole arrived.
May 8	— Twelve orioles (nine males and three females) ate from the orange halves and grape jelly feeders.
May 15	— Orioles started gathering nesting material.
May 20–23	— This is the peak of nest building.
June 19	— Orioles are eating inch worms. Female orioles were at the grape jelly feeder for the first time in about three weeks. The orioles have been quiet for the last three weeks, but today they began singing loudly. It must be nearing the launching time of the young.
June 27	— Oriole young left their nests.
August 21	— Orioles are busy at the grape jelly feeder.
September 4	— The numbers are dwindling. Only nine orioles were counted at the feeders.
September 6	— Only three orioles are still coming to the feeders.
September 7	— Two orioles appeared early this morning at the feeders.
September 8	— No orioles.
May 5, 1980	— First orioles returned to Al's yard; two males arrived at noon.

The last of the northern orioles left the Minnetonka area to spend the winter in Central America on these dates:

September 11, 1975	September 7, 1979
September 8, 1976	September 6, 1980
September 5, 1977	September 3, 1981
September 13, 1978	September 3, 1982

September 8, 1979 Sulphur Butterflies

A few early season apples that were overlooked during harvest are now overripe and rotting on the trees and attract red admiral and mourning cloak butterflies that unroll their coiled, sucking tubes to feed on the juices. As I looked at our alfalfa meadow, I also saw hundreds of sulphur butterflies, quick-moving yellow wisps, darting back and forth in the sunlight. There are several species of sulphurs found in Minnesota, but I'm sure that I saw mostly common sulphurs, also called clouded sulphurs. The butter-yellow of European sulphurs probably suggested the name "butterfly."

This year I observed the first sulphur butterfly on the wing May 25. The males can be identified at once by their rich butter-yellow wings with black margins while females have the dark borders of their forewings interspaced with yellow dots. Each has a wingspread of up to about two inches, but in spring and fall they are somewhat smaller. These predominantly-yellow insects may well be one of the most plentiful butterflies in the state and even in most of the United States east of the Rockies. They are often seen on the edges of mud puddles sipping the water or over flower-covered meadows.

The species tends to increase in number with each successive brood until early September. The eggs are laid singly beneath the leaves of clover and alfalfa plants. The green caterpillars then feed for nearly three weeks, growing to one inch and forming chrysalids that hatch in about ten days. Their short life cycle allows for several broods each growing season.

In 1979 the last sulphur butterfly was seen in the Arboretum area on October 29.

September 9, 1978 September Heat Wave

Since the first of September we have been having temperatures about ten to twenty degrees above the normal highs. Two days ago the Twin Cities had a high of 96°F; Redwood Falls, 103°F; St. Peter, 99°F; but the high temperature in Duluth was only 58°F. Yesterday the Twin Cities again had an air temperature of 96°F.

This afternoon we are in the low 90s as the cicadas buzz and the catbirds call. A continuous stream of monarch butterflies is passing over our yard, headed in a south-to-southwest direction. We saw a ruby-throated hummingbird zipping around in the spray from the lawn sprinkler as we ate a picnic lunch nearby. Soon its bath was over, and the wet hummingbird landed on a branch of the silver maple where it preened its feathers carefully as we watched. At the same time a white-lined sphinx moth was visiting some of our annual flowers in hummingbird-like fashion. Late in the afternoon I took the temperature of the surface water of Lake Waconia and found it to be 80°F and perfect for swimming.

The hot weather is making some crops mature too fast. An example of this is the sweet corn that is drying in the fields. About 20 percent of Minnesota's sweet corn crop has not been harvested yet. As the farmers try to get it in as quickly as possible, the processing plants are working at full capacity but can't take care of the corn that is ready. Soybean plants are drying and yellowing, and field corn is drying and turning tannish-brown before either crop is fully mature.

September 10, 1977 Shaggy Mane Mushrooms

The surface temperature of Lake Waconia was 67°F, cool for swimming, but I took a quick invigorating dip anyway. I saw more than 300 slate-gray coots in a raft on the west end of the lake, but naturalist Dick Gray spotted the first fall American coot on Lake Minnetonka on August 20.

Rain has brought out the mosquitoes again, but it has helped to make our lawns a lush green and encouraged the appearance of mushrooms, especially the shaggy manes.

Mushrooms are the fruiting bodies of thread-like plants that must grow on other organic material, living or dead, because they have no chlorophyll to produce their own food. Each mushroom has specialized cells for the development of spores, which, like seeds, serve to reproduce and spread the species.

Shaggy mane mushrooms *(Coprinus comatus)* appear infrequently during hot and dry weather but are now commonly seen in grassy areas. These beautiful mushrooms are snowy white against the green grass and can be spotted easily. At first a shaggy mane appears as a narrow egg emerging from the ground, but as it grows the cap rises and the stem appears tightly clasped by the bottom of the cap. The caps are cylindrical, about one to two inches across and three to six inches high, with the surface of the cap covered by shaggy white or tan scales. There is no other mushroom like the shaggy mane and little possibility of confusing it with anything else. It will more than double in size before the cap begins to expand, and at this stage, the bottom of the cap turns to pale pink, and it's time to collect the mushroom for food. When the cap expands, its edges begin to turn black and watery, while self-digestive enzymes turn the tissue into black ink-like liquid that drips off and carries the spores to new spots for germination and growth.

Shaggy manes are considered to be one of the tastiest mushrooms. They are found in open grassy areas, compost heaps, along roadsides, in silt along streams and in decaying sawdust near old logging roads. Delicate in texture and excellent in flavor, they must, however, like inky caps, be picked before the caps begin to liquify. After being washed, the shaggies can be cooked in several ways or eaten raw, one of the few mushrooms that can be. To do this, cut the young plants into sections, stems and all, and put on lettuce to make a salad that goes well with any dressing. Alcohol in any form is likely to make an unwholesome combination with shaggy manes.

September 11, 1978 The Green Darner

This afternoon millions of monarch butterflies and green darner dragonflies passed through parts of southern Minnesota just ahead of a big cold front moving in from Canada. Sightings of the migrating insects were reported to me from Appleton, Wayzata, Eden Prairie, Stillwater and points in between.

I was in the Arboretum about 3 p.m. and was disappointed in seeing only about twenty-five of the regal orange and black butterflies working the plants on the prairie area. However, to my surprise, several hundred others were feeding on the red clover flowers in the crabapple collection and pine areas. As the temperature was 90°F and the mosquitoes were bothersome, I decided to make my note-taking visit

Shaggy Mane

a quick one. I was leaving in the car at 3:35 when the build-up of cumulus clouds caught my attention. I stopped my car to take a better look at the clouds and noticed that a few monarchs were flying over. Then within minutes I saw hundreds in the air, and soon thousands were coming from the Lake Minnewashta area and heading south over the Arboretum. At the same time I observed thousands of darner dragonflies also headed south.

I watched in front of the Arboretum Snyder Building at 4 p.m. as thousands of monarchs continued to pass over. It was an unforgettable sight; some were traveling close to the ground, one to five feet up, but most were flying south at an elevation of 100 feet or more above ground. Again I observed thousands of darner dragonflies, but not once did a dragonfly attack a monarch. Both species just kept heading south.

I called Dan Hertsgaard at WCCO Radio, who enthusiastically announced some of my observations to listeners and invited them to call their monarch and dragonfly sightings into the station. Many people responded, and we were able to determine that the migration was a massive one across southern Minnesota and into Wisconsin. I had read that the monarchs migrate at heights up to about 1,000 feet, but a pilot who called WCCO Radio reported that although many dragonflies were flying at his level of 1,200 feet above ground, he didn't see any monarchs up that high.

The peak of the migration came about 4:15 p.m., with still a few monarchs and dragonflies flying at 5:20. I was amazed and excited by what we had witnessed, but although I knew that monarchs migrated, I was puzzled by the dragonflies. With a wing-span of three inches they were easy to recognize with their large, net-veined, clear wings and green bodies.

Dr. Edwin Cook, University of Minnesota entomologist, later told me that the green darner dragonfly *(Anax junius)* is a widely distributed species in North America. Soon I found library references stating that other observers had recorded the migration of green darners over the years, even having seen them riding the air waves of mountain valleys with hawks and eagles.

September 12, 1972 Arrival of White-throated Sparrows

The whistling of the white-throated sparrows, opening on one or two clear notes followed by three quavering notes on a different pitch, is one of my favorite bird sounds. Their songs are often translated as "Old Sam Peabody, Peabody, Peabody," or "Sweet Sweet Canada, Canada, Canada." The latter rendition is probably more appropriate, since most of these birds nest in Canada and some in the northeastern and north central regions of Minnesota. White-throated sparrows pass through the Twin Cities in large numbers during their spring and fall migrations with the first ones seen today on their fall flight. Since the majority will be migrating through the next couple weeks, we will be able to hear their songs then.

During migration times we attract white-throated sparrows to our feeding stations that are located near forests or shrubbery. They are ground feeding birds, and although they seem to prefer millet seeds scattered on the ground when they are at our station, their main food throughout the year is grass seeds and seeds from other low plants and insects. A few white-throats overwinter at our area feeders occasionally, but the majority migrate to southern states.

For beginning bird watchers who may be confused trying to identify the dozen or more sparrow species that appear in their yards and neighborhoods in a year's time, the white-throat is one of the easiest to identify. First we listen to its plaintive song, and then we look for a sparrow with a gray breast, a white throat patch, a yellow spot between the eye and bill, and black and white head stripes. In fall and winter its colors are duller, and sometimes the yellow spot near each eye is inconspicuous.

September 13, 1976 Gray Catbirds

As I looked out the window on this rainy day, I saw gray catbirds eating ripe common buckthorn berries. Although they are largely insectivorous during the summer, catbirds can now be seen feeding on many of the fall fruits. They are members of the mockingbird family, so in addition to their songs they also imitate calls of other birds and animals. The cat-like whines coming from dense thickets are distinct and indicate their presence.

One of the first birds I learned to identify as a child was the gray catbird. It is a slate gray bird, smaller than a robin, slender, with a long tail and a black cap. It is found in low dense thickets, tangles of vines, edges of forests and often on the borders of marshes and roadsides, the latter location causing many birds to be killed by traffic.

The small gray catbird is a dearly loved dooryard bird in America. It is a summer resident throughout Minnesota but leaves in autumn for its winter range in southern United States and an area from the West Indies to Panama. When catbirds leave in September, they fly mainly at night, with TV towers and tall buildings sometimes becoming a hazard in their flights.

September 14, 1974 Zigzag Goldenrod

Until a few years ago when I made a serious effort to study and learn about the native plants in Minnesota, the zigzag goldenrod was unknown to me. I was under the impression that all goldenrods were

Common Milkweed

sun-loving plants of the prairies and meadows, but to my surprise, I discovered that a forest plant that had clusters of golden flowers at the base of each upper leaf was a native goldenrod species. This plant called zigzag goldenrod or broad-leaved goldenrod *(Solidago flexicaulis)* has stems that zigzag and broad coarse-toothed leaves. There are many now in bloom in the shady forests of the Arboretum, a sharp yellow note in the green surroundings.

The annual flower garden is colorful along with the garden roses, mums and dahlias. These flowers, together with the muted red fall color of pagoda dogwoods, bright reds on red maples and yellow leaves on basswood trees, attract people to the Arboretum now.

The acorns from the white, the red and the bur oak are falling, and since eastern chipmunks live where there are oak trees, their "chipping" and "munking" sounds can be heard throughout the forests today. Birding is quite good now. Two dozen species can easily be spotted on a hike across the Arboretum bog boardwalk, along the forest edge and up into the meadow areas. Red admiral butterflies that are especially numerous now can be seen on marigold, aster, white snakeroot and stick-tight flowers.

September 15, 1975 First Common Milkweed Pods

More than 100 species of milkweeds grow in North America. From August into winter pods of various species of milkweeds, well-known perennials with a milky juice, burst open releasing seeds.

The common milkweed is found in meadows and along roads throughout Minnesota. The warty-looking seed pods, flat at the bottom and pointed at the top, make it easy to identify. I noticed the first open pods today. The plant is dropping its leaves, and the gray fruit pods are opening down the middle so that the wind can carry away the seeds that have fluffy white tufts of silky hairs.

In a few weeks some of the pods will have dried and started opening, and then a sunny, warm day will force the pods to burst open in great numbers. A beautiful sunlight scene will ensue as brown milkweed seeds on silvery parachutes, puffed up in masses, flow out from the pods in the late afternoon sunshine.

First common milkweed pods began opening in the Arboretum area:

September 17, 1974	September 19, 1978
September 15, 1975	September 20, 1979
September 8, 1976	September 8, 1980
August 23, 1977	September 9, 1981
	September 17, 1982

September 16, 1975   Black Swallowtail Butterflies

It's easy to attract butterflies to your yard if you provide a few of their favorite flowering plants like bergamot, blazing star, butterfly-weed, asters and goldenrods. However, a small price must often be paid. If you want mourning cloaks, the caterpillars will eat some of your elm and willow leaves. They will not kill the trees, but they will leave holes in the foliage. Another insect, the black swallowtail female, will lay her eggs on wild and cultivated plants of the carrot family, such as parsley, parsnip, dill, carrot and Queen Ann's lace. After the eggs hatch, the larvae will feed on the foliage and in about two weeks will become handsome, two-inch long, green and black caterpillars that will each form a chrysalis. When the adults emerge, they will enjoy the nectar of delphinium and other garden plants.

I have butterflies on my mind because this is a very good butterfly year. On a short hike this afternoon I saw monarchs, black swallow-tails, sulphurs, Milbert's tortoise shells, cabbage butterflies and a viceroy. Of the six black swallowtails I saw, three were on the flowers of one bull thistle plant.

Eastern black swallowtails are common and widespread throughout the eastern United States. They have an average wingspread of three inches and are best identified by the twin rows of yellow spots on their black wings. The first adults usually appear in May. We see two broods of black swallowtails annually in Minnesota, most often en-countering them on the wing in June and August. This year there appears to be a late second brood or even a third now in September.

September 17, 1979   Painted Lady Butterflies

Painted lady butterflies, which are numerous this fall, were feeding today on the nectar of many flowering plants. Some of the plants were asters, dahlias, marigolds, miniature roses, mums, phlox, showy stonecrop, verbena and zinnias. People around the state tell us they are seeing hundreds of painted lady butterflies. During favorable years these butterflies often erupt over the countryside in great num-bers with nearly every field and flower garden swarming with the insects by late summer and into fall. This species is known for its extremely large numbers one year and very few the next.

Another common name for the painted lady butterfly *(Vanessa car-dui)* is the thistle butterfly. Caterpillars of the painted lady feed chiefly on thistle and other plants of the composite family. The butterfly is predominantly orange, brown and black on the upper body with four eyespots on the underside and a wingspread of about two inches. There are two broods annually; a new generation is seen in July and a second one in late August. The last brood flies well into autumn, and some adults may overwinter, with the butterflies that survive appearing very faded in spring.

Some painted lady butterflies were still flying in October and November, 1979. Three were spotted November 17 feeding on dandelion flowers as the temperature reached 64°F that sunny afternoon.

September 18, 1977 — Notes from the North Shore of Lake Superior

Lake Superior is the world's largest body of fresh water with a shoreline that is marked by great forests, rocky cliffs and beautiful beaches. The rugged natural beauty was more spectacular than usual because the peak of the autumn colors had reached this area when our family spent the weekend there.

Next to the water's edge in the crack of imposing rocks, we saw the three-toothed cinquefoil, a tiny shrub with red, yellow and green leaflets. A much larger shrub, the common ninebark with red leaves and brown clusters of fruit, grew there also.

Just a few feet from the shoreline the forest begins. There we saw thimbleberry shrubs with leaves that are turning yellow and orange, moose maples with red, orange and yellow foliage, and highbush cranberry shrubs and pin cherry trees both at their peak of red fall color. Along the highway between Duluth and Grand Marais we noticed that the mountain ashes have a good crop of fruit and that their leaves are yellow on some trees and mostly red on others. Many of the aspens and paper birches are yellow and gold.

It was a relaxing and entertaining weekend. We fed the herring gulls, watched migrating warblers move quickly from branch to branch, gathered and ate a few lingering wild raspberries, skipped flat pebbles, enjoyed the sounds of the waves and the feel of the cool, refreshing air, and noticed a few flowers. Some wildflowers like the harebell, butter-and-eggs, spotted touch-me-not, evening primrose and large-leaved aster are still in bloom. A quick jaunt up the Gunflint Trail and another to Caribou Lake revealed more colorful, beautiful fall colors.

Although rain and fog were present most of the weekend, I feel they helped to make the fall colors even more captivating.

September 19, 1971 Hawk Ridge in Duluth

Hawk Ridge in Duluth is known as one of the major global sites for the observation of fall hawk migrations. Hawks, eagles and other birds of prey concentrate over this single geographic point during their migration to wintering areas as close as southern Minnesota or as distant as South America. They pass here quickly, probably because they are reluctant to cross a body of water as large as Lake Superior. A further funneling effect occurs as the hawks use updrafts along the shoreline, but after passing Hawk Ridge they quickly disperse.

Hawk-watching begins in mid-August and continues into December, with the biggest flights usually occuring from September 8 to 23. The best time to observe the migrating birds seems to be from about 10 a.m. to 2 p.m., but there is almost no migration on days with an easterly wind or precipitation. Clear skies and a northwest wind provide the best conditions for flying. On one particular mid-September day with a south, southwest wind, only fifty hawks were seen. However, the very next day 19,225 birds were counted after the wind had switched to the northwest and skies had cleared. Most of the birds were broad-winged hawks that are about the size of a crow with distinct tail bands. Fourteen species including turkey vultures, bald eagles, ospreys, marsh hawks and red-tailed hawks are regular fall migrators over Hawk Ridge.

Today was my first trip to Hawk Ridge. There was a spectacular flight of over 19,000 birds yesterday, but we couldn't expect so many today as the light wind was from the south, the wrong direction. It was a good day, nevertheless, as by 2:30 p.m. about 500 birds had been counted from this vantage point, which is about 800 feet above the city. They were mostly sharp-shinned hawks, but there were also some sparrow hawks, marsh hawks and broad-winged hawks.

Besides learning to identify hawks moving overhead and sometimes below us, my father and I enjoyed the panoramic view of Duluth and the blue water of Lake Superior, together with the patches of fall color on the hillsides.

September 20, 1975 Highbush Cranberry

There are definite signs of fall. Butternut trees have lost most of their leaves; sumacs, Virginia creeper vines, basswood and sugar maple trees are showing nice fall color; autumn crocus is in bloom, and the dahlias and mums have colorful flowers. Along the Arboretum bog boardwalk, red maples are scarlet and the highbush cranberry has red foliage and fruit.

The highbush cranberry *(Viburnum trilobum)* is a tall shrub that grows wild in Canada and northern United States where it is common in coniferous forest areas. It likes cool woods, thickets, shores and rocky slopes. Highbush cranberries grow to twelve feet, have three-lobed leaves and tart, juicy red fruit. The shrubs have clusters of berries, each berry a little more than one-fourth inch in diameter, that remain on the bushes through the winter and provide food for cedar waxwings and ruffed grouse.

Although not related to cranberries, the fruit of the highbush cranberry is often used in their place for sauce, cold drinks and jelly. It is normally too tart to be eaten raw, but the berries are excellent when cooked with some lemon peels, the seeds removed, and sugar added. The result is very much like cranberry sauce and is rich in vitamin C. The sweetened juice can be diluted for drinks or made into jelly with the addition of pectin.

September 21, 1979 Rafts of American Coots

This year the first few coots appeared in Lake Waconia on September 3, but it wasn't until today that they returned in large numbers. Flotillas or rafts of them were seen bobbing in the water. Although last year some of the gregarious coots stayed until the lakes froze over in November, they generally reach their highest number on area lakes in mid to late October. A few will overwinter in Minnesota

American Coot

in spots where there is open water and food available, but nearly all of them move south to open water, even to saltwater bays and inlets.

The American coot — also known as mud hen, crow duck, mud duck and pond crow — has a large range. It is found between Canada and northern South America. Coots are present on area lakes in spring soon after the ice cover leaves, but they are not seen here in the summer although they nest in other parts of the state. Their slate-gray color, hen-like conspicuous white bills, greenish legs and big-lobed green feet make them easy to identify. The necessity to patter over the water before they are airborne is another of their definite characteristics. They are the most aquatic members of the rail family, are excellent swimmers and divers and move in open water like ducks and often feed with them. They graze on muskgrass *(Chara)* and other aquatic plants, small fish, tadpoles, snails and insects. Occasionally coots come up on land, and sometimes flocks can be seen far from water, feeding on seeds and grasses in meadows, on lawns and on golf courses.

September 22, 1976 First Official Day of Autumn

Today our sun is in a position relative to the earth to make days and nights of equal length on all parts of the globe. Sunrise occurred at 6 a.m. (local solar time), and the sunset was at 6 p.m. at all places on earth except at the poles where special conditions prevail. The sun rises at a point due east on the horizon and sets at a point due west on the horizon at all latitudes except at the two poles. At the poles the sun remains on the horizon all day, traveling one complete circuit of the horizon in twenty-four hours. In the northern hemisphere we will notice that the sun shines for an increasingly shorter time each day as the nights get longer until the winter solstice. The autumnal equinox occurs on September 22 or 23.

Today the Virginia creeper vine *(Parthenocissus inserta)* is at its peak of fall color with brilliant red foliage. Virginia creeper trails or climbs and often covers shrubs and trees. With its tendrils or small modified stems that are capable of twining around objects, it is a loosely climbing vine. Each leaf of Virginia creeper, also called woodbine, has five to seven leaflets with five the most common. The leaflets are two to five inches long. Virginia creeper is sometimes feared as something poisonous to touch, on the order of poison ivy. One needs only to remember that the Virginia creeper has five finger-like leaflets, suggesting that one's own fingers can safely handle it, while the poison ivy has only three leaflets.

Virginia creeper is planted occasionally. The vine does not cling to buildings but is ornamental on fences, trellises and for covering rocks. Its most colorful period is now, when the deep green leaves have turned to brilliant scarlet. In the deciduous forest areas of the state this native woody vine is quite common on banks, in thickets, along fence rows and growing up into some trees.

Peak of fall color for Virginia creeper vines in the Arboretum area:

September 25, 1971	September 17, 1977
September 19, 1972	September 27, 1978
September 28, 1973	September 27, 1979
September 19, 1974	September 25, 1980
September 20, 1975	September 24, 1981
September 22, 1976	September 25, 1982

September 23, 1978 Carver County Pioneer, Andrew Peterson

The sumacs and Virginia creeper are colorful plants now, but still the total landscape looks like early September. Our hot weather in the first part of the month, together with the moisture, must be holding back the colors. Many types of mushrooms are prevalent in large numbers, and common nighthawks still can be observed as they migrate through.

With clear skies and a high temperature in the mid-70s, the weather was perfect for the Harvest Festival at the former Andrew Peterson farm, a little more than five miles west of the Arboretum. Jo Mihelich, festival chairperson, and the Heritage Committee of the Carver County Historical Society organized this tribute to the memory of Andrew Peterson and other settlers of Scandia, a settlement of Swedish Baptists who first arrived and homesteaded in the area near the southeast shore of Lake Waconia in 1855. Our family enjoyed the hayride, an old fashioned threshing demonstration, the booths featuring historical displays, the slide-tape show about Andrew Peterson and the Scandia people, and the buildings that were part of the original Andrew Peterson farm.

Because of Andrew Peterson's diary, which he faithfully kept from 1855 to 1898, we are able to trace the development of his farming and horticultural activities. The diary is a priceless sociological record that details the seasonal rhythm of the hard labor that was a pioneer's life and the system of barter, shared labor and cooperative effort that was needed for a homesteader's success. His farm, which was diversified and served as a model for his neighbors, was highly successful. We learn that the farm produced wheat, oats, barley, corn, alfalfa, potatoes, rutabagas, vegetables of many kinds, sugar beets, many apple varieties, pears, grapes, plums, cherries, gooseberries, currants, raspberries, strawberries, maple syrup, molasses, wine, eggs, butter, cream, milk, cattle, swine, sheep, geese, poultry, cordwood and logs. These products insured a multiple income, above a mere subsistence level.

Although in many respects Andrew Peterson seems to be typical of the many Swedish immigrants who built their homes and farmed in America, one of his activities was not typical — his devotion to horticulture. The son of a farmer, Andrew was born in 1818 in Sweden. He may have developed his interest and skills in horticulture while working for a nurseryman in Iowa before coming to Minnesota; and on his own farm he worked with apples, pears, plums and other fruits as he experimented to determine which varieties could survive Minnesota's winter, bear well and resist disease. It's interesting that 100 years later this type of work is going on at the University of Minnesota Horticultural Research center just a few miles east of his former farm.

Soon after coming to Minnesota, Andrew set out an orchard. He probably tried more than 100 kinds of apples and raised thousands of trees over the years. Although he tried Swedish varieties as well as others, he had the greatest success with Russian varieties. He helped to prove that apples could be grown profitably in this section and that some of those imported from Russia were especially dependable.

Andrew Peterson's diaries were written in Swedish and were translated into English by Emma Margareta Ahlquist during the 1930s as a Work Progress Administration (WPA) project. Copies of the English translations are in the libraries of the Minnesota Historical Society and the University of Minnesota Landscape Arboretum where I read them. Like many hardworking Scandinavians, he seldom expressed his feelings or revealed his inner thoughts. The following eight entries help to give an idea of what it was like to be a pioneer farmer and horticulturist in Carver County:

> March 31, 1857 — A.M. Made 20 troughs for the sap. P.M. Erickson and I made plans for his house. Later he and I bored more maples. In all there are 66 maples bored for syrup.
>
> June 9, 1857 — Finished planting potatoes. Altogether I have planted 7½ bushels of potatoes.
>
> May 19, 1858 — Split shingles all day. Today we have something unusual. There has fallen three inches of snow although the leaves are half grown.
>
> September 15, 1858 — In the morning I was over at Johannes and chopped cornstalks. At noon John went with me home and started plowing for the wheat. In the evening at 5 o'clock Elsa and my expectations became a reality, a marriage.
>
> August 20, 1862 — We had an Indian scare so we fled out on the island in Clearwater (Waconia) Lake. We stayed until the evening of the 21st then went home.

March 8, 1873 — Grafted apple trees. This winter I have grafted 404 apple trees, 13 pear trees, 30 plum trees, and 12 cherry trees.

August 31, 1874 — First I went to Waconia and had the plow hardened and sharpened. In the afternoon I moved the clover and timothy field. Elsa and the children cut off corn.

April 28, 1881 — Sture rolled wheat and then sowed oats. The other boys grubbed out stumps, and I tied up the grape vines. The 25th we finished cooking down the maple sap. We made 20 gallons of syrup this spring.

September 24, 1978 Field Corn Picking

Sumacs are at fall color peak, and the birches are half yellow in the Ely area. I received word that it's sugar beet harvest time in the Red River Valley, with the possibility of the best harvest in a long time, while southwestern Minnesota farmers have started combining both field corn and soybeans. In the Arboretum area where black walnuts are dropping, both red and gray squirrels and people are picking up the nuts. Concord grapes are ripe, and two days ago I saw Waconia area farmers starting to pick field corn.

Not being a farmer, I was curious about field corn harvest time and the methods used, and after talking with a farmer and using a reference book, I learned some interesting things. Corn is considered mature when the grain has about 30 to 32 percent moisture, but the time to harvest depends on the farmer's harvest and storage system. Generally, an early harvest of field corn is best because ear drop is smaller, there is less chance of waterlogged fields that delay or prevent harvesting and less loss from stalk rot and severe storms results.

A farmer who has a moisture tester can save time and money since without one he has to take samples to an elevator to decide when to start harvesting or how long to continue drying. For long-term storage shelled corn should be down to 13 percent moisture. If moisture is even a few percentage points higher, the center of the bin will heat from the natural respiration of the grain causing the humidity to rise enough to allow mold to grow.

Although ear corn storage has declined in the United States, the safe moisture level for ear corn stored in a crib is higher than for shelled corn because air easily passes through it to remove heat and to dry the corn. For storage in narrow cribs the ear corn can have a moisture content as high as 25 percent.

Some farms have drying systems to handle high-moisture, shelled corn while others, instead of drying field-shelled corn, put it directly into an air-tight silo. Corn can then be harvested at 28 to 32 percent moisture. When high-moisture corn has been put into a silo, it must be used to feed animals, whereas with dry grain the farmer has the choice of feeding or selling.

September 25, 1975 First Juncos Arrive

The first juncos arrived at the Lowry Nature Center feeding station today. I saw only two birds, and it's good to have these winter birds back, even if they are a signal of the end of another growing season. In the next few weeks we can expect to see an influx of juncos, also called snowbirds, at our fall and winter feeding stations. They are handsome, gregarious, musical visitors the size of a sparrow; about five and one-half inches long, gray, with white bellies and white showing on their tails when in flight.

Juncos nest in the northern coniferous forests of Canada, Alaska and northeastern Minnesota but migrate in autumn. They spend the winter anywhere between southern Canada and the Gulf of Mexico, in city parks and suburbs as well as in the country.

By banding I have found that individual juncos can return to the same winter feeding stations. They often feed in the company of other birds, especially house sparrows in the city and tree sparrows in the country. At feeding stations they like millet and cracked corn and prefer to feed on the ground. Away from feeding stations we usually

Slate-colored Junco

see them in flocks, eating seeds of trees and herbaceous plants as they hop on the ground to pick them.

First slate-colored (dark-eyed) juncos arrived in the Arboretum area:

October 3, 1971	September 16, 1977
September 28, 1972	September 20, 1978
September 29, 1973	September 27, 1979
September 26, 1974	September 25, 1980
September 25, 1975	September 28, 1981
September 20, 1976	September 24, 1982

September 26, 1978 McIntosh and Sweet Sixteen

McIntosh and Sweet Sixteen, along with Minjon, Red Baron and Red Haralson, are now being picked at the University of Minnesota Horticultural Research Center. After McIntosh apples are picked, they should be kept for two weeks before they are eaten to bring out their best flavor. Those aromatic apples are hard to resist. I don't think a bag or bushel would last two weeks in our house before being eaten.

McIntosh is a mid-season, crisp, juicy, red apple that keeps until after Christmas and is good for fresh eating, sauce, baking, pies and freezing. The original McIntosh apple tree was discovered in 1796 as a chance seedling of unknown parentage in Dundas County, Ontario, Canada. The trees are vigorous and productive and suitable for growing in the southern two-thirds of Minnesota.

Sweet Sixteen is a new introduction from the University of Minnesota. The fruit has an appealing characteristic flavor combined with high sugar, moderate acid, and crisp, juicy, fine-textured flesh. It has good storage features and rates high as a pie and sauce apple. Sweet Sixteen trees show resistance to fireblight, scab and cedar-apple rust and are winter-hardy in central and western Minnesota.

September 27, 1977 Cranberries from a Minnesota Bog

Itasca State Park in Clearwater County is beautiful any day of the year, but today it was especially so. Many trees like the basswoods and American elms are almost bare, but paper birches and quaking aspens are yellow, sumacs and red oaks add a bit of red, and along with the dark green on spruces and pines, it is a spectacular scene.

I am with a group of junior high students and teachers in the Itasca area for two days to study parts of its unique ecology. I took the group to a bog so they could have the experience of walking on a sedgemat and become acquainted with a few of the plants. We noticed that the tamaracks were turning golden-yellow and bog birches had red and yellow leaves, but the big find was ripe cranberry fruit. The native cranberries are low creeping shrubs with small green leaves and many-seeded, juicy red berries, less than one-half inch in diameter. Although one of my guide books says that the fruit is sour and nearly inedible when raw, some of us picked and enjoyed them anyway. The berries are usually gathered while still firm, just before or just after the first frost, but those that are not gathered will remain on the stems during the winter.

We visited the jack pine forest of Lake George, seven miles east of Itasca State Park, where we also saw lichens, mosses and other plants. The jack pine forest is known for its blueberry shrubs that are low, woody plants, and there were still ripe blueberries that we picked and ate. The foliage on the blueberry shrubs was at its fall color peak, mostly red and very showy.

September 28, 1974 — Late September Arboretum Observations

The fall color near Longville and Hackensack was at its height today. Mountain maples, sugar maples, aspens, birches, oaks — red, white, and bur — were especially striking mixed with the green pines and spruces.

In the Arboretum we had a cold, cloudy day, but it was Fall Festival day, and many visitors were here. While working on the grounds today, I made over fifty quick notations in my field notebook. A few of those follow:

Herb collection — most plants are still nice although we did lose some on September 22 when the temperature dropped to the upper 20s.

Scotch pine — this species and other pines have many yellow-brown needles (leaves) that are dropping, a natural happening each autumn.

Red Splendor crabapple — trees are loaded with bright red fruit and nearly one-half the leaves are red and yellow, the rest green.

Blue beech tree — they are at their peak of fall color with red and yellow leaves.

Korean barberry — these shrubs have bright red foliage.

Nannyberry — the fruit is purple and the leaves are about 90 percent red.

Amur maple — they are at their peak, glowing red.

American elms — the leaves are yellow.

Hybrid tea, miniature and grandiflora roses — they still have good bloom.

Autumn crocus — they have light purple flowers, probably at bloom peak.

Water striders — they are active on the surface of the stream.

September 29, 1977 Fall Color Peak

Today is the peak day for autumn foliage colors in the Arboretum area in a year marked by unusually brilliant colors. In our yard on Lake Waconia the amur maple hedge has red foliage, one of our green ash trees is yellow, and our neighbor's pin cherry is also yellow. Driving and hiking around the Arboretum today I saw elegant yellow fall color on paper birches, shagbark hickories, black cherries, bigtooth aspens, quaking aspens, eastern cottonwoods and wild grape vines. Bitternut hickories are a beautiful golden color, the white oaks are red-brown, and the sugar maples with their yellow, orange and red leave are glowing. Nowhere in the world are the fall colors more rich and varied than in the climax woodlands of the United States east of the Rocky Mountains. Each September and October we marvel at the color of the many woody plants, sadly acknowledging that it is only a brief pleasure.

The fall coloring is the result of chemical processes in the leaves as the seasons change from summer to winter, many leaves turning before the first frost. Because of the decreasing amount of fall daylight and the lowering of average daily temperatures, leaves stop their food-making process. As they do, the chlorophyll breaks down, the green color disappears, and the yellow pigment that was covered up becomes visible, giving the leaves part of their fall splendor. At the same time, other chemical changes occur and cause the formation of additional pigments that vary from yellow to red to blue.

Some pigments give rise to the red and purple fall colors of the sumacs and dogwoods, but others give the sugar maple its brilliant orange and fiery red. The quaking aspen, birch, green ash and basswood show only yellow color. Familiar trees with red or scarlet leaves are red maple, amur maple, red oak and sassafras. Within the same species, the degree of color may vary from tree to tree or branch to branch as leaves exposed to the sun may turn red, while those on the shady side may be yellow. The foliage of some tree species just turns dull brown from death and decay and never shows bright colors.

Weather conditions that favor brilliant red autumn colors are warm sunny days followed by cool nights with temperatures below 45°F. Sugar is made in the leaves during the daytime, but cool nights prevent the movement of sugar from the leaves, trapping it to form the red pigment, anthocyanin. When there is warm, cloudy, rainy fall weather, leaves may have less red coloration, as the sugar that is made in reduced sunlight moves out of the leaves on warm nights.

September 30, 1979 Some Arboretum Autumn Activities

It's Sunday afternoon, and I just took a quick hike on some of the Arboretum trails and paths, studying fall's progression. I'm certainly not the only one seeking the beauty of fall, as an estimated 7,500 people have visited here this weekend. Fall color has not reached its peak yet, but we can see large patches of red, orange and yellow on the big native sugar maples. Virginia creeper vines are loaded with purple fruit and dark red leaves, and dahlias, mums and garden roses are still blooming.

The best part about walking around this 638-acre site is that in this way one can get close to the plants and animals to discover more interesting happenings. This afternoon I saw the small yellow flowers of the full-blooming shrub called common witch hazel, clusters of purple wild grapes, a sassafras tree draped with red leaves and golden-yellow color on our native bitternut hickory trees. Black walnuts are falling, cicadas buzzing, and monarch butterflies are busy feeding on dandelion and red clover flowers.

Another reason for so many visitors here this weekend was the thirteenth Fall Festival yesterday. The Arboretum Auxiliary sold dried plant materials and arrangements, dried and potted herbs, herb vinegars and breads, a large assortment of spring flowering bulbs and fresh-cut flowers, bags of apples and garden produce, with the proceeds going to Arboretum projects.

Mrs. Henry S. Crosby, a long-time Arboretum member and auxiliary worker, has been in charge of dried materials and arrangements for thirteen festivals, specializing in collecting and drying plant materials. To get the best quality and selection of dried grasses and herbs, she begins collecting them in late May from swamps, woods, fields and gardens. Each material has its own special time for harvesting. Cattails are gathered in late June or early July so they will remain small and will not shatter and shed seeds, and goldenrod is picked just before it is in full bloom. In the garden, baby's breath, zinnias, daisies, strawflowers, hydrangeas and black-eyed Susans are harvested. Strawflowers, if picked early, will keep their colors, and petals should be removed from the black-eyed Susans and just the centers dried. Most of the plants are tied singly or in small bunches on hangers and hung upside down in a dry place away from direct light until it is time to use them for the Fall Festival.

This is a successful enterprise, entailing work and effort on the part of hundreds of volunteers and professionals who have started a tradition that should continue for many years.

Red & White Oak, Maple & Aspen Leaves

October 1, 1979 Poison Ivy

Poison ivy *(Rhus radicans)* has reached its peak of red, orange and yellow coloring. Although people generally fail to find anything interesting about poison ivy, they usually want to know how to control or get rid of the plant. As a naturalist, I'm interested in poison ivy, which I use in my outdoor lessons, as part of our state's flora. Because it causes serious skin irritations, most people consider it a nuisance, but its compensation lies in its use as food by wildlife and as a natural esthetic groundcover.

We have no poison oak in the Upper Midwest; only poison ivy and occasionally poison sumac (*Rhus vernix*). The latter is a coarse shrub, six to twenty feet tall. It has compound ash-like leaves with each having seven to thirteen leaflets, and it grows in bogs and swamps where tamaracks grow or along streams and wet ditches in the east central part of Minnesota. Greenish-white berries distinguish the poison sumac from the harmless staghorn sumac and the smooth sumac, which have red berries. The conditions of poisoning and the toxic principles are the same for poison sumac as for poison ivy. This species is said to be more poisonous than poison ivy.

There is an old saying that many people believe, "Leaves of three, let it be," but since we encounter numerous plants with three leaves or leaflets, we need more information than that to recognize poison ivy. Poison ivy is a woody perennial growing as a small shrub or a vine that climbs by aerial rootlets. Although the trailing or climbing form is not common in Minnesota, when it is found, it's usually in the southeastern corner of the state. The shrub form, usually one to two feet tall, is common in the Upper Midwest. It can be found in dry fields, pastures, rocky exposures, banks, along fence rows and roadsides as well as in thickets and woodlands. The leaves are alternate on the stem and divided into three leaflets, each about four inches long, oval-shaped, pointed at the tip and rounded at the base. The center leaflet has a longer stalk than the two lateral leaflets. The leaflet surface may be glossy or dull green, and the margins may be without teeth or may be toothed or somewhat lobed. Small yellow-green flowers appear in June but pass almost unnoticed. The grayish-white, berry-like fruits, up to one-fourth inch in diameter, which appear later in clusters, persist through winter.

Contrary to popular opinion, poison ivy is a beneficial plant if left alone. Fifty-nine species of birds — catbirds, flickers, white-throated sparrows, sharp-tailed grouse, ring-necked pheasants, among them — feed on the berries, primarily in winter when other foods are scarce. When eating the berries, the birds spread the seeds over large areas. In addition, the foliage and berries provide food for bears, deer, muskrats and mice.

Nationally, about two million persons suffer from poison ivy to some degree each year. A more accurate name for poison ivy might be "allergic ivy" as itching areas and runny blisters are the skin's allergic response to poison ivy's plant oils. As with any allergy, the body must be exposed to the offending substance at least once before the blood can produce antibodies that stimulate the allergic reaction. University of Minnesota dermatologist Robert Goltz says that nobody is born allergic, so a European visitor in the United States could literally roll in poison ivy once and not be bothered because Europe has no poison ivy plants; however, Captain John Smith, who stumbled into it several times, was the first victim from Europe on record.

The resin ducts of roots, stems, leaves, flowers and fruits contain oils that cause the rash, and only the pollen and leaf hairs are not poisonous. The oils are active year-round, but the amount and availability of the poison varies.

A person cannot be affected by breezes blowing over the plant toward him as contact must be made, but indirect contact, such as handling clothing or shoes or even petting dogs or cats that touched the plant, can also give a person a case of poison ivy. The oils that cause irritation can cling for months to clothes and shoes and can only be removed by washing. Smoke from burning plants must be avoided as it causes severe irritation when the oil sticks to particles of soot and is carried to the skin.

Some people are more susceptible than others and may even be more susceptible at one time than another. Some people seem to be immune to the problem entirely. If you're strongly allergic, you will break out soon after touching poison ivy; if you're weakly allergic, it can take several days. Symptoms may appear in a few hours or days but are usually noticeable within twenty-four hours.

If you are in contact with the plant, wash the invisible oil off as soon as possible with any kind of soap as water alone usually isn't sufficient. Since the reaction of the poison to the skin is nearly instantaneous, washing with soap will only remove excess poison, but this is necessary as the excess poison may otherwise be transferred to unexposed skin parts. Washing with strong soap and water must be done before the oil has been on the skin for six hours, and if you repeat the washing three times, you usually can avoid having any reaction according to some experts in the field. There is, however, no universal agreement on the effectiveness of washing. Under no circumstances should a person eat a leaf of poison ivy with the mistaken idea that it

SEPTEMBER

September is a transition month; the month of summer's ending. The first days of the month are usually definitely summer but the last days are true autumn.

161

162

163

164

Garden roses continue to bloom. **(161)** Mountain ash fruit is ripe. **(162)** Goldenrods bloom and soldier beetles feed on their pollen. They are *not* hayfever plants. **(163)**Wild asters bloom. **(164)**

165

Edible giant puffballs can be found. **(165)** The poisonous fly mushroom appears. **(166)** Shaggymanes are numerous. **(167)** Garden mums are showy at the U of M Landscape Arboretum. **(168)**

166

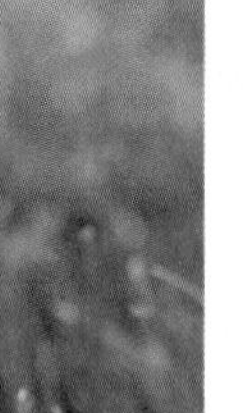

167

168

Compton's tortoise-shell butterflies sun on warm days before going into hibernation. **(169)** Painted-lady butterflies visit dahlia flowers for nectar. **(170)** Katydids call. **(171)** First common milkweed pods open. **(172)**

169

170

171

172

173

Virginia creeper vines reach fall color peak at the end of September. **(173)** Each year we marvel at the fall color of the trees and shrubs. **(174)** Green ash leaves turn golden. **(175)** Bitternut hickory leaves turn yellow. **(176)**

174

175

176

OCTOBER

October is the month of clear skies. We expect frost several times and Indian Summer days after the frosts. Our forests begin to look bare and field corn is harvested.

177

Minnesota forests in early October are gorgeous beyond compare. **(177 & 178)** Staghorn sumac shows mostly red fall color. **(179)** Leaves on small native sugar maples on the forest floor turn from green to yellow. **(180)**

178

179

180

181

Highbush cranberry fruit is ripe. **(181)** A wide center band on a woollybear is believed to foretell a "warm" winter. **(182)** Sugar maples in the open usually turn red and red-orange. **(183 & 184)**

182

183

184

185

186

187

188

Late apples of many varieties become ripe. **(185 and 186)** Marigolds continue to bloom. **(187)** It is natural for 3-year-old needles on red (Norway) pines to turn yellow-brown and drop in October. **(188)**

189

Daylight decreases and temperatures cool so leaves stop their food-making process and we see autum colors at their best. Native red oak. **(189)** Introduced ginkgo trees turn golden-yellow in late October. **(190)** The introduced winged euonymus is a shrub known for its red autumn coloration. **(191)** Native tamaracks of Minnesota bogs have needle-like leaves which all turn golden and drop. **(192)**

190

191

192

will produce immunity as severe gastric irritation, and even death, can result.

If rash and blisters form, calamine lotion and a cold wet dressing can help relieve the itching. Symptoms remain about two weeks. The fluid inside the blisters and the oozing produced will not spread the rash to other areas as only the plant oil itself can do that. If people have applied the lotion without first washing, the action may spread the exposure to a wider area.

Histamine, the substance in the skin cells that causes the intense itching, is released by heat, so hot showers and baths may possibly help. By gradually making the water as hot as tolerable, the heat draws most of the histamine out of the skin cells, and the itching subsides for about eight hours of relief. The best advice is to see a physician if the blisters and itching are severe.

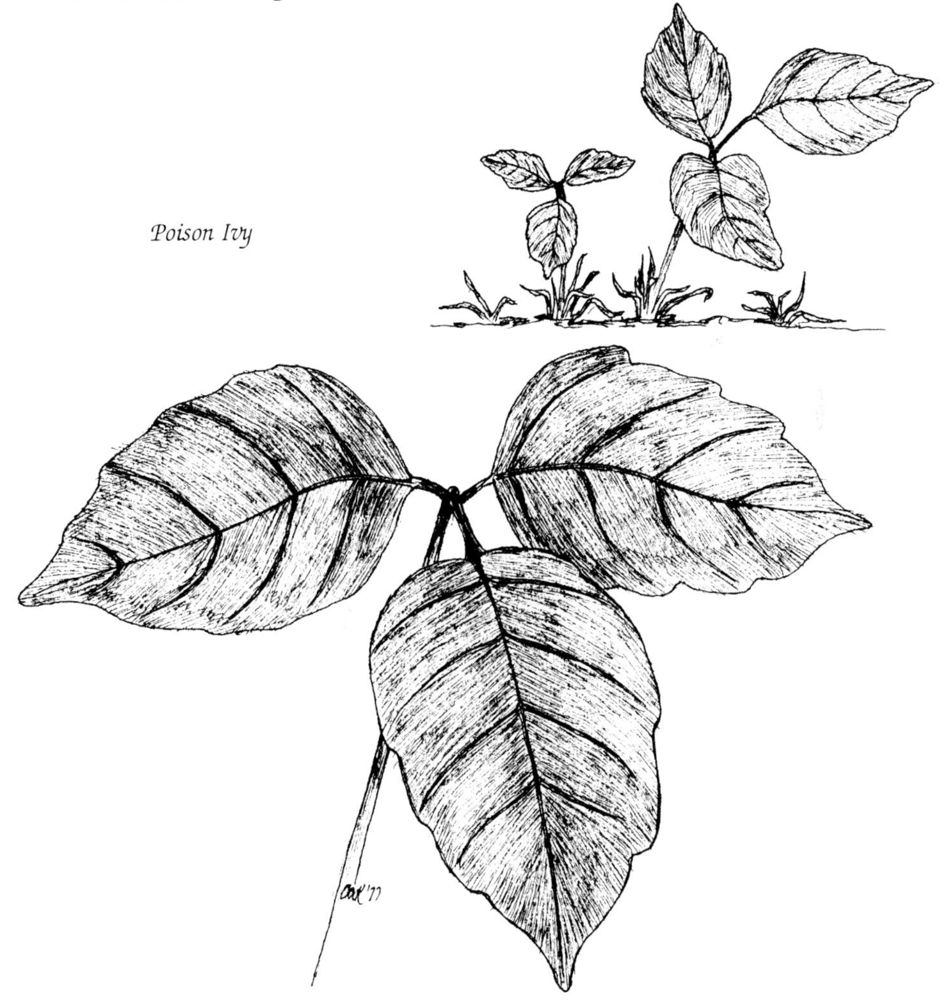

Poison Ivy

October 2, 1979 Harvest of Haralson Apples

Most wild grape leaves are yellow. Many area green ash trees are at their fall color peak of golden-yellow. However, some trees are way past peak and some are still all green. The garden roses are colorful, and mums are blooming. This is the week to pick the Haralson apples, the earliest of the late season varieties.

In 1922 the Haralson was introduced as an all-purpose apple by the University of Minnesota Horticultural Research Center, which was then called the Minnesota State Fruit Breeding Farm. Charles Haralson was at that time its superintendent. When introduced, the apple promised to meet the demand of growers for an apple that had the taste quality of the Wealthy and the keeping quality of the best late winter apples.

The Haralson is probably still the most popular winter apple among Minnesota growers. It is medium-sized, deep red with white, firm flesh that is medium-tender and crisp and juicy with a mildly acid flavor. This apple will keep until late winter in cold storage and is good for fresh eating, pie, sauce, freezing and baking. The trees are hardy and vigorous, relatively small, and can be grown throughout the state. Haralson trees are highly productive but tend toward biennial bearing.

October 3, 1978 Bears Heading for Dens

I called to check on fall color at the Environmental Learning Center at Isabella in northeastern Minnesota. I was told that the aspens are showing beautiful yellow foliage, the birches have faded, and there is still some nice color along the North Shore of Lake Superior. The black bears in the area have started going into their winter dens, and, in fact, two bears were seen in their dens two days ago.

About leaf-change time in mid-September the black bears in northeastern Minnesota become lethargic, and at least by mid-October they have usually fed so well that they have built up a heavy fat layer. Food gathering becomes more difficult so the bears begin looking for dens. The peak time for bears going into their winter sleep in northeastern Minnesota is between September 24 and October 24. They pull in pine needles and other leaves for a bed in a winter den that is usually dug under an overturned tree, but may also be a sheltered cave in a rock outcrop, a hollow tree or stump, a dense thicket or a stand of small evergreens. Generally the bear is somewhat exposed and later becomes partly covered with snow, but its breath melts a hole in the snow so a bear den can be located.

Black bears are found in more than thirty states, and although they were originally found throughout all Minnesota, they now live only in the northern woodlands. They are retiring, elusive animals who lead solitary lives except when the females are rearing their young or when concentrations of food bring them together. They are seldom seen in the wild. Much of what we know about our Minnesota bears is the result of a bear research project that is being conducted in northeastern Minnesota by Lynn Rogers of the U.S. Forest Service. He began his work in 1968, and up to now he has logged more than 1,000 bear captures. The bears are tagged and some are fitted with radio transmitters before being released. Lynn is studying their habitat requirements and is trying to discover how their social organization is influenced by their food supply.

Being omnivores, black bears eat both plant and animal food. They feed on grasses, berries and other fruits, buds or leaves, honey, mice, squirrels, insects and their larvae, and dead animals; in fact, they will feed on anything that resembles food in looks, smell or taste. Probably less than 10 percent of a bear's food is animal matter. Research has found that bears supplementing their food with garbage do better than bears subsisting on wild food alone. A bear never gets up in the winter to eat but uses its fat storage until April when it comes out of hibernation. It sleeps with its nose tucked down on the chest between the front legs, a fecal plug is formed, and the moisture from the kidneys is reabsorbed.

Although the bear's winter sleep is called hibernation, it is not in a complete deep sleep like thirteen-lined ground squirrels. It is rare, indeed, that a bear cannot easily be aroused from its winter slumbers in spite of the fact that it acts very drowsy.

October 4, 1978 Sumac Shrubs

Smooth sumac *(Rhus glabra)* and staghorn sumac *(Rhus typhina)* often grow together in thickets as both will grow in sandy soil and rocky hillsides and by means of their extended roots take possession of large areas. The scientific name *Rhus* is derived from a Greek word meaning "run" because the roots spread underground for a considerable distance. Since they are able to control areas to the exclusion of other plants, we now see great masses of brilliant red foliage along Twin Cities area roads and the hills sloping to these roads. They have reached their autumn peak of beauty. The leaves are mostly red, but we can see some brighter orange and yellow too.

Both sumacs are shrubs or small trees and have feather-like compound leaves, each leaf containing eleven to thirty-one leaflets. Both have dense clusters of dry, red fruit that cling to branches through the winter, making a distinctive silhouette. Each year I need to tell my new students that these sumacs that grow in dry soils and have red berries are not poisonous, but the sumac with greenish-white berries that grows in wet places is.

Not known to many people is the fact that sumac fruit is on edible plant lists. Two ways to use the fruit are by making jelly and by making a cold drink tasting something like lemonade. To do this it is necessary to collect the entire fruit cluster, rub gently to bruise the berries and soak for about fifteen minutes in cold water. Remove the cluster and pour the pink juice through cheesecloth to strain out the hairs and any extra berries and then sweeten to taste and chill. The clusters must be gathered before heavy rains or melting snow wash out most of the acid.

Several bird species, ruffed grouse, ring-necked pheasant, bob-white quail, bluebird, robin, brown thrasher and others, rely on the clusters of red fruits for food when other foods are scarce in winter and early spring. White-tailed deer feed on the twigs and foliage of sumacs, and cottontail rabbits eat the bark and fruit.

Smooth and staghorn sumacs are good plants for highway slopes and for erosion control on banks. The natural range of staghorn sumac is not as large as smooth sumac, which is native from Maine to British Columbia and south to Florida and Arizona. Staghorn sumac is common in the southern part of Minnesota in the hardwood forest area but seldom found in the north towards Duluth. Staghorn sumac twigs and leafstalks are always clothed in velvet and are hairy while smooth sumac has hairless twigs and leafstalks. Some natural hybrids occur between the two sumacs.

October 5, 1969 Notes from the Sugarbush

Although rain and cool temperatures kept some people away from the second annual Arboretum Autumn Festival sponsored by the Arboretum Auxiliary, many who came visited the three new picnic shelters located on the north side of the grounds overlooking Lake Minnewashta. The shelters housed the Festival's country schoolhouse, country kitchen and general store, where dried plants, rare and unusual house plants and bulbs, herbs and nature crafts were on sale. Some people enjoyed the gardening demonstrations while others went on tours and hikes to see the Arboretum near its height of fall color.

My job today was to lead people through part of the sugarbush, and while waiting for the next hiking or bus group, I jotted down a few observations in my journal:

> Leaves are dropping continuously from the weight of water on them. Yesterday was the fall color peak for sugar maples this year. Amost every sugar maple had kept most of its leaves until then and each tree had at least some fall color, but today many trees are starting to look bare. Sugar maple colors in the forest are yellow with some green and a few orange and red leaves. Most of the red leaves are on trees that have good exposure to long periods of sunlight near the edge of the forest and along roads and clearings. In the sugarbush the wet, dark bark of the maple trees is beautiful next to the yellow foliage.

October 6, 1979 Banded Woollybears

Picking up a woollybear is difficult; it rolls into a little ball, and the hairs are so elastic that it's difficult to seize it. These hairs are, no doubt, a protection from birds that do not like bristles for food. When the caterpillar is safely rolled up, the bird sees only a little bundle of bristles and leaves it alone.

In late August or early September we begin to notice woollybear caterpillars scurrying across highways. This year I saw my first one on August 23. They seem to reach their peak numbers in October, although I have seen them crossing roads on warm days in November and December and sometimes crawling about on unseasonably warm days in January and February. Yesterday I counted twenty-five crossing a one-mile stretch of paved county road as I drove slowly and tried to avoid squashing them. All seemed to be in a hurry, on their way to find some cozy place to spend the winter. A woolly caterpillar overwinters as larva, curled up under boards, leaf piles or other protective spots and makes its cocoon in spring. By spinning silk about itself, each makes its cocoon, weaving in the hairs that it sheds easily at that time, so the cocoon looks as if it were made of felt. The adult, called an Isabella moth, emerges about the last of May and is yellow-brown with three rows of black dots on its abdomen.

The woollybear I have been describing is the banded woollybear *(Isia isabella)*; reddish-brown in the middle and black on both ends, about one and one-fourth to two inches long. It's difficult to measure one, however, as it stretches and contracts quickly. Its head is a polished black, and the antennae are two tiny yellow projections that can easily be seen with the naked eye, but the eyes are minute. Because the woollybear cannot see very far, it must feel its way about the landscape.

There are really thirteen segments, excepting the head, but since the last two are joined, only twelve segments are counted. The caterpillar's appearance is variable. Several front segments are black, the middle segments are reddish-brown, and the hind ones are black, with different numbers of segments in these colors.

Folklore says that the woollybear foretells a warmer than normal winter if the center band is wide (long), but if the center band is narrow, the coming winter will be colder than normal. A more exacting way of putting this superstition is to say that if the middle band of reddish-brown is narrower than either of the black bands on the front and rear, then the coming winter will be severe; if the three bands are about equal, it will be average; and if the middle band is the widest, the winter will be mild. It is fun to observe hundreds of woollybears and then make a prediction as to what winter may be like. Scientists have observed them closely and, surprisingly, the forecast has proved true more often than not, although the results may be coincidental. Actually, it is thought that the relative amounts of black and reddish-brown are due to conditions of temperature and possibly moisture during a woollybear's early life.

Banded woollybear caterpillars feed on plantain, dandelion, dock, many grasses and other low-growing plants but do not eat much after we find them in autumn because their growth is completed. Since they are adapted to be outdoors hibernating in the winter, keeping woollybears indoors will prove fatal to them, and they cannot be kept as pets by children who are curious about them. Generally they can be enjoyed by watching and holding them carefully outdoors or, for short periods, indoors. For someone interested in studying their life cycle, they could be kept in a box with leaves, soil, pieces of bark and some food plants and placed outdoors so that the mini-habitat can have ordinary winter temperatures.

Woollybears

October 7, 1978 Dahlias

The dahlias in the Arboretum look beautiful, in a collection sponsored by the Minnesota Dahlia Society as a north central trial garden. It has a wide array of flower colors, sizes and forms, developed over many years, and produces blossoms from the first week in August until frost kills them.

The dahlia *(Dahlia pinnata)* is native to the highlands of Mexico and was grown by the Aztecs near the present site of Mexico City. Dahlias first flowered outside their native land after 1789 when seeds or tubers were sent from the Botanic Garden of Mexico to the Royal Gardens at Madrid. Because of their origin, they require well-drained soil and fairly sunny locations.

The flowers are of many colors at the Arboretum: white, yellow, orange, red, pink, purple, maroon and many combinations of these colors. Dahlias come in all flower colors except true blues. Ranging from one-inch pompoms to the dinner plate size, twelve inches or more in diameter, there are many forms including daisy-like single types, fully double types and intermediate ones. Looking at them, it is easy to see why there is great enthusiasm for dahlias and why they have special appeal to exhibition flower growers.

October 8, 1978 Frost on the Pumpkin, Ice on the Birdbath

Not only was there frost in low spots but also on rooftops, windshields and on Arboretum area lawns. This was our first frost, and it was quite widespread in southern Minnesota. After a friend had called to report the first ice on the birdbath, I began getting reports of squash vines, cucumber vines, tomato plants and zinnias that had succumbed to the frost.

Area lake temperatures are dropping, and 55°F is an average surface temperature. Thousands of American coots remain on the lakes, giant puffball and shaggy mane fruiting bodies can be found, to the delight of mushroom fanciers, and potatoes are being dug amidst reports of big crops. Both the Kentucky coffee trees and bitternut hickories are approaching fall color peak.

On the fertile plants of American bittersweet, bright red-centered fruits have appeared. The fruit of the climbing and twining bittersweet vine is a yellow-orange capsule about one-fourth inch across that bursts to expose a red seed cluster, which can make a semi-permanent fall and winter indoor bouquet.

October 9, 1979 Snow Geese Migrating

An apple-growing friend reports that Honeygold, Northwestern Greening, Prairie Spy and Redwell apples are ripe. Area gardeners are still harvesting green beans, green peppers, tomatoes, radishes, spinach, broccoli, Brussels spourts, cauliflowers, carrots, buttercup and acorn squash, together with Fallred and Fallgold raspberries. Robins and common grackles are appearing in large flocks. Although people reported seeing snow geese flying over the Twin Cities in V formation, I didn't see any today. I must have been too busy watching the still-active garter snakes and the American toads and leopard frogs. However, I did hear and count twenty-four snow geese flying over our house three days ago.

The migrating snow geese and gray phase snow geese, called blue geese, are coming from their summer breeding grounds along the Arctic Coast from Alaska to Baffin Island and are going to the salt marshes and marshy coastal bays along Louisiana, Texas and Mexico. Snow geese are white with black wing tips, and blue geese, now regarded as a color morph of the snow goose, are dark gray with white heads. Both are seen together. Until recently, the two color phases were considered separate species, but it is now known that they interbreed where their ranges overlap. It's thrilling to see a flight of snow geese high overhead in wedge formation as they make their way south.

October 10, 1977 First Snowmen Appear

Two days ago we had our first snow flurries, and today we had our first measurable snowfall, which means one-tenth of an inch or more. Less than that amount is recorded as a trace. In the Twin Cities area we received about two and one-half inches while six to twelve inches fell in the Isabella area. Our air temperature was about 30°F when the snow fell this afternoon. At times large aggregate flakes, more than an inch across, floated down on the landscape. Some of the snow melted upon hitting the ground so there was no more than about one and one-half inches at any one time. This, however, was enough to bring out the children, eager to make the first snowmen and the first snowballs of the season.

This early snowfall brought down many forest leaves, and many such areas are starting to look bare. Dahlia, mum and garden rose flowers were decorated with white, and in our garden I found a big ripe strawberry that I ate as snow crystals fell about me — a strange but interesting experience.

October 11, 1979 Sugar Maples

John Burroughs, a renowned American naturalist and writer, described October as "the time of the illuminated woods," to which I add "colorful and vibrant" as I think of the forests in the Arboretum area today. One of the most spectacular sights was the native sugar maples.

The maples that are out in the open had the first tinge of fall color in August. They are now at their peak of orange and red, but the rest of the maples are a glowing yellow. Just as the sap of the sugar maple is a valued item in the early spring, so its autumn foliage splendor is valued as it contributes to the beauty of our landscape now.

If someone is looking for a fine shade tree to plant in a yard, I would recommend the sugar maple whose main cultural requirement is a reasonably productive, well-drained soil. The best time to select a tree is in fall when the leaves have their fall color as some trees are more colorful than others. There will be little transplanting difficulty, especially if the work is done a little later in the autumn or in early spring; and as the growth is reasonably rapid, in only a few years even a small tree will reach a respectable size. Each year the unsurpassed

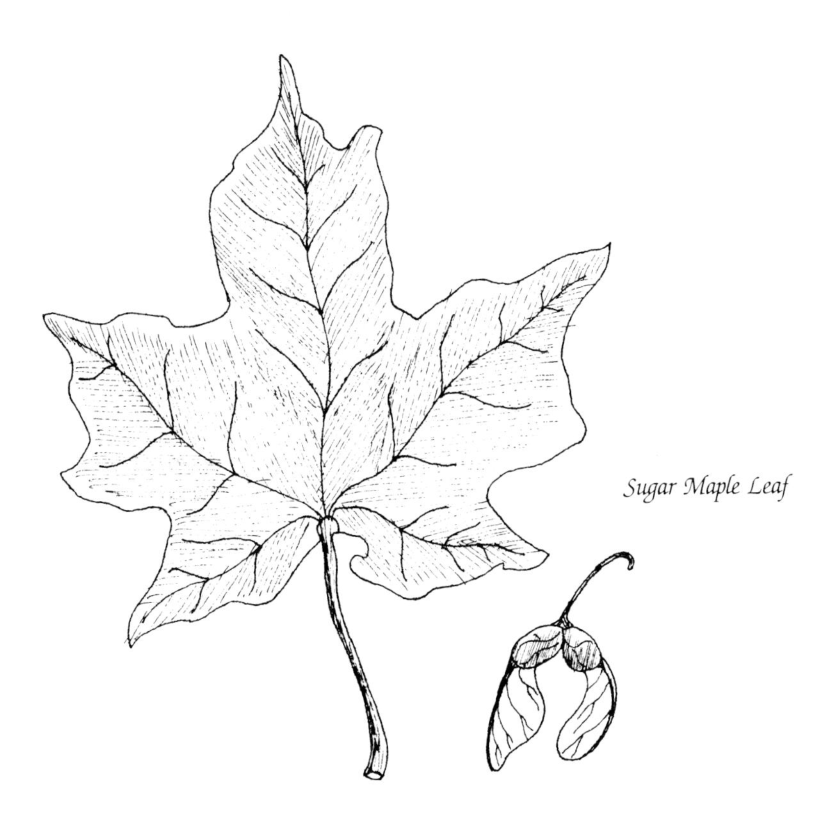

Sugar Maple Leaf

autumn colors can be enjoyed from a homegrown sugar maple, but, if that's not possible, hopefully a person can get out to the country roadsides and see the many sugar maples in their full splendor on future autumn days such as we had today.

Peak of fall color for Arboretum area sugar maples *(Acer saccharum)* located in the open or on forest edges:

September 30, 1976	October 11, 1979
September 29, 1977	October 2, 1980
October 11, 1978	October 3, 1981
	October 3, 1982

October 12, 1979 Late Fall Color Peak

Today was probably the overall peak day for autumn colors this year. Ironwoods, largetooth aspens and quaking aspens are yellow, bitternut hickory trees have golden-yellow foliage, red oaks are a dark red, and sugar maples are an unbelievable blend of reds, oranges, and yellows. In the interior of the forest the still-green trees are a sharp contrast. Cold temperatures during the day froze annual flower and vegetable gardens, and the green ash, catalpa and apple leaves shriveled and died on the trees, still green when they froze.

Taking the many trees, shrubs and vines together, the peak days for autumn foliage colors in the Arboretum area are listed below.

October 4, 1969	October 1, 1976
October 5, 1970	September 29, 1977
October 5, 1971	October 12, 1978
October 4, 1972	October 12, 1979
October 4, 1973	October 5, 1980
September 27, 1974	October 6, 1981
September 30, 1975	October 5, 1982

Since the University of Minnesota Landscape Arboretum is located near Chanhassen, the dates listed above could be used also for the Twin Cities area in general.

It's interesting to note the peak of fall color in other parts of Minnesota. These dates are a bit later than normal, but still they show the progression of colors from northeast to southeast.

Fall color peak (1979)	*Area*
September 23	Finland
September 28	Bagley and Grand Rapids
September 30	Bemidji, Cromwell, Deerwood and Palisade
October 6	Alexandria and Sandstone
October 12	Excelsior and Minneapolis
October 17	Faribault

October 13, 1977 Why Leaves Fall

The forest areas are starting to look bare. At the end of the growing season deciduous plant leaves fall, in contrast to the evergreens, which keep their leaves (needles) for several seasons. The chemical called auxin, a growth-regulating substance produced by plants, creates a process that makes deciduous plants lose their leaves at approximately the same time each year. When the leaves unfold in the spring, each new leaf makes large amounts of auxin. In some way auxin signals the leaf stem (petiole) to grip its branch tightly, but as the leaf gets older, it produces less auxin. At about this time, two thin layers of cells called the abscission layer grow across the base of the leaf stem where it is connected to the branch, probably initiated by the decreasing daily light period. As the supply of auxin slows to a trickle, the cells in the abscission layer separate from one another. As the leaf stem's hold on the branch grows weaker, a gust of wind can easily blow the leaf free and it falls to the ground.

A few deciduous plants, such as red oaks, keep many dead leaves on their branches throughout the winter. This is usually attributed to the lack of an abscission layer and to the failure of the tough vascular bundles in the petiole to break.

October 14, 1979 Paper Birches

Betula papyrifera, the scientific name for the well-known paper birch, comes from *Betula*, the Latin name of the birch, and the scientific term *papyrifera*, meaning paper bearing. Two other popular common names for the same tree are canoe birch and white birch. The gleaming white bark, which frays and separates into thin papery layers, is a distinguishing characteristic of this species. Today we are also enjoying the golden-yellow foliage of these graceful trees.

Paper birch is native from Alaska to the south shore of Hudson Bay, east to Labrador, south to Pennsylvania, Nebraska and Montana. It often grows in nearly pure stands on wooded slopes and along borders of streams and lakes. Since it prefers cool moist soil, it's not surprising that when it is planted on an open lawn it is subjected to moisture stress as well as being vulnerable to attack by the bronze birch borer. The bronze birch borer mines in irregular winding galleries just under the bark which is then loosened, but the first sign of injury is the dying back of the top of the tree. By this time, however, it's too late for control measures. If a moist site is selected and the tree is watered during dry weather, the ravages of the borer can be reduced since it usually gains entrance during dry periods.

Wood from paper birches is used for toothpicks, ice cream sticks, clothespins, toys, house trim, and for wood pulp and fuel. American Indians made their lightweight birch bark canoes by stretching the bark over white cedar or spruce frames, sewing with thread from tamarack roots and caulking the seams with pine or balsam fir resin. The bark was also used for covering tepees and for receptacles in which to store or carry food. The sap, collected in early spring before the leaves unfold, was prized by the northern Indians as a pleasant, sweet drink and was also boiled down for syrup.

Souvenirs of birch bark should always be taken from a fallen log. Stripping bark from living trees is often fatal to the trees, and it is invariably disfiguring, leaving permanent ugly black scars.

October 15, 1979 Fall-blooming Witchhazel

The common witchhazel, the latest blooming shrub, is full of flowers. In the midst of the pomp and circumstance of our northern autumn, one of the most remarkable plants is the witchhazel that bursts into a luxuriant bloom of bright yellow flowers when some of its leaves begin to fall. Three or four flowers, each about an inch across and with four long, crumpled strap-like petals, appear together, with several clusters on each branch. They began blooming in September and will continue into November.

Common witchhazel *(Hamamelis virginiana)* is native from Canada to Georgia and west to Nebraska. It is found occasionally in the southeastern part of Minnesota but commonly in Wisconsin. Several of these large shrubs, now about nine feet tall, were planted in the Arboretum more than ten years ago. The alternate toothed, straight-veined leaves provide landscape interest, especially in the fall with the yellow blossoms and the yellow and brown leaves. Witchhazel fruits, which are woody capsules, will not ripen and open until next year's flowers appear.

October 16, 1979 Indian Summer Day

Although our fall color seems endless this year, we still see a large number of green leaves on deciduous trees and shrubs. There certainly are environmental factors in addition to the decrease in length of daylight that bring on fall color and leaf fall. This year we had a late spring, late summer and now a late fall.

Today is an Indian summer day; a day with light winds and above

Katydid & Annual Cicada

normal temperatures after the first official day of fall. To verify my understanding of Indian summer, I called my friend Bruce Watson, a consulting meteorologist who specializes in the study of Minnesota weather. He said that Indian summer follows autumn's first cold and takes place when high pressure dominates. Necessary ingredients for an Indian summer day are that the sun must shine, the air must be smoky and still or nearly so, and the temperature must be above normal. Today fits that description, Bruce said. At this time of the year, American Indians would burn grassy areas to drive the game for one last big hunt before winter, which may be the origin of the idea of smoky and hazy air.

By counting the number of snowy tree cricket chirps in fifteen seconds and adding forty to the number, I get 66° F, a good approximation of the air temperature. Indian summer today — with its banded woollybears and leopard frogs crossing the roads, garter snakes out sunning, last buzzing cicada, honey bees visiting perennial salvia and aster flowers — seems for a few hours to hold back the hands of the clock. I saw several monarchs heading south this afternoon and also on the wing were cabbage, sulphur, alfalfa, Milbert's tortoise shell and painted lady butterflies. Amur maple and Korean barberry shrubs are red, and there are still some garden roses, phlox and delphinium flowers that escaped the below-freezing temperatures we had a few days ago.

October 17, 1979 Chrysanthemums in Bloom

Dr. Snyder has said that garden chrysanthemums can withstand some frost and freezing temperatures as low as 28°F, or a bit lower for some varieties. The temperature in the mum garden in the Arboretum was close to that on October 12, but about ninety varieties continue to bloom.

The chrysanthemum, which has become our most popular autumn flower, has been cultivated for centuries in the Orient. It is certain that it was cultivated in China 500 years before the birth of Christ and introduced to France and England in the 1700s. Chrysanthemums were introduced to America in 1798 by John Stevens of Hoboken, New Jersey, and in 1826, twenty-six varieties were listed by a Long Island nurseryman. The origins of the perennial garden chrysanthemum are lost in antiquity, but at least two native species in China are involved in the genetic makeup.

During the past 150 years, hybridists have produced thousands of greatly improved varieties of both garden and greenhouse chrysanthemums. Beginning in the late 1930s, with the development of early flowering varieties by the University of Minnesota's Department of

Horticultural Science, gardeners have been able to extend their relatively short gardening season by a month to six weeks. Until breeding work was begun at the University, along with the work of private breeders and other institutions, only a few single-flowered varieties bloomed early enough to escape our fall frosts. Today we have the choice of many varieties that bloom prolifically in September and October with a few still flowering in early November.

Chrysanthemums require well-drained soil, bloom best in full sun and should be divided each spring, or new plants started from cuttings then. Most varieties grow up to two feet tall, and flowers vary from very small button-shaped blossoms to large six-inch blooms. There are single, semi-double and double flowers in white, yellow, bronze-orange, pink, red, purple and different shades and combinations of these.

More than sixty varieties of garden chrysanthemums have been introduced by the University of Minnesota since 1941. Some of my favorites, which still bloom well in October, are listed below along with the year of introduction.

Minnehaha (1958) — light-red and orange, double, about two and one-half inches in diameter.

Wayzata (1961) — yellow, fully double flowers about three inches in diameter.

Superior (1965) — bright bronze-orange, double, three-inch flowers.

Cream Top (1966) — attractive, fully double, three-inch white blossoms with yellow centers.

Minnruby (1974) — dark red, two-inch double flowers. The prefix "Minn" is used to designate varieties with a cushion type of growth habit introduced by the University of Minnesota.

October 18, 1975 Arboretum Bird Hike

We walked through the fog on frosted paths and saw ice on the edge of Green Heron Pond. At least ten male red-winged blackbirds called on territory, song sparrows and fox sparrows sang, and juncos and robins were numerous. We were on an early morning bird hike, and the people who joined me observed eighteen bird species. Those who attend these sessions are good birders, but they also enjoy all plant and animal life and being with people who also share their interests. We all have fun making discoveries about nature.

Most of the garden roses continue to bloom, the mums are bushy and colorful, and a few colorful dahlias can be seen. The dahlia plants have been touched by frost, but if the garden had not been located on a high spot they would have been killed much earlier by the cold.

The native tamarack foliage and the Norway maples are now a golden-yellow, but the English ivy is still green. Even red clover, dandelion flowers and marigold blossoms remain. In my few minutes of observation I saw seven species of butterflies, honey bees and bumble bees, three species of flower flies and three moth species attracted to the marigolds.

October 19, 1979 Native Oaks

Three native oaks — white, bur and red — are commonly seen in the Lake Minnetonka area. All three have the traditional look of strength and ruggedness that give our neighborhoods a feeling of continuity. Today all reached their fall color peak.

Quercus is the scientific name for oak and is probably of Celtic origin, meaning beautiful tree. White oaks *(Quercus alba)* can be grown from seed, the acorns germinating within a few weeks of ripening and producing a long tap-root before winter. The *alba* refers to the pale bark. Glossy leaves with five to nine rounded lobes are characteristic of this long-lived species, some known to be 800 years old. From a distance the foliage varies from light reddish-brown to dark reddish-brown, but a closer look shows purple autumn coloration on the backs of the leaves. Some white oak leaves will stay on the trees through the winter.

The bur oaks *(Quercus macrocarpa)* lack the brilliant fall colors of the red and white oaks. The scientific name *macrocarpa*, meaning large-fruited, refers to the large nut with a sweet, white edible kernel. Most have foliage which is about one-third brown, one-third yellow and one-third green. The rounded, lobed leaves, wedge-shaped at the base, are the largest of all the oak leaves; six inches or longer and three to six inches across the upper half. Both white and bur oaks grow to a height of sixty-five feet or more.

The red oak *(Quercus rubra)* is seldom planted because it is susceptible to oak wilt disease. Every effort should be made to protect these native trees that can grow to eighty feet. The red oak has leaves about five to nine inches long, with unequal point-tipped lobes, and today their colorful foliage varies from brown to red, with some trees partly yellow.

October 20, 1979 Time to Cover the Roses

All garden roses — hybrid teas, floribundas, grandifloras, miniatures and tree roses — are injured when the temperature drops below 20°F, so winter protection must be given before temperatures go that low. The garden roses in the Arboretum were still putting on a floral show this morning. Many plants had buds and fully open flowers, but it was time to put them underground. Members of the Minnesota Rose Society came to the Arboretum today and completed the job in a few hours.

Many methods of covering roses have been tried, but the "Minnesota Tip" is the best method of winter protection. The canes of each plant are tied in a tight bundle. Then a trench that is the depth and width of a spade and as long as the plants are tall is dug from the base of each plant. Next a spading fork is used to loosen the soil around the base of the plant, and each cluster of canes is bent into its trench and covered with soil. After this is done, the soil in the garden is practically level.

It is best to tip all the plants in the same direction and mark the base of each with a stake as this will make it easier to lift the plants next spring. When cold weather arrives in November, at least six inches of leaf or straw mulch should be applied to the rose beds, with boards or chicken wire put over the mulch to keep it from blowing away. About the first of April the mulch can be removed, and as soon as the soil dries in mid-April, the rose shrubs can be lifted out of the soil.

October 21, 1977 Red Crossbills

We can't count on seeing red crossbills every year, but I have entries for two different years that describe flocks of these erratic travelers when they have been here towards the end of October. More than fifty have been seen lately in Waconia, extracting seeds from spruce cones. A birder from Deephaven called to say that about a dozen were eating from blue spruce and red pine cones in his yard. Although I seldom see red crossbills, I always marvel at their behavior and special adaption when I do.

Red crossbills are the size of sparrows. Both sexes have black wings and tail, but the males have a distinctive brick-red plumage and females, olive-gray tinged with yellow. The most outstanding characteristic of the red crossbill is the crossed mandibles of the bill; the slender point of the upper mandible curves down and the point of the lower mandible curves up. When feeding in trees, they crawl about using their bills and feet much like small parrots. The crossed bill is used to force open and hold the cone scales apart while the tongue lifts the seeds out. Besides feeding from cones of conifers, red crossbills eat insects and the seeds from birches, alders, elms and maples. Because they are attracted to calcium chloride (salt) spread on highways to melt ice and snow, many are killed by cars.

The conifer forests of the Northern Hemisphere are the habitat of red crossbills. Ordinarily they live in their broad nesting range, but when their population is large or a natural food shortage occurs they will wander great distances. Their numbers and distribution are unpredictable, especially in southern Minnesota, but when they appear, evergreens are most appealing to them.

October 22, 1978 Blackbird Roost

Beginning at 7:30 this morning and continuing for more than five minutes, several thousand blackbirds flew in a narrow band, like a fast-moving stream, over our yard. They came from a low area on the northwest side of Lake Waconia where they had spent the night. Then tonight between 5:45 and 6 p.m., a steady stream of blackbirds moved back to their roost. This is a common sight regularly seen in many areas of Minnesota at this time of the year.

Soon after the adults stop caring for the young, blackbirds begin to flock together. Each night in summer until they move farther south later in fall, huge congregations of common grackles, red-winged blackbirds and brown-headed cowbirds, all members of the blackbird family, will fly from their feeding grounds to their roosts. They create the largest and most commonly observed groups of land birds in North America. Assemblies of red-wings reach a height in about mid-October, and grackle flocks are at their height a bit later. Slowly, as the season progresses, the huge flights drift south.

In 1978 I saw the last large flocks of blackbirds on November 15.

October 23, 1979 Golden Tamaracks

Yellow-leaved ginko trees are almost at fall color peak in the Arboretum. The shellbark hickory is beautiful. Its foliage is about one-third tan-brown, one-third yellow and one-third green. A third tree species that has good autumn color is the American beech with its brown and yellow foliage. I think more people should plant trees and shrubs in their yards with the thought of extending and intensifying the fall color season.

A native tree that we planted in our yard about seven years ago is the tamarack *(Larix laricina)*, also called the American larch. This and the ones growing in cold swamps in the Lake Minnetonka area are now golden-yellow. Since the tamarack is a deciduous conifer, the leaves (needles) will fall soon, and its branches will be bare until next spring. The soft, flexible needles, which are bright green in summer, are unique. They are one-half to one and one-fourth inches long and grow in clusters of twenty to forty on wood from previous years or singly on new shoots.

The tamarack is abundant in the coniferous forest region in Minnesota, chiefly in bogs together with black spruce. Occasionally it is also found in upland areas where it grows larger. It is also native from Alaska and Canada to Wisconsin, Michigan and Pennsylvania. The broad, shallow root system is adapted to swamp ground, and yet the best growth is in well-drained soils. The slender straight tree is seldom more than fifty to sixty feet tall with a trunk about one and one-half feet in diameter. Young trees and those crowded together form narrow, conical heads with short horizontal branches; older trees, or those in the open, form broader crowns.

Fall color peak for native tamaracks in Carver County:

October 29, 1969	October 25, 1976
October 23, 1970	October 15, 1977
October 23, 1971	October 23, 1978
October 23, 1972	October 23, 1979
October 26, 1973	October 20, 1980
October 12, 1974	October 19, 1981
October 22, 1975	October 25, 1982

October 24, 1978 Turn-over of the Lake

In the summer our lakes have warm water on and near the surface and cold water below. When this occurs, only the warm top layer circulates, and the oxygen supply can become depleted in the deep water. It's not unusual for the surface temperatures of Minnesota lakes to be in the upper 70s and 80s during July and August, but with the onset of cooler weather, the temperature in the upper layer drops until it is the same as in the lower layer. When the temperature is the same throughout the lake, it is called the fall overturn. A temperature of 50°F throughout the lake is the average for Lake Minnetonka and other area lakes now.

The uniform temperature allows mixing, induced by wind and density currents. The currents bring all of the lake's water to the surface from time to time where it absorbs oxygen from the air. As the water in the lake circulates, oxygen is returned to the depths during the fall overturn, and nutrients are brought to the surface. In this way lakes store oxygen for the fish, frogs, turtles, worms and other living things that spend the winter under the ice.

The temperature of the lake, which will continue to drop until the lake freezes, is a result of the mixing water. The cool surface water goes to the bottom of the lake since cold water is heavier than warm, and as it sinks, warmer water from below is forced to the surface where it in turn is cooled. The whole lake will cool to 39°F, the temperature at which water is the heaviest. As the surface water continues to cool below 39°F, it expands, becomes lighter and remains on the surface to freeze.

October 25, 1978 Return of the Tree Sparrows

Friends from Isabella tell me that the bodies of the snowshoe hares are now one-third white and the rest brown; in about two weeks they should be all white. The American goldfinches are in their somber winter dress here, and the tree sparrows that have been in the Arctic for the nesting season are returning to our area for the winter. Although they will fly up to the feeder to eat, they prefer to feed on millet seeds on the ground, so I'll have to put some there for them.

Male and female tree sparrows are similar. Each is streaked brown on its upper body and plain gray below, with a dark spot in the center of the breast. It has two white bars on each wing, a red-brown cap, a dark upper mandible and yellow lower one. In the two years I have been banding birds, I have had several tree sparrows that had been banded the previous winter return to our feeding station. Banded tree sparrows wearing bands for seven, eight and nine years have been reported by others, verifying our speculation that many may make several trips during their lifetimes back to their wintering territories.

October 26, 1980 Woodpeckers Attacking Homes

I have been watching a downy woodpecker working on a roosting cavity in a dead limb of a red oak. It is well-known that each woodpecker roosts at night in a separate roosting hole. These are found or excavated in fall and are often vigorously defended against other hole-roosting birds. We enjoy watching woodpeckers in the forests, on our trees, and at our bird feeding stations, but they become unpopular when they begin making holes in our houses and outbuildings. Downy and hairy woodpeckers are seen working on buildings most often. They begin their attacks in early to mid-September, build up to a peak in October and gradually decline in November.

There are several theories why woodpeckers, who are particularly

Downy Woodpecker Attacking a Home

attracted to houses with cedar siding, drill and excavate holes in houses. One theory is that a bird may have selected an inappropriate site in which to make a winter roosting hole. Another idea is that drilling is done to obtain insects that crawl under the siding to hibernate in the fall, but a woodpecker on a house does not mean that there are termites. A third idea is that the bird may be hearing noises from household electrical appliances, transmitted by vibration through the house frame, and it interprets these noises as chewing insects that it tries to obtain.

People usually want to know how to discourage the woodpeckers from attacking their homes, regardless of why the birds do it, but we have to admit there is not a sure way to do that. There is no spray or paint that can be applied to the house to discourage them, shooting them is illegal, and plastic owls and rubber snakes are ineffective. They can be harassed by chasing them away, squirting with a hose and shouting at them, or a piece of plywood or heavy plastic can be put over the affected area. This latter way may discourage the birds from attacking, and the covering can be removed about a week or so after they have stopped.

October 27, 1980 Boston Ivy

Dr. Francis de Vos, Arboretum director, says, "We can still find pockets of fall color." It's late in the year, but there are still red leaves on pin oaks, European larches have beautiful golden-yellow needles, and Korean barberry has red leaves and bright red berries. American elms have some golden-yellow leaves, and colorful foliage can still be seen on a few aspens and red oaks.

A plant that I have been observing the last few days is the Boston ivy *(Parthenocissus tricuspidata)*, a high-climbing vine with tendrils ending in sucker-like disks that is growing on the main building at the Arboretum. Its shining green leaves have now changed to shades of crimson, and the vines are loaded with blue fruit.

Boston ivy, which is a native of Japan and China, is a popular, quick-growing climber that clings to stone or brick walls. Although it only borders on hardiness in the Twin Cities area, it is still commonly seen here. If dieback occurs following a severe winter, new growth from the base will soon cover the wall again. Even the branching pattern against a wall is attractive after the leaves have fallen.

October 28, 1978 Lombardy Poplars

Flocks of American robins continue to feed on the ripe fruit in the Arboretum crabapple collection, and the sugar maple leaves that are thick on the ground in the sugarbush make a crunching sound as we walk on them. The winged euonymus shrubs with their corky winged stems are a vivid red, while the tall Lombardy poplars have reached their peak of fall color. Their broad triangular leaves, about three inches long with rounded marginal teeth and flattened petioles, are golden-yellow.

Populus nigra variety *italica* is the widely planted fast-growing tree commonly called the Lombardy poplar and is hardy in southern Minnesota. A tree that is sixty feet tall may be only ten feet wide, giving it a slim columnar shape that is, perhaps, its most distinctive feature. The Lombardy poplar was known to be growing before 1750 and was propagated by cuttings from a European black poplar tree in Lombardy, in northern Italy. It was first introduced into America in 1784, and although once a highly esteemed tree that was planted in formal, impressive rows, it has fallen into some disfavor. It is susceptible to diseases that make it short-lived, and formal landscaping using long rows of Lombardies is not as popular as it was. An irregular grouping of these tall, graceful trees as an accent or as a planting mixed with other trees for a variety in outline is preferred now. Since only the male trees are common, the Lombardy poplars don't produce a spring snow storm of cotton.

October 29, 1979 Active Cold-blooded Animals

Only birds and mammals among the animals are truly warm-blooded and can maintain a high constant body temperature. All other animals are cold-blooded or of variable temperature, and their body temperatures are dependent upon the environment. Snails, earthworms, millipedes and wood ticks are common cold-blooded animals.

On this sunny afternoon with a high temperature of 66°F, I recorded quite a list of active cold-blooded animals: I saw one monarch butterfly headed south along with comma, mourning cloak, sulphur, alfalfa and painted lady butterflies. Flower flies, honey bees and a bumble bee were feeding from the last late blossoms of asters and mums. Daddy-longlegs were out on their long slender legs, feeding chiefly on plant juices and insects, although most daddy-longlegs winter over in the egg stage in the North.

Fish are also cold-blooded animals, and the walleyes and northern pike from Lake Minnetonka were biting well today, according to local anglers. One lone painted turtle crawled up on a log on a pond's edge to sun, but being surprised by my presence it slid into the water again. Garter snakes were sunning themselves, leopard frogs jumped toward the safety of lakes, and woollybear caterpillars scurried along. A katydid and common skimmers — medium-size dragonflies with red abdomens — appeared long enough to be counted and disappeared.

The last cold-blooded species I was aware of were the snowy tree crickets. Two or three chirped in our yard just before midnight.

December, 1979

Looking back in my field notebook, I can see that October 29 provided the final observations for the cold-blooded animals I have listed:

Last bumble bee and honey bees of the season feeding on flowers.

Last painted turtle was sunning.

Monarch, comma, sulphur and alfalfa butterflies, plus common skimmers and a katydid, seen for the last time this year.

October 30, 1978 Purple Finches

With the appearance of a male three days ago, purple finches began returning to our feeding station. Although they nest in northeastern and north central Minnesota, they usually are not seen in the Twin Cities area until this time of the year. I enjoy listening to their rich musical warbles and watching them go after sunflower and millet seeds on tray feeders.

To describe a male purple finch as having purple feathers is hardly accurate; it is more a raspberry or cranberry color. As someone told me, "A male purple finch looks like a sparrow dipped in cranberry juice;" but the females and young are heavily streaked with dull brown, and all have thicker bills than the sparrows. Thousands of purple finches were banded in Michigan, but the average bird lives no more than two years although one that was retrapped there was at least ten years old.

Purple finches are gregarious in winter, but they can be quite aggressive toward each other when feeding. When darkness comes they roost together, generally in dense evergreens. In late fall, winter and spring, when they eat seeds, they prefer the seeds of trees, grasses and other herbaceous plants, together with aspen, maple and birch buds, and fruits of shrubs.

October 31, 1979 A Halloween Hike

First I heard their "zeee, zeee" calls, and then I saw them; fifteen cedar waxwings, their black masks and yellow-tipped tails making them easily noticed as they perched at the top of a green ash tree. Flocks of cedar waxwings are often seen in the fall and winter here, where they eat berries and other fruits still hanging on trees and shrubs.

The roses are beautiful with white, yellow, light pink, dark pink and red petals, and we can still also enjoy their fragrance. Shrub and old fashioned roses are not put underground for the winter, and a few are still blooming. Although most of the old roses have green foliage, some plants have yellow, orange and red leaves. Many mums and a few delphiniums continue to bloom, and the Boston ivy vines are colorful.

White oak leaves and tamarack needles are falling. Our native tamaracks appear to be about two-thirds bare, and yet the European larch is approaching its color peak with handsome golden needles.

Not many people hike in the Arboretum on cool fall days when it's raining. Today, as I did, I noticed that the juncos, bluejays, chipmunks and other animals were not deterred by the rain. My Halloween treat was to enjoy the sights, sounds and smells of this wet autumn afternoon. Then I went home to help pass out treats to neighborhood children and to take our two young boys out in their costumes to ring doorbells.

Pond Freezing Over with Canada Geese

November 1, 1975 What's Blooming?

Last night I covered the alyssum, marigolds, petunias and geraniums, and they all endured the frosts and are still blooming next to our house. None of the plants at the Arboretum has been covered, but some chrysanthemums are still blooming there together with the New England aster, blanket flower, verbena, delphinium and common periwinkle. Even a half dozen old-fashioned roses have survived the first frosts and have some buds and blossoms. A few red clover and dandelion flowers can be found near the roadsides while on the forest edge a common witchhazel shrub has the last of its yellow blossoms.

Juncos, tree sparrows, fox sparrows and Harris' sparrows are busy eating the millet seeds on the ground below a large tray feeder at the edge of a forest. Our two largest sparrow species, fox and Harris', nest in Canada and will spend the winter south of us.

The fox sparrows, boldly striped and each sporting a rufous tail, have an interesting way of searching for food. They scratch in fallen leaves using both feet in unison and often make a great deal of noise. They are not inconvenienced by moderate snowfalls and make the snow fly as well as the leaves. Harris' sparrows with black crowns, faces and bibs and pink bills also scratch vigorously in the leaves and soil for food.

November 2, 1978 Leopard Frogs on the Move

The leopard frogs have the most beautiful coloring of our common frogs. They are better known than others, not only because they are found in much of North America but because they have the habit of traveling long distances from ponds and lakes. We often meet them when we are walking in fields and meadows. They jump out from under our feet in long, low leaps but seldom appear above the grass. Although most frogs are in hibernation now, a few stragglers took advantage of the weather and could be seen going from the grassy areas to lakes as today was unusually warm with a high temperature in the 70s.

The frogs' food of insects, worms and spiders, which must be caught live by the quick flip of a sticky mucous-coated tongue and swallowed entire, is becoming scarce now. A cold-blooded animal, the frog can reproduce, feed and grow during the warm weather but must hibernate in cold weather. To keep from starving and freezing it burrows into the bottom mud or finds other places under submerged rocks or logs in a pond or lake for a winter sleep. In this inactive state its body metabolism drops to a low level, and its heartbeat slows.

November 3, 1978 Record High Temperature

As the high pressure continues to dominate, we enjoyed another Indian summer day and a new record high temperature for the second day in a row. The Twin Cities had a high today of 74°F, passing the old record of 72°F that was set in 1975. Redwood Falls recorded 77°F, and International Falls has a new record high of 66°F.

The last pairs of wood ducks seem to be hesitant to leave this warm north country, and a few painted turtles crawled up on half-sunken logs above the cold water to bask in the sun. Garter snakes, leopard frogs and woollybear caterpillars moved about, and I saw honey bees on red clover flowers as well as grasshoppers, ladybird beetles and a large bumble bee. Sulphur butterflies were on the wing, and I even saw flower flies and a Milbert's tortoise shell butterfly on chrysanthemum flowers. A friend recorded a mosquito bite, his last of the year, he hopes.

With drying winds, frost-killed vegetation and very little precipitation lately, there is a danger of forest and grass fires in Minnesota, but these same conditions have given farmers the opportunity to work in the fields and finish the field corn harvest.

We still have some interesting fall color. Weeping willow leaves are about half yellow and half green, apple trees have yellow foliage, and the Sungold and Moongold apricot trees are yellow and red. A spectacular November sunset contributed to the fall color this afternoon. The sky had been clear earlier, but just before sunset at 4:59 p.m. CST, cirrus clouds, about 25,000 feet up, moved in and created a flaming red sky. As we viewed this beauty, about two dozen honking Canada geese flew by and landed on a pond that was reflecting the bold atmospheric colors.

November 4, 1979 European Larch

Larches are cone-bearing trees of grace and beauty that belong to the pine family, but being deciduous they lose all their needle-like leaves in autumn. Our native larch, commonly known as the tamarack, is now nearly bare, but the European larch *(Larix decidua)* is a beautiful golden-yellow. An excuse to visit the Arboretum in early November could be to come and see the European larches near the Ordway Shelter.

This tree is native to northern and central Europe and was introduced into North America by early settlers. It is tall with a pyramidal form and leaves about one inch long. It is cultivated on tree farms and used in shelterbelts or as an ornamental in Europe and North America. European larches are hardy in both northern and southern Minnesota, but because of the size at maturity, which can be eighty feet tall and forty-five feet wide, they should not be planted in the average small yard.

November 5, 1979 Local Bird Observations

While listening to a great horned owl calling just after sunset last evening, I saw and heard seventeen whistling swans as they flew in a southeastern direction. They were the first ones I had seen this fall. We still have tens of thousands of red-wings and common grackles roosting each evening in a marshy area near Lake Waconia, and big flights of Franklin's gulls in V formation fly in around sunset and spend the night on the lake. At least 1,000 American coots remain on Lake Waconia.

I banded birds today, the first time since last spring as my research involves mainly winter-feeder birds. Ten species came to the feeders: downy, hairy and red-bellied woodpeckers, Harris' and white-throated sparrows, blue jays, black-capped chickadees, white-breasted nuthatches, cardinals and dark-eyed juncos, but only sixteen juncos and four chickadees could be enticed into the traps. It's much easier to encourage birds to visit the traps containing sunflower and millet seeds as bait when there is snow on the ground.

It is only a few minutes from the time a bird is caught in the wire-mesh trap until I release it, but in that time I read the numbers on a previously banded bird or apply a small ring-band to its leg, examine it and fill out a data sheet. Banding gives us information on bird territory, movement and longevity.

Green-winged teal, buffleheads, mallards, common goldeneyes and eight common snipes have been seen on local lakes and ponds but no common loons. They are, however, still on some northern lakes.

November 6, 1979 Cold Weather Vegetables

Carrots are a cool season vegetable, and given the proper cool storage they will last for months. Arboretum librarian June Rogier recently covered her carrot rows with hay, which, when followed by a covering of snow on top, will keep the soil from freezing. This will make it possible to uncover the hay and dig fresh carrots from the garden throughout the winter. Another local gardener dug all his carrots yesterday and will store them in a barrel of sawdust in a cool cellar where they will stay fresh for several months.

Brussels sprouts, broccoli, cabbage, cauliflower and kohlrabi continue to grow even in the cool weather and are being harvested by area gardeners. Those that planted leaf lettuce, radishes and spinach in early August have been enjoying a good fall crop. From the herb garden, salad burnet leaves with their cucumber flavor and onion chives can still be cut for use in salad, fresh tarragon leaves are available for chicken dishes, and green sprigs of parsley can be picked for an attractive garnish.

All of the plants I have listed can withstand light frost and some freezing temperatures. With proper planning and selection of crops, the garden season can be extended late into the year.

November 7, 1980

The white-tailed deers' bark rubs on trees and soil scrapes can be found and are signs that the rutting season has begun. Although the silver and green leaves of the Russian olive are dropping, common buckthorn trees continue to have green leaves, and indoors our Thanksgiving cactus has begun to bloom. Some people regard November as a drab, uninteresting month, but there are always changes as the earth moves in its charted course around the sun. I try to get my students involved in outdoor discovery activities to show them that this month can be exciting, too.

If you are looking for another way to step up activity at a backyard feeding station, consider providing the local resident and visiting birds with fresh water, which they like and need the year around. They are attracted to a yard that has water for them to drink and to bathe in. People sometimes ask why some birds bathe in freezing weather. To keep warm, their feathers must be efficient, and to have efficient feathers a bird must go through the preening ritual that often starts with a bath.

Glycerine or antifreeze should never be used to keep water in a birdbath free of ice as these chemicals should not be drunk, and they will also cause havoc with a bird's feathers at a time when the feathers must keep the bird warm. Immersion heaters designed to keep baths permanently icefree work well and are available commercially.

November 8, 1979 End of the Growing Season — The Freeze

The growing season, which began in early April this year, came to a close today with a low temperature of 16°F and a high not above freezing. The last of the delphiniums and chrysanthemums froze, fringe ice formed on ponds and small lakes, and the first measurable snow of about one-half inch fell.

A dozen robins worked on some frozen tree fruit while fifty or more snow buntings circled over the Arboretum and soon landed on a windswept grassland. Snow buntings are gregarious birds, the size of sparrows, and identified by their large white wing patches. It is a circumpolar bird, often called "snowflake," that nests on the tundra, but in severe winters large flocks appear in our northern states where they search for seeds of low-growing plants in barren places.

November 9, 1978 Weeping Willows

Today was another unusual, warm fall day. The bright sunshine and 59°F air temperature brought out one last painted turtle to bask in the warmth, a few sulphur butterflies flew around, and some woollybear caterpillars crawled on the sidewalk. The weeping willows have had some fall color for a long time, and today they reached their peak of golden-yellow foliage.

The weeping variety of the white willow *(Salix alba)*, called the

Weeping Willow

golden weeping willow, is a native of Europe and Asia and probably the most commonly planted willow in Minnesota. It's the one we now admire for its fall color and will also easily spot in very early spring with its golden twigs. The pendulous branches are beautiful at all seasons of the year. The golden weeping willow is best when planted along lakes and streams, for if planted in a yard, its shedding branches can be messy and the drooping branches a nuisance when mowing the lawn.

November 10, 1979 Area Ponds and Small Lakes

I received word that Caribou Lake in Cook County, Lake Itasca in Itasca State Park, and Traverse Lake near Wheaton froze over yesterday, and today the ponds and small lakes in the Arboretum are frozen.

A lake or pond cannot freeze over until it reaches 39°F throughout the water. Hibbert Hill, a local scientist and student of freshwater life, explained it to me this way: "Freezing and the final formation of a permanent ice cover on our lakes are processes controlled in large part by a unique characteristic of water. Most materials, for example, mercury in a thermometer, shrink as they cool. Water also shrinks as it cools from summer temperatures to 39°; that way cooler water sinks, and the lake mixes and becomes a uniform 39°. At 39°, however, water goes into reverse and swells as it cools below that temperature. For this reason, water cooler than 39° is lighter than water at 39° and so will float on the surface. Ice forms at 32°. The temperature of the water just in contact with the ice sheet in winter is 32°, the freezing temperature, but a few feet below the ice, the water temperature is 35° to 38°. The colder water floats on the warmer water at these temperatures. On the first calm, freezing day or night after the lakes and ponds reach 39° throughout, an ice cover will form."

The temperature of water beneath the ice cover will range from 32° to 39°, the 39° being on the bottom. If water cooler than 39° continued to shrink and to become more dense and sink, ice would form from the bottom of the lake upward. Our lakes would then have permanent ice covered by a layer of water in the summer.

We have about two inches of snow on the ground bringing out sliders and opening some downhill ski areas near the Twin Cities where snowmaking equipment has been used to set an adequate base. The big flocks of blackbirds are gone, most of the American coots have left the lakes, a large flock of whistling swans flew high overhead, and a bald eagle made its fall appearance on the shoreline of Lake Waconia.

November 11, 1979 The Deciduous Tree with Green Leaves

Deciduous is the term applied to trees and shrubs that shed their leaves in the autumn. Most of our deciduous trees and shrubs are bare or nearly bare now, but there is one species that still has dark green, broad leaves and gives our landscape a welcome touch of green. This plant is common buckthorn *(Rhamnus cathartica)*, a shrub or small tree that grows to a height of twenty feet. When its leaves finally fall in very late autumn, they will still be green with little or no change of color.

A Eurasian species that was introduced into North America by early settlers, common buckthorn was once widely planted for hedges and thick screens as it will grow well even in poor soil and can withstand severe clipping and shaping. The plant has now escaped from cultivation and is naturalized in Minnesota and other areas. The two-inch leaves are oval and have prominent veins and small teeth on the margins with a thorn between the buds at the tip of each branchlet. Common buckthorns still have clusters of blackish-purple, berry-like fruits, each about one-third of an inch in diameter, which robins and other wildlife consume. The fruits are messy when eaten by birds because of their laxative effect, and animals that eat these fruits scatter the seeds freely.

November 12, 1979 Christmas is Coming

We have seen trucks loaded with Christmas trees on the highways for several days, and today while driving through the Glen Lake area near Hopkins, I saw trees set out for retail sale.

The Christmas tree is mainly a horticultural product planted, cultivated and harvested for the purpose of selling. Until about twenty-five years ago the Christmas tree was cut in its natural state, and while some cutting of evergreens in natural habitats still occurs, most Christmas trees are grown on tree farms. In Minnesota thousands of acres are in production. Because many people enjoy selecting and cutting their own trees, a number of growers have opened "choose and cut" tree farms.

At one time the balsam fir was harvested from native stands of trees before the cultivation of pines on tree farms became popular. Because it is not very adaptable to modern methods of tree culture and is slow growing, the fragrant balsam fir, which was once the standard Christmas tree in our area, is now quite scarce. The balsam fir needs partial shade and cool, moist conditions for growth, but sunny, open sites are usually chosen by tree growers who plant pines and spruces by machine, approximately 1,200 trees per acre. Grasses and other weeds are kept down to provide good growing conditions for the small trees, and growers must watch for insect attacks. Shearing is necessary both for shaping the trees and to increase their density. From the time they are about three feet tall until they are harvested, the pines need to be sheared each summer and spruces in fall, winter or spring.

Most of the Christmas trees grown are made up of Scotch and Norway pines, while the spruces include Norway, black, white and Colorado blue. Pines take about seven to eight years to mature, spruces about ten years. Before harvest many growers spray their trees with a non-toxic, water-based pigment to color the trees green as the Scotch and Norway pines, more than the spruces, lose their bright green as fall approaches. Harvesting usually begins in late October and continues through Thanksgiving. Although most consumers who choose to cut their own Christmas tree expect it to be fresher than one selected at a pre-cut lot, it may not be. According to some growers, freshness depends on the moisture in the needles, which is influenced more by weather than by the date the tree is cut.

Whistling Swan

November 13, 1978 Migration of the Whistling Swans

Whistling swans were migrating over Minnesota today. I was fortunate to see eighty-three on Lake Waconia and to enjoy hearing their muffled, musical whistles. The mature swans are all white with black bills, and the immatures are a very light brownish-gray with pink bills. As they are three feet tall and have a seven-foot wingspread, they are easy to spot and identify.

The swans are coming from their summer range mainly north of the Arctic Circle. Large numbers pause briefly each fall on lakes and rivers in the Great Lakes area before moving to their winter headquarters along the Atlantic coast from Chesapeake Bay to North Carolina. Whistling swans fly with speed and power, their long necks stretched straight ahead, feet back under their tails and wings beating slowly and regularly as they travel in V-shaped wedges, sometimes at a height of six to eight thousand feet.

November 14, 1979 Crows and Owls

Since great horned owls go into crow roosts at night to take crows for food, we often see bands of common crows chasing and generally harassing owls in the daytime, which I saw today. The voices of the crows carry the hysterical fear of their nights over into the day. It is also possible that the owl will go to the crow roost again and repeat its ritual.

Mobbing is the customary response of birds to certain predators that pose a threat, such as cats, foxes and large snakes. Presumably this behavior has survival value to the mobbers by drawing attention to the whereabouts of a killer. When owls are discovered, the action that best ensures survival of the local birds seems to be exposing the enemy by mass display or mobbing, and even chickadees and other small birds can be seen engaged in this activity against small owl species. Since crows must spend a good part of their day finding and eating food, they eventually lose interest in the owl, and the mobbing response discontinues.

Common crows are omnivorous, consuming great numbers of grasshoppers, cutworms and other insects. In late fall and winter they eat the kernels of corn in a field after harvest and also large numbers of weed seeds and wild fruits, animal matter collected near water, traffic-killed animals and garbage. Crows often feed in small groups, and usually one or more will stay on a perch and warn of approaching danger.

In the southern half of Minnesota, common crows are seen regularly in winter. These stocky black birds have a wingspread of about three feet and weigh about a pound. They gather in communal roosts of many thousands in fall and winter for reasons not known to ornithologists. Roosts of these interesting birds can be located by watching the direction toward which groups are flying in late afternoon or the direction from which they come at dawn. They disperse every morning from their roost in small groups to feed and then return in the same way at sunset.

November 15, 1979 White Coats on the Snowshoe Hares

Naturalist Mark Rosen from the Environmental Learning Center at Isabella called to say that the snowshoe hares in his area are now white. Each fall in response to photoperiod, they turn from their dark-brown summer coats to white winter ones. The change takes about seventy-two days with most of it occurring in the last month. About a

Snowshoe Hare

month ago Mark noticed that the hares had white feet and legs; about three weeks ago the white was seen about an inch up on the sides of their bodies, and now they are completely white and can blend with the snow. It's interesting that the fall change in fur color is from the bottom up, but the spring change in March and April is from the top down, which helps ensure survival at these particular times. It's harder for hawks and other enemies to see them. The eastern cottontail rabbits we see in the Twin Cities area are brown all year.

Snowshow hares are found in the northern half of Minnesota. They are gnawing animals with ears about four inches long, a short tail, soft fur, long hind legs, and they weigh about two to four pounds. Their name is derived from the soles of their large feet that are well-furred, enabling them to run on soft snow without sinking down. In summer the hares eat green vegetation and in winter, buds and bark. Although the home range of a snowshoe hare is about ten acres, it may travel up to about a mile.

There are fundamental differences between hares and rabbits. Hares are precocial at birth, having a full fur coat and functioning eyes and ears, and they can hop around within a few hours. Newborn rabbits are confined to the nest after birth, are naked and helpless, and do not open their eyes for some days.

November 16, 1980 Snowy Owls

Snowy owls have been seen recently in the Princeton area, around Minneapolis and near Weaver in Wilkin County, but the first report of a snowy owl came from the Bongards area in Carver County on October 27.

Snowy owls are large with about a five-foot wingspread, almost pure white with occasional dark spots, a rounded head and yellow eyes. Being circumpolar, snowy owls are found throughout the arctic regions in North America and Europe. In North America they nest on the treeless tundras in Alaska and Canada and go farther south in fall and winter. They are seen at irregular intervals in the United States, occasionally as far south as California, Texas and Georgia. Roughly every four years the great white owl appears in large numbers in southern Canada and the northern states. These invasions coincide with a decrease of its favorite prey, the tundra-inhabiting rodents known as lemmings. Lemmings undergo periodic population changes owing to population explosions and succeeding epidemics, and when their numbers decrease, the snowy owls must move southward to avoid starvation.

From the number of reports I have received, this appears to be an invasion year for snowy owls in Minnesota. When they are here, they hunt during the day in fields for rabbits and other small game, they prey on Norway rats in shipping centers, and they even feed on dead fish on beaches. The imposing white owl is a beautiful sight as it sits upright on a fence post or flies over an open field. Strictly a bird of the open country, it is practically never seen in a tree. It perches instead on the ground, on roofs of buildings, haystacks, utility poles and on ice near open water.

Minnesota Gopher (13-lined Ground Squirrel)

November 17, 1975 Late Gopher

While driving around the Arboretum today, I saw a gopher searching for food in the grasses under the trees in the nut collection. I suppose it was taking advantage of the 50°F air temperature and sunshine to look for its last meal before going into hibernation.

The Minnesota gopher is also known as a grass chippie, grass runner, striped ground squirrel, striped gopher and thirteen-lined ground squirrel. This little mammal has thirteen lines alternating from light to dark on the upper part of its body. When it runs, it can be distinguished from a chipmunk by the way it carries its tail straight out behind it while a chipmunk holds its tail vertically. It prefers dry meadows, pastures, golf courses and parks where it digs burrows which are usually less than two feet below the surface. The home range of a gopher is somewhat restricted and rarely exceeds three acres or a radius of about two hundred feet.

To locate a gopher, look for the animal itself on a bright day and look for entrances to its burrow in grassy areas. At a first glance the gopher may appear like an upright six-inch wooden peg. A person may, with silence and deliberation, approach to within fifteen feet of it before it ducks into its burrow and then slyly reappears for another peek at the intruder. Often a gopher will run through the grass and dive into its hole uttering its sharp rolling chirp as it does so, and if a person withdraws a few feet and remains quiet, it probably will come entirely out of its burrow. Some brave gophers may even accept potato chips or bread thrown or dropped on the ground.

Gophers prefer bright sunshine and warm weather and dislike exposing themselves on cold, dark, or rainy days. They are true hibernators and usually begin hibernation during October and remain dormant until the middle of March or the beginning of April. Although I observed my first gopher on March 17, 1974, I did not see one until April 6, 1975. The gopher grows fat by the last of September, its spring weight doubled. Then, after solidly plugging the entrances to the burrow with soil, it curls itself into a ball and becomes still. While its temperature lowers to nearly that of the air about it, its body functions are reduced to a minimum.

The gopher is omnivorous in food habits. It eats grasses, weed seeds, berries, acorns and other plant material, but it is also fond of insects and other animal matter. During summer months or about half the time of its active existence, it feeds extensively on harmful insects such a grasshoppers, June beetles, both larvae and adults, and cutworms.

November 18, 1979 A Warm Day

A warm day like today is a special treat. The joggers are back in their shorts, tennis players and golfers are out, and boats with fishermen are on area lakes. With high temperatures in the mid 60s the last two days, our boys and I enjoyed some short bike hikes, a few neighbors mowed their lawns, and area farmers picked corn and plowed in comfort.

Today I watched small spiders ballooning, traveling through the air on long strands of silk, as a mourning cloak butterfly flew within inches of me. On the south side of the house ladybird beetles, boxelder bugs, flies and a daddy-longlegs basked in the sun's rays.

For those who hadn't done so earlier in the fall, this was a good time to place a cylinder of one-fourth-inch mesh hardware cloth around the base of young fruit and ornamental trees and shrubs to protect them from rabbits and mice that feed on the bark during winter months when food is scarce. If the bark is chewed through all around the main stem, the plant will die from starvation of its roots as food manufactured by the leaves moves downward to the roots through the inner bark.

November 19, 1979 Green Garden Parsley

The parsley has survived freezing temperatures and a little snow, and it is still green and healthy in the herb garden. With some protection, this annual will continue to grow outdoors into December. It can also be potted in fall and brought indoors to grow on a cool, sunny windowsill where it will produce fresh leaves all winter.

Parsley is native to the Mediterranean region. It is an excellent source of iron, calcium and vitamins A, B and C. Parsley leaves can be harvested as soon as a plant is six inches tall and can be refrigerated to use fresh or frozen or dried. The curly variety is often used raw as a garnish. Culinary artists make good use of parsley in green salads, cream sauces, egg dishes, vegetable dishes and stews.

November 20, 1970 Late Garter Snake

Temperatures only a few degrees above freezing stimulated a hardy garter snake into activity about the mouth of its hibernation den today. My students and I found one in Carver Park as it was sunning on an open hillside on the edge of a forest. Picking up the snake, I found that it felt warm although the air temperature was only in the 30s.

Snakes do not dig the dens in which they hibernate. Rotting tree stumps give them access to areas below ground level where the roots grew, and old chipmunk and woodchuck burrows along banks also provide winter dens. Garter snakes are the most common snakes in Minnesota. They are cold-blooded animals that congregate in the fall in denning areas and disappear during cold spells. They reappear on warm days until cold weather finally forces them into hibernation for the winter.

During six autumns the naturalists at Lowry Nature Center in Carver Park Reserve observed and recorded the date the last active garter snake was seen above ground. As you can see, the November 20 date was indeed late.

November 4, 1975	October 30, 1979
November 4, 1977	November 3, 1980
November 8, 1978	November 17, 1981

November 21, 1972 First Skaters

November is a good month for nature observations. There is plenty of natural food for the furry animals, trees are silhouetted against blue skies and fantastic cloud formations, dried grasses and herbs stand tall, winter birds are colorful, beautiful sunsets enchant us, and new ice appears. On November 15 ponds and small lakes froze over, and today people were skating on ponds in Hopkins and St. Bonifacius. Although I love to skate, I have been waiting for some colder weather to thicken the ice.

Here is an ice thickness table that should be followed for skating safety.

One inch — keep off!
Two inches — one skater
Three inches — three or four skaters
Four inches — safe for skating groups

The table above assumes that there is clear, solid ice in contact with stationary fresh water. Ice near the mouths of streams or streams flowing out of lakes or near springs is dangerous. Test the thickness of the ice first, and as you do, remember that ice seldom freezes or thaws at a uniform rate. It can be a foot thick in one spot and only an inch thick ten feet away.

If you should break through the ice, the first thing to do is to grasp the edge of the ice lightly to support yourself and then kick your feet to keep your body as flat as possible. Crawl forward on the ice on your belly until your hips are at the edge, then quickly roll sideways and try to roll away from the hole. Once you're on safe ice, get to a shelter to warm yourself immediately.

To help rescue someone who has broken through the ice, form a human chain if no equipment is available. You alone may be able to rescue someone if you lie flat on the ice and push a plank, ladder, pole or tree branch within reach of the victim or throw a rope or article of clothing. Then hang on to one end, being sure the victim doesn't pull you into the ice hole also.

November 22, 1979 Christmas Landscape on Thanksgiving Day

Among my blessings today was the opportunity to see our area conifers with snow on them. A snow-covered evergreen is a beautiful sight. Wet, heavy snow fell most of the day and stuck to everything, producing a true winter wonderland. At Marshall twelve inches of snow fell, and in the Twin Cities area we received four inches.

Strangely enough, one of my favorite occupations is to shovel our

NOVEMBER

November is the month of great transition from the warm season to the cold season. The month usually starts out like autumn but ends up being wintery.

193

Some chrysanthemums continue blooming early in November. **(193)** The common witchhazel is the last shrub to bloom. **(194)** Boston ivy continues to show fall color **(195)** as does the European larch. **(196)**

194

195

196

197

198

199

200

Many mallard ducks stay if they can find open water and a food source. **(197)** Some Canada geese may also stay for the winter. **(198)** Whistling swans migrate through but stop to rest. **(199 & 200)**

201 202 203 204

A white-breasted nuthatch and downy woodpecker feed on beef suet. **(201)** Suet is also relished by red-bellied woodpeckers. **(202)** Snowshoe hares turn from brown to white for the winter. **(203)** Deer have an acute sense of smell, sensitive hearing, and eyes that are especially good for detecting movement. However, they are color blind. White-tailed deer can run 30 mph but depend on camouflage and keen senses to survive. **(204)**

205

206

208

207

November, being the month of clouds, provides some spectacular sunsets **(205)** as well as fog. **(206)** The majority of Minnesota lakes usually freeze over in November. **(207)** Remember, ice fishing and skating require at least 4 inches of clear, solid ice. **(208)**

DECEMBER

The month of gentle snows, sunshine is at a minimum for the year, and the coldest part of the month is usually the last week.

209

210

211

The lack of snow can result in a beautiful sunrise over an ice covered lake **(209)** and great ice boating. **(210)** Refraction of light by ice crystals in the atmosphere causes solar halos and sundogs (bright colored spots of light), especially during very cold weather. **(211 & 212)**

212

213

214

215

216

A Droll Yankee feeder with thistle and sunflower seeds attracts pine siskins. **(213)** A tray feeder or a glass jar feeder will draw many birds. **(214 & 215)** Several bird species, such as the cardinal, prefer eating seeds scattered in protected spots on the ground. **(216)**

217

218

An evening grosbeak likes sunflower seeds **(217)** but a northern shrike comes to a feeding station looking for chickadees or other prey. **(218)**

Animal tracking is a fun activity in winter. December snows usually cooperate so we easily can find cottontail rabbit tracks **(219)**, red squirrel tracks **(220)**, ring-necked pleasant tracks **(221)** and Canada goose tracks. **(222)** Deer tracks **(223)** and weasel tracks and snow tunnels **(224)**, surprisingly are often seen even in metroplitan areas.

219

220

221

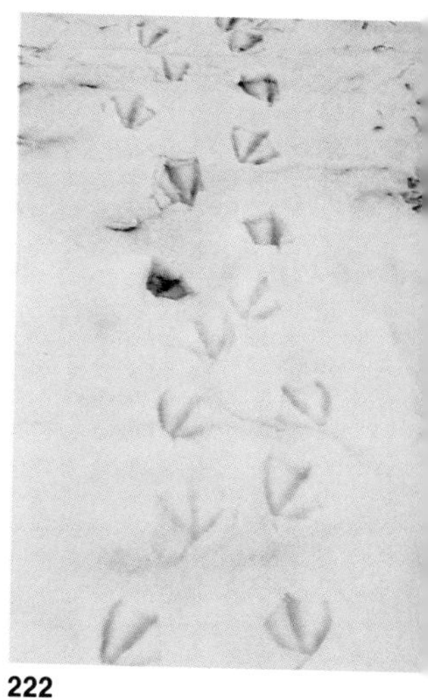

222

223

224

long driveway after a snowfall, but I like to do it alone in the evening when it is quiet. Studies have shown that sounds are reduced when there is fresh snow on the ground. The roar of traffic in a large city is muffled, and the wail of a distant siren, whistle or horn is lost in the country. A similar reduction in audibility has been noticed by researchers in the Antarctic in freshly dug snow tunnels where people must shout to be heard if more than fifteen feet apart. Snow surfaces absorb sound just as acoustical tile on a wall or ceiling does since fresh snow is filled with a myriad miniature air spaces like tile. As snow becomes more packed, the air escapes, and the sound-deadening effect disappears.

November 23, 1971 Tracks in the Snow

I am a naturalist who enjoys the beauty of snow, and as an outdoor education teacher I have still another reason to look forward to the first snowfall. My students love it and can hardly wait to go out in it. Snow is nature's peanut butter, someone once told me; it's crunchy, kids love it, and it sticks to the roof of your house. When I awoke this morning, I noticed we had about four inches of new snow, which was our first snowfall amounting to more than one inch.

Our outdoor lesson for today was to observe and record signs of animals. We would have done it without snow, but the new white cover helped us even more. Besides the old bird nests, leafy squirrel nests, woodpecker holes, goldenrod galls, cocoons, scats, browsed twigs and humpy muskrat houses in the marsh, we found animal tracks in the snow. At the same time we could hear Canada geese honking and red squirrels chattering. Mice left tiny footprints that always led to thumb-sized holes in the snow where they went down for cover. Numerous squirrel tracks led to and from the bases of trees, small birds left four-toed imprints, a fox left a walking-set of tracks, the weasel tracks showed us how small this active hunter really is. We could see where several deer had walked in each other's steps making a narrow path in the forest.

The traveling and feeding activities of many animals were studied without ever actually spotting them, but my students agreed that we learned more by observing the tracks than we could have if we had seen the animals.

November 24, 1979 Growing Icicles

Today in the Twin Cities, our temperature went from a low of 17°F to a high of 35° turning the rooftop snow into icicles. During winter weather one of the most beautiful and interesting phenomena is the formation of icicles.

An icicle is a tapering, pendant mass of ice formed by the freezing of dripping water only when the temperature of the air is below freezing. These ice sticks grow with freezing temperatures and recede with thawing temperatures. Under freezing conditions, snow on a roof can still melt from heat coming through the roof or from the sun's heat. If the roof of a house is poorly insulated, it can be easily detected by noting that the snow disappears faster than from a house roof with good insulation.

Snow melting from automobiles may cause icicles to form on bumpers and fenders, water seeping from rock layers may be the cause of icicles on a cliff, and icicles sometimes form on the outer branches of snow-covered evergreens. We occasionally see some that have been misshaped by strong wind action or ones that were originally straight but were pushed inward when the snow began sliding off a roof. If you are going to collect icicles to study their shapes and sizes, be cautious because these ice sticks, which add charm to our surroundings, can be dangerous when they fall.

November 25, 1978 Freeze-Over

As I wrote on November 10, we cannot expect ice to form on a lake until after the lake cools down to 39°F throughout the whole body of water. After that an ice cover will form on the first calm, freezing day. Because the lakes located in any one area vary in depth, area size, shape and water movement, it's not surprising that some lakes freeze over much sooner than others. Lake Waconia with an area of about 3,100 acres and a maximum depth of thirty-seven feet froze over four days ago, but Lake Minnewashta, also located in Carver County but having an area of about 700 acres and a maximum depth of seventy feet, froze over today. In this case the shallower lake cooled down faster and froze over sooner.

This fall I contacted people around the state and asked them to note the date when lakes near their homes froze. They were to record the first day when at least 90 percent of the lake was frozen over and stayed that way. The following is a list of Minnesota lake freeze-up dates for 1978 compiled from the reports of the interested observers.

Town or Post Office Near Lake Reported	*County in Which Lake is Located*	*Date Lake Froze Over*	*Lake*
Isabella	Lake	November 14	Flat Horn Lake
Lake George	Hubbard	November 15	Lake George
Wheaton	Traverse	November 15	Traverse Lake

Lake Itasca	Clearwater	November 16	Lake Itasca
Lutsen	Cook	November 17	Caribou Lake
Deerwood	Crow Wing	November 20	Bay Lake
Buffalo	Wright	November 20	Buffalo Lake
Faribault	Rice	November 21	Cannon Lake
Ray	St. Louis	November 21	Kabetogama Lake
Chanhassen	Carver	November 21	Lotus Lake
Darwin	Meeker	November 21	Stella Lake
Sturgeon Lake	Pine	November 21	Sturgeon Lake
Longville	Cass	November 21	Woman Lake
Bemidji	Beltrami	November 22	Lake Bemidji
Laporte	Hubbard	December 1	Kebekona Lake
Sandstone	Pine	December 2	Grindstone Lake
Mound	Hennepin	December 2	Lake Minnetonka

November 26, 1978 First Fish Houses

Although ice fishing requires a clear, solid ice cover at least four inches thick, eight inches to a foot of ice is necessary to drive an automobile on it. Lake Waconia, which froze over on November 21, now has an ice cover of about four inches, but that may not be absolutely accurate as ice doesn't freeze over a lake at a uniform rate. People who test the ice in a couple of spots and then decide to drive a vehicle on a lake early in the season are setting up the situation of an accident looking for a place to happen.

No cars went out on the ice today, but the first ice fishing houses were pushed across the smooth new ice. I counted three and about fifty people scattered across the ice film on the south end of the lake. Lake Waconia is known for its good fishing, and people were catching crappies and sunfish.

Since we moved to the shore of Lake Waconia, I have been recording freeze-up dates for the lake, and the date when the first ice fishing house appears each year.

Freeze-up, Lake Waconia	First ice fishing house appears
November 30, 1971	December 4, 1971
November 29, 1972	December 2, 1972
December 6, 1973	December 8, 1973
December 1, 1974 (Mostly frozen over on November 28.)	December 1, 1974
November 27, 1975	November 28, 1975
November 15, 1976	November 20, 1976
November 25, 1977	November 27, 1977

November 27, 1979 Muskrats on Ice Sheets

It's a cold day, and on the still-open area lakes ice is forming in big sheets. The muskrats are taking advantage of the ice sheets, using them as platforms on which to rest and eat. They are largely vegetarians, and I watched them bring various aquatic plant parts like tubers up for food for their picnics on the ice.

A muskrat is a furry animal about the size of a small house cat, weighing two to three pounds and always found near water. The long, shiny guard hairs of its coat are a rich brown, and beneath these is a dense mass of thick under-fur that is impervious to water. A long scaly tail that's flattened on the sides and functions as a rudder and partially-webbed hind feet to assist in swimming make it possible for a muskrat to live an aquatic life.

Muskrats are found in most parts of the United States and Canada. They are more active by night than day, and while they do not hibernate they build houses shaped like miniature beaver lodges up to about four feet high and eight feet in diameter in preparation for winter. These houses are made of cattail plants, mud and small water plants that they build up into mounds. Then like the beavers, they eat and dig out a chamber inside and an underwater entrance where they can enter and leave unobserved from shore. Muskrats may also burrow into banks and have their homes in tunnels above high water, but the entrance is always sufficiently below water level to be difficult to observe and below the winter ice level.

November 28, 1977 A Permanent Resident

Adult hairy woodpeckers are not regularly migratory, and when settled on a territorial range they tend to stay there for life. I was reminded of this again today while I was banding birds at the Lowry Nature Center. I recaptured a male hairy that had been wearing a band since June 4, 1971 and had been originally banded here in the same feeding area. It was now at least seven years old. Checking longevity records, I found that another Minnesota bander had listed one that was still alive at fourteen years.

Hairy woodpeckers are residents in all types of forests from the tree limit in Alaska and Canada, south throughout the forty-eight states, Mexico and the mountains of Panama. Although they are more shy than the downy woodpeckers, they are also more active and noisier. They save both forest and fruit trees by destroying harmful insects such as wood-boring beetles that are extracted from the holes by the hairies with their barbed tongues. They also eat other beetles, ants, some spiders, a few wild fruits and nuts like blackberries and acorns, drink sap at wells of sapsuckers, and at our feeding station they come often to feed on the beef suet.

A bit smaller than an American robin, a hairy woodpecker is black and white, with a broad white stripe down its back. The male has a small red patch on the back of its head that is missing on the female. Hairy woodpeckers appear to be semi-paired throughout the year. Both sexes drum on their territories, the females often as intensively as males in November and December. The hairy is almost identical in its plumage pattern to the downy woodpecker but distinguished from it by its larger size, longer and heavier bill and unmarked outer tail feathers.

November 29, 1978 — Northern Shrike at the Feeding Station

A northern shrike has been coming to the Lowry Nature Center feeding station lately, and, in fact, one hit a window yesterday while chasing a chickadee and stunned itself but was revived, banded and released. While other birds come to our feeding station to eat the seeds and suet, the shrikes, a few owls and some small hawks come to prey on the small birds and mammals that are feeding there.

If northern shrikes were common visitors in our feeding station area, I would feel that it was our fault that animals could be easily caught by them there, but we seldom see shrikes. They nest in Alaska and northern Canada and are migrators. They can be found wintering as far south as the central part of the United States, but I would consider them uncommon winter visitants in Minnesota. The same species is also found throughout much of Eurasia.

The name shrike comes from the word shriek in reference to their shrill calls. Linnaeus, in naming the bird, suggested that its cries on sighting a hawk might be a warning to small birds. A northern shrike is the size of a robin, gray on its upper body and white below, with black and white wings and tail, a black mask across the eyes and a stout, hooked bill.

Shrikes are solitary throughout most of the year except when nesting. They like open woodlands and open grasslands with fence posts and scattered trees where they conspicuously perch, or they can be seen on utility wires along a highway. From these places they have a good view and can swoop down to catch prey or look upward for possible attacks by hawks.

Despite their habit of killing small birds, rodents, snakes and frogs, they prefer insects when they are available, and they eat grasshoppers, crickets, dragonflies and bumble bees. They are fond of meadow mice, but also eat lemmings, white-footed mice, gophers and many small birds such as redpolls, goldfinches, house sparrows, starlings and cardinals. Their prey is often impaled on thorns or barbed wire for storage. Now and then a carcass is left to hang for a week or more before eventually being eaten by the shrike. Shrikes hunt only by day, and they have remarkable eyesight, comparable to that of hawks and eagles. One observer reported watching a northern shrike sight a flying bumble bee at least 300 feet away, fly after it and pluck it out of the air.

November 30, 1978 Squeaking, Creaking Snow

Snow sometimes squeaks when we walk on it. With seven inches of snow on the ground and below-zero temperatures, we can hear that unusual sound when the snow is pressed against the ground and sidewalks by the heels of our boots. When the temperature is a little below freezing, the pressure of a person's foot melts the snow, and no sound is heard. But when the temperature is well below freezing, near 0°F, the snow does not melt, but instead it yields abruptly as the crushed snow crystals slip over one another. It is the sudden breaking and slipping of the dry crystals that produce the familiar cold-weather squeaks and creaks when we walk.

Birds at Feeder with White Spruce

December 1, 1977 Feeding Birds

We have over nine inches of snow on the ground, and the winter birds are active at the feeding station. In a few minutes of casual observation one could see downy, hairy and red-bellied woodpeckers, blue jays, black-capped chickadees, white-breasted nuthatches, cardinals, American goldfinches, juncos, tree sparrows and house sparrows. With more time and a little luck, a birder might also see a pileated woodpecker, a small flock of evening grosbeaks or a couple of purple finches.

It isn't really necessary to feed wild birds as they usually have the ability to obtain sufficient food themselves. However, feeding is worthwhile if only for the education and pleasure of the people who feed them and to encourage birds to visit yards and gardens. In the winter, feeding may also tide birds over periods of deep snow and severe ice storms when natural foods are buried.

The first rule when feeding birds is that once it is begun in the fall or winter, don't quit. Feeding stations tend to influence certain species to remain far north of their normal wintering grounds, and if a feeder has been established and birds induced to stay in that area for the winter, the station should be maintained well into spring and summer when insects and fruits become available. For many people, the pleasure of the birds' company is worth the trouble of maintaining feeding stations throughout the year.

It is doubtful that artificial feeding keeps birds from eating insects and weed seeds, which is obvious as you observe that most visit the feeders only periodically and spend the rest of the time gathering their normal foods.

Birds that visit feeding stations generally fall into three groups: birds that feed mostly on seeds, those that feed chiefly on insects and other small animals, and the ones that are omnivorous. A mixture of sunflower and millet seeds will attract the first group, beef suet will be devoured by the insect eaters and the omnivorous birds will eat practically any food on the feeder. A typical bird food mixture is sunflower seeds with lesser amounts of cracked corn, safflower seeds, millet, wheat, peanut hearts, raisins, suet and grit. However, a feeding station with sunflower seeds and a smaller amount of millet and suet has proved successful in our yard.

Birds are not interested in the architectural beauty of a feeding station but only in the food. Some of the most successful feeding stations are those where the seed is merely scattered on the ground or poured into cracks of a log and the suet is tucked into natural cavities in trees. In yards and gardens many people find a homemade feeder easier to keep neat, and they put up shelves, covered or uncovered, that are nailed to tree trunks, suspended from branches, supported by poles, attached to clothes lines or fastened to windows. There are many commercial feeders on the market, but people will have as much success with a simple, shallow, home-made tray. Big feeders are better than small ones because more birds can be accommodated without fighting, and they need not be refilled as often. It's also a good idea to have several feeders of various types so that squirrels or big birds cannot dominate all of them.

People who feed birds should accept all visitors and enjoy each species for its particular characteristics and habits. I derive as much pleasure from observing wild mammals such as squirrels, mice, chipmunks, gophers, weasels and deer visiting feeding stations as I do from the birds. Rather than fretting about the squirrels at a feeding station, it would be better to spend one's time protecting birds and other wild animals from domestic cats.

December 2, 1978 The Freezing of Lake Minnetonka

Ice appeared on area roadside puddles November 14, small ponds froze over on November 14, small lakes on November 20 and medium-size lakes, Lotus, Steiger, Virginia and Waconia, November 21. Some small bays of Lake Minnetonka were frozen over by November 22, but then a strange thing happened. To quote naturalist Dick Gray: "For the first time according to all of the records I've gleaned from here and there and per my own, the Lower Lake of Minnetonka froze over before the last of the Upper Lake. Along with Jim Gilbert, the date of November 30 was agreed to by Sewell Andrews and Millard Skarp as to the freezing of the Lower Lake whereas I know the West Upper Lake wasn't fully frozen until December 2."

Browns Bay in the Lower Lake of Minnetonka, which is usually the last bay to freeze each year, froze on November 30 this year. Today, when the last of the Upper Lake froze over, ice boats were already skimming the ice on Browns Bay. It's difficult to record the date that a large body of water is fully frozen over because on cold mornings like this (−10°F) we can see wisps of vapor coming from cracks and a few small open water spots. The test is whether or not the sheet is at least 90 percent complete. Today we reached that point, so we can say that Lake Minnetonka is now frozen over. Although that's true, it's also true that the lake is not safe yet.

December 3, 1978 A Snowy Landscape

Since last evening we have received about eight inches of very light fluffy snow. Melted down this was the equivalent of four-tenths of an inch of rain, a ratio of 20:1; a ratio of 14:1 is average; and 9:1, a heavy snow. Many cross-country skiers were out on the Arboretum trail today enjoying the snow and scenery.

I was surprised to hear from naturalist Orwin A. Rustad that some farmers in the Faribault area are still plowing even with fourteen inches of snow on the ground. He said that if a field is plowed so that snow gets underground, a farmer can't plant oats in early spring as the seeds would germinate poorly in the extra cold soil, but corn and soybeans could still be planted at a later date.

December 4, 1970 Flying Squirrels

Flying squirrels are common in Minnesota although they are seldom seen. This afternoon I saw one as it left its home, an old woodpecker hole in a large basswood tree. The time was 4 p.m., which is early for flying squirrels to be out. This one was, no doubt, very hungry and wanted to beat the others to the sunflower seeds in a feeder near the base of a nearby American elm.

Flying squirrels sleep during the day and are active at night in the same trees that their larger tree-squirrel relatives occupy by day. They cannot really fly but glide. They have light, flattened bodies and a folded layer of loose skin along each side of their bodies that extends between their wrists and ankles, and with front and hind legs spread wide, they can sail through the air for considerable distances. They can glide ordinarily about twenty to thirty feet but occasionally as long as one hundred and sixty feet. They cannot rise nor keep on a horizontal line but can only descend. I have watched them run to the top of a tree and begin their glides to a lower branch or another tree, often at an angle of thirty to fifty degrees.

The southern flying squirrel, which prefers heavy deciduous timber near water, is found in hardwood forests throughout the eastern United States but seldom where coniferous trees predominate. Northern flying squirrels are found in mixed coniferous and deciduous forests from Alaska, across Canada and into the United States, and both species live in Minnesota. Since the habitat of the southern species is hardwood stands, this is the species we are likely to see in our area where they are often more numerous than red squirrels, their

Flying Squirrel

cousins. They are gregarious and live together in communities where favorable habitats may support three to five or more per acre.

A southern flying squirrel, which is smaller than the northern flying squirrel, is about ten inches long and weighs about two ounces. Both species have thick soft fur that is brown on the upper body and white below. The hairs of the underparts of southern flying squirrels are completely white, but a close examination of the undersides of a northern flying squirrel shows the hairs to be slate-colored at their bases.

The young are born in April or May, usually three or four in a litter, after a forty-day gestation period. Nests are generally made up of bark shreds, dry leaves, mosses and feathers or other soft materials, and they are built in hollow trees, attics, farm buildings and bird boxes. Sometimes outside nests of twigs and leaves are built, or deserted bird or gray squirrel nests are taken over. Their food consists of seeds and fruits, buds and blossoms, fungi, insects and occasionally birds' eggs and young birds. I have seen flying squirrels eating May beetles (junebugs) that were attracted to brightly lighted windows on a warm spring evening.

The value of an animal to its habitat is an often-discussed question, but it seems easy to see the importance of flying squirrels to the woodlands. By feeding on the buds of trees, they probably stimulate better tree growth; their foraging for wood-burrowing insects helps destroy these pests; and by burying seeds and fruits they assist in the continuation of the forest that protects and feeds them. Their body wastes add organic matter to the total contributed by all wildlife, and because they are preyed upon, they serve as a link in the forest food chain. Their enemies include owls, hawks, ravens, bobcats, raccoons and weasels. Owls are their main enemy, and they are always wary of them. The squirrels' large eyes, often characteristic of nocturnal animals, enable them to gather in enough light for excellent nighttime vision, and this, together with their running speed and the ability to glide, insures their survival in a forest.

Flying squirrels are, however, poor swimmers because of their gliding folds. Their fondness for water often causes them to be drowned in wells and water buckets while some are known to have drowned in sap buckets, lured by the sweet maple sap in early spring.

December 5, 1974 Sounds of Ice

The loud, long sound of ice cracking and booming is not a sign that the ice is unsafe. Once ice forms, it expands when heated and contracts when cooled, which causes the noise we hear. Lake ice becomes anchored on shorelines, and when the ice contracts from cold weather, cracks form that may be two or three inches wide or up to a foot, depending on the air temperature and the size and layout of the lake.

We observe the opposite in the spring or anytime that a warming trend causes the ice to expand. As it expands, the ice buckles and pushes up on shore, sometimes uprooting trees and changing a shoreline in the spring.

December 6, 1972 Evening Grosbeaks

Three inches of new snow provided a pristine backdrop for the winter birds at the feeding station today. Our regular customers — the cardinals, blue jays, black-capped chickadees and tree sparrows — were there, but so was a new one, an elegant male evening grosbeak. Evening grosbeaks aren't common in the Twin Cities area, but if there are some around they will probably be at feeders with sunflower seeds.

The evening grosbeak is a stockily built, beautiful bird, shorter than an American robin. Like all grosbeaks, it has a large conical bill that is particularly well adapted to feeding on seeds and is even strong enough to crack cherry pits. Their colors are striking; the male has a predominantly yellow body with white patches on black wings, and the female is silvery-gray with enough of the yellow, black and white to make it recognizable.

They are summer residents in the northeastern and north central part of Minnesota, but outside of the coniferous forests they are irregular fall, winter and spring visitants. They appear regularly, however, in large numbers around Brainerd and Bemidji and other northern locations in the winter. Evening grosbeaks usually appear in southern Minnesota during November or early December, but no rule can be made for them as they move in an erratic manner. Some winters they are abundant, but other years they appear only for a short time or are absent entirely, a condition that is probably related to their food supply farther north. When they appear in southern Minnesota, they are commonly seen in groups of six to a dozen in the fall and until spring, and if a single bird or a pair is at a feeder, it is probably temporarily separated from the flock. When you see them in the wild, they may be in calling-flocks overhead or feeding on seeds of maple, boxelder, ash, conifer trees, shrubs or herbs. If they eat crabapples or highbush cranberries, they reject the skins and pulp, eating only the seeds. Since boxelder and ash seeds hang in clusters in the winter, they are a certain source of food for them.

December 7, 1970 Cross-country Skating

Tonight I tried one of my favorite sports, cross-country skating, again. Two days after Lake Minnewashta froze over, we received five inches of snow. Then several days later the snow melted on the ice, and tonight the lake looked good for skating.

Cross-country skating is dangerous if one is not familiar with the lake and the ice, which should be two inches thick to hold one person safely. Although the ice on Lake Minnewashta is now much thicker than two inches, one must still be aware of thin spots that are caused by springs or the action of fish schools or the movement of water from one bay to another. This lake is familiar to me as I grew up on its north shore and have spent many hours exploring it and studying its ice condition, but to be on the safe side, I always skate on the edge of the shoreline over very shallow water.

It took my dog Frosty, running and slipping on the ice, and me, skating carefully to avoid the cracks and bumps, about an hour to travel several miles. It was a beautiful night and a wonderful way to travel. Light from the gibbous moon reflected on the ice, and in the northeast I could see the aurora borealis and above us the winter stars. Orion, the brightest constellation, is associated with winter, and this bright region was a lively scene tonight. Orion, the mighty hunter, accompanied by his dogs, stood with uplifted club awaiting the charging Taurus. Taurus the bull never charged, and after taking a good look at them and at Gemini, I turned and headed toward Polaris and home. It was late, and Frosty and I needed to be getting back.

December 8, 1978 Evergreens

It was cold, minus 17°F, but the air was calm, and white frost covered every twig, grass blade and goldenrod plant. Our feeding station was extremely active with chickadees, tree sparrows and juncos. Overhead a mature bald eagle was seen gliding and dipping.

When I look at the winter landscape, it's the snow that contributes most to its beauty. Because we have had more snow than normal, about one foot on the level, the evergreen trees have been draped in white for days, and a snow-covered evergreen is one of the most splendid sights of nature. In the Twin Cities area we expect to see snow-covered evergreens for thirty or more days a year as wind and thaws remove the snow during the rest of the time.

Professor William C. Rogers from the University of Minnesota who has been studying ways to make winter cities more livable says, "It's as clear as the nose on our faces that there is nothing like a conifer to grace the winter scene." Anyone who has been in the Arboretum lately to see the snow-covered species and varieties of pines, firs, spruces and junipers was favorably impressed, I'm sure. They are natural, beautiful trees and shrubs to plant for our northern winters, and they do many things for us. They fill in for deciduous trees that drop their leaves and look bare and cold in the winter. When maples, oaks and elms lose their leaves in fall, evergreens give us bulk. They protect from the cold winds, give us privacy and make us feel sheltered as they add their shades of green to the white winter scene. Evergreens provide food and nesting and roosting places for many birds and other animals.

December 9, 1978 Where Do the Birds Go

Our thermometer read minus 20°F this morning, and the forecast is for a similar reading tomorrow morning. Looking at the birds at our feeder, I started thinking about where these birds had spent the night.

Several years ago as I stood at the window in the new Arboretum Education and Research Building an hour after sunset looking out toward the bird feeding station where all activity had ceased, one of the employees stopped to talk. As he wondered out loud where the birds went on a cold, winter night, I remember saying something like, "Oh, they go into tree holes, and some roost in evergreens." That was hardly a complete answer, and it led me to spend my spare time for the next few weeks doing some observing and reading on the subject. Although I learned things then, I have a few more answers now, after more observations and discussions with birders.

Even before the leaves fall, the downy and the hairy woodpeckers prepare for winter by finding or digging out cavities usually high in a tree, which become their roosting holes, often vigorously defended against other hole-roosting birds. Each woodpecker roosts at night in a separate roosting hole and will retreat there during daylight hours if the weather is bad. A friend told me about a downy that retired each night to a bluebird house in his Minnetonka area yard. Deserted woodpecker roosting holes are popular with other birds such as chickadees and nuthatches and even with flying squirrels.

Black-capped chickadees are often observed during the winter in noisy flocks of about six birds formed around a dominant pair that had bred the previous summer. Other members may be juveniles, which may or may not be the young of the dominant pair, as well as a few stray adults. A flock generally has a roosting area within its feeding territory to which the birds return each night. It is often a dense evergreen, but individual birds may also roost in small tree holes nearby.

Both male and female white-breasted nuthatches remain in the same territory the year around, and because they do, tend to select the same mates in successive years. Within the territory the male and female have separate roosts in holes in the trees, probably chisled out by downy or hairy woodpeckers.

Ducks and geese stay on the ponds during cold nights floating in the 32°F water while pigeons and starlings often seek ledges of concrete buildings that have retained some heat from the sun during the day. English sparrows tend to like haylofts, garages and martin house apartments, and American goldfinches, cardinals and juncos often roost in pines and spruces.

A naturalist from Michigan reported spending a night observing juncos roosting in dense sumac shrubs near a building that offered shelter from the wind. The birds jostled for position on a branch since they are social birds and roost according to status. The oldest and biggest demand the best site, usually in the center of the group, which is the area best protected from predators and the wind, but they all roost close enough to share the radiant heat from the group.

I have seen cardinals, juncos and tree sparrows feeding on the ground at our bird feeding station one-half hour before sunrise and up to twenty minutes after sunset. The tree sparrows come and go as a group of about twenty but seem to prefer a solitary roost. After dark I have been able to flush only scattered individuals that prefer cattail marshes when available, cavities on or near the ground, corn shocks, haystacks or pines. One tree sparrow that I observed spent the winter nights roosting in an open rural mailbox.

Ring-necked pheasants are basically ground-dwelling birds. Roosts are usually in lowland swamps where cattails and other vegetation provide cover and insulation although I have also seen them roosting in trees. A naturalist from Faribault reports that he has seen small flocks roosting three to four feet off the ground in mature Norway spruces, and other observers have seen them roosting higher in spruces and pines.

December 10, 1973 Short-tailed Weasel

Although it was cold outside, my students were willing to spend a few extra minutes there anyway as they quietly watched the antics of a sleek, short-legged white mammal with black on the tip of its tail. While several called it an ermine, others called it a weasel, and both names are correct. An ermine is any of several weasels of northern regions with fur that is brown in summer but white in winter. This time the weasel was interested in the suet feeders, but another day out on Maple Trail we watched a weasel catch, kill and carry away a mouse.

The animal we saw today was about ten inches long and called a short-tailed weasel. It is dark brown in summer with white underparts and feet, and it is white during the winter in Minnesota, always with a black-tipped tail. It rarely destroys poultry but is an expert mouser. In fact, the short-tailed weasel is adapted primarily to catching mice and small rodents as its small head and narrow sides enable it to enter mouse runways. It is frequently seen near barns and sheds where mice spend the cold months, and its home may be nearby in wood piles or under buildings. Weasels seem to be distributed fairly evenly over the country in woods, fields, around farms and the outskirts of cities. They are the most active at night using their sense of smell to hunt, and although we have watched them climb trees, they seem to be more at home on the ground. Populations as high as twenty per square mile can be expected in a good habitat.

December 11, 1973 Tracks in the Snow

So far we have very little snow on the ground, but the one inch that fell two days ago gave us the opportunity to see many animal tracks. For every wild creature that's seen or heard, at least a hundred pass by unobserved, and it is only when we begin to notice the many and varied tracks in the snow that we realize the amount of activity occurring. Size and differences in structure and pattern help to determine what animal has passed. Besides revealing the identity of an animal, observing an animal's tracks can help one discover many things about its habits including what it eats, where it sleeps, where it goes for protection and how it moves through snow.

I saw raccoon tracks this morning, which surprised me as I didn't know a raccoon would still be active this late in the year. Muskrats are fairly well prepared for winter in their lodges made of cattails, mud and small water plants. When you see their tracks, characterized by dragging tail marks, the tracks will always be near water, which was true today as the tracks were on the bog boardwalk.

Jumpers were out also, their track pattern of paired footprints immediately recognizable. Cottontail rabbits, red squirrels and gray squirrels are good jumpers. The rabbit's forefeet are usually not side-by-side but are diagonal to each other; but squirrels jump with their front feet together, and their tracks are paired side-by-side. Small bird and mouse tracks in the snow show that they are jumpers, also.

The ring-necked pheasant, a ground dwelling bird, is a walker that travels precisely with one foot ahead of the other, the middle toe pointing straight ahead. I saw pheasant tracks as well as those of another walker, the red fox, which also leaves little evidence of dragging its feet as its prints are in a definite straight line, twelve to eighteen inches apart.

A weasel with its short legs moved by bounding, its hind feet often landing on the tracks made by the forefeet. Looking at a weasel trail today, I noticed how erratic it was, suddenly changing direction and even doubling back as it zigzagged over the snow in search of a scent. When the snow gets deeper, we will be able to see where weasels tunnel.

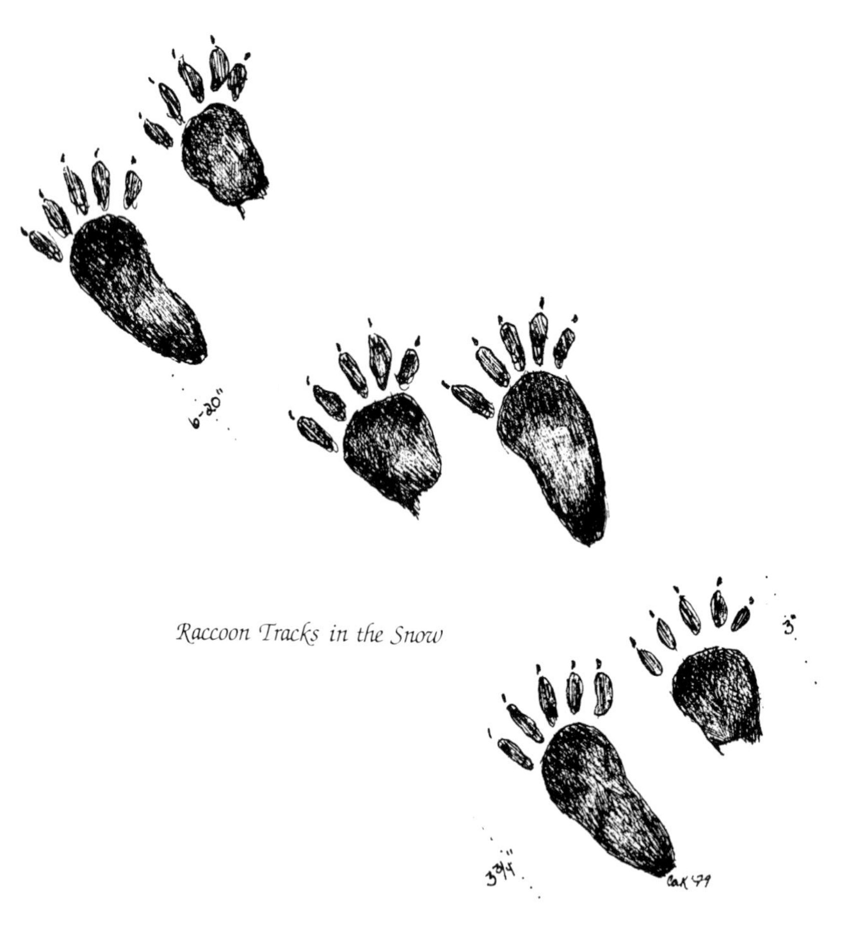

Raccoon Tracks in the Snow

December 12, 1973 Colorado Blue Spruce

Since today was the day we had decided upon for cutting our Christmas tree, my wife Sandra, our son Andrew and I went out to a planting of Colorado blue spruce trees to pick ours and cut it. Although I did not like to cut the twelve-year-old tree, there were so many trees close together that thinning was needed.

The Colorado spruce (*Picea pungens*), the state tree of Colorado, is found in large numbers on moist slopes and along streams in the Rockies west of Denver. Its natural range extends from the mountains of western Montana through Colorado into the mountains of New Mexico and Arizona. Under the name Blue Spruce, it is a popular tree in the eastern states where it is probably planted more than any other western conifer. It is widely used for lawn plantings and also for windbreaks and close-growing hedges. Trees in their native haunts are predominantly dark green, but the foliage varies from green to blue, the blue ones often being selected out and given cultivar names.

December 13, 1977 The Whistling Chickadees

Two black-capped chickadees were whistling "fee-bee" over and over again near the feeding station this morning. It is a matter of speculation whether the "phoebe" call is the true song of the chickadee. It is heard most often in early spring, but we hear it throughout the winter also, many times on cold, cloudy days. I have even heard chickadees whistling in the heat of summer and on crisp autumn days.

In a clear sweet whistle the chickadee sounds two notes of equal length, the second tone lower in pitch than the first making the whistled "fee-bee" sound. Frequently the second note has a slight waver in the middle as if the bird sang "fee-beyee" rather than "fee-bee." Those who confuse the "phoebe" song of the black-capped chickadee with the well-enunciated "phoe-be" or "fi-bree" of the eastern phoebe might be interested to know that their call is not whistled like the "phoebe" song of the chickadee. Since the eastern phoebe is a summer resident, usually arriving in April and leaving in September, its song is only heard in the spring and summer.

December 14 1976 Springtails or Snow Fleas

It was warm today with an afternoon temperature of 42°F. Thinking that the snow fleas would surely be out, I took a hike to a likely habitat. There I was rewarded by a sight that few people ever see; hundreds of dark, tiny bodies were moving and jumping on the snow.

On a warm winter day in a snow-covered forest, especially one near wetlands, people who are interested in one of nature's phenomena should look at the snow near the base of trees. Quite often there will be a mass of black specks, which resemble sprinkled pepper but are six-legged snow fleas. A snow flea is one of the most primitive insects in the world. Winter is the best season to study them, and if one looks closely, it can be seen that periodically they spring like mechanical toys. From this action comes the name springtail, their other common name. The name springtail refers to the two appendages that they have on their last body segment and that are like two extra legs. They are normally folded against their abdomens and held in place with two clasps. When the clasps open, these two appendages spring against the ground, propelling the insect a couple of inches, and it is this flea-like, leaping motion that has given winter-active springtails the name snow fleas. They are usually vegetarians, feeding on algae, pollen, decaying plant material and fungi.

Snow fleas are creatures of winter thaws and seem to come up through the snow by following the small spaces around the stems of herbs, shrubs and trees. When colder temperatures force them down again, the ones that have remained close to the plants go back the

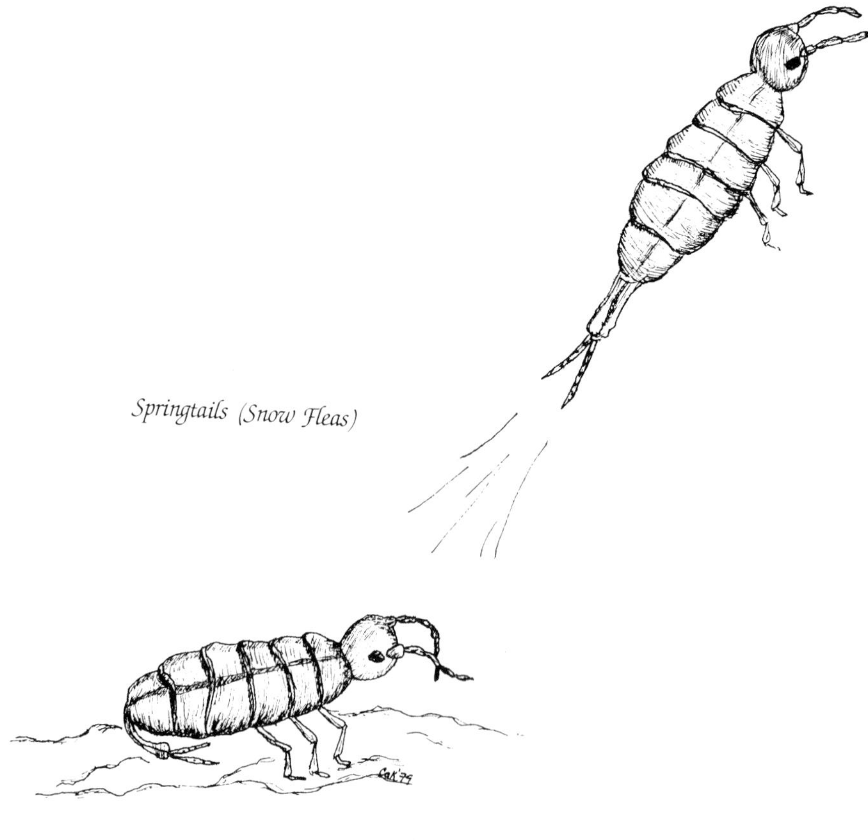

Springtails (Snow Fleas)

same way, but many others will attempt to work their way straight down through the snow. Most of these snow fleas probably freeze when they strike layers of icy snow and can't reach the earth.

December 15, 1973 Arboretum's Bird Feeding Station

The Arboretum has its first bird feeding station consisting of two suet feeders and two seed feeders. We began feeding the birds here in October. In just a few minutes' time this morning, I observed a red-bellied woodpecker, several downy woodpeckers, blue jays, black-capped chickadees, purple finches, American goldfinches, slate-colored juncos, house sparrows, a white-breasted nuthatch and a female cardinal.

December 16, 1977 Late Chipmunk

An eastern chipmunk is still visiting our feeders but returns to its burrow located at the edge of a forest below a prickly gooseberry shrub about one hundred feet away. The chipmunk carried innumerable loads of food in its bulging cheek pouches to its underground storage spot as it worked tirelessly to lay away more food than it will ever consume in the remaining winter months.

Late summer and fall is a busy time for chipmunks as each one becomes a hoarder. Because of its habit of caching large stores of nuts and other seeds beneath its nest in its underground pantry or in small holes dug under logs and rocks, the chipmunk does not need to put on fat as a thirteen-lined ground squirrel does. I'm not sure how many seeds our late-appearing chipmunk is carrying although cheek-pouch loads of sixty to seventy sunflower seeds have been recorded. With several inches of snow on the ground now, these trips to the feeders will soon stop. Most in this area retired to their burrows between late October and the end of November, and soon this one will also remain at home at least until the end of February.

December 17, 1978 The Flight of Birds

This is the seventy-fifth anniversary of the famous flight in 1903 at Kitty Hawk, North Carolina, by Wilbur and Orville Wright who flew the first powered, man-carrying airplane. They had designed and built the airplane. The first flight with Orville as pilot covered about 120 feet and lasted twelve seconds; Wilbur, on the fourth and longest flight of the day, flew 852 feet for fifty-nine seconds. Of particular interest to me is the fact that some of their design ideas came from observing the flight of birds. With this in mind I attempted to be a keen observer of birds in flight today as I watched downy woodpeckers, black-capped chickadees, tree sparrows, dark-eyed juncos and cardinals as they approached and took off from the feeding station.

Flight demands greater intensity of effort than any other animal locomotion. This can be observed by noting a bird's heartbeat, breathing rate, metabolism, body temperature and amount of food eaten. A bird's heart beats many times per second. The heart of a black-capped chickadee beats about 400 times a minute when asleep but about double this when active. A bird's breathing is correspondingly rapid. All birds have a high rate of metabolism, and they have the highest body temperatures of any animal, averaging 110°F. To illustrate how large their food consumption is — robins are said to eat as much as fourteen feet of earthworms in a day, and young crows have been known to eat more than their own weight in food per day.

Bird skeletons are very flexible, strong and light. Their feathers combine lightness with extraordinary strength, and the shape of the wing is a basic factor in flying effectiveness. All these features, plus highly developed flight muscles, streamlined bodies and tails that help them to steer and to brake, make bird flight possible.

The speed of a bird's flight varies considerably among individuals and from one species to another depending upon the circumstances. The majority of small land birds travel at speeds between twenty and thirty miles per hour, geese and ducks usually range from forty to sixty miles per hour, and our summer-resident chimney swifts fly sixty to seventy miles per hour. A further example of their speed comes from Mesopotamia where swifts were timed, almost incredibly, at two hundred miles per hour.

December 18, 1974 Snowflakes

Snowflake or snow-crystal watching opens up a new world of discovery each time it snows. This afternoon, between observing deer eating from the bird feeders and seeing a brown creeper work over the bark of a large basswood, I enjoyed watching the snowflakes falling. Snow-crystal watching is done best by catching snowflakes on a dark surface such as the arm of a jacket or on a cold square of black construction paper, and although some will be too tiny to appreciate without a small magnifying glass, most snowflakes can be enjoyed

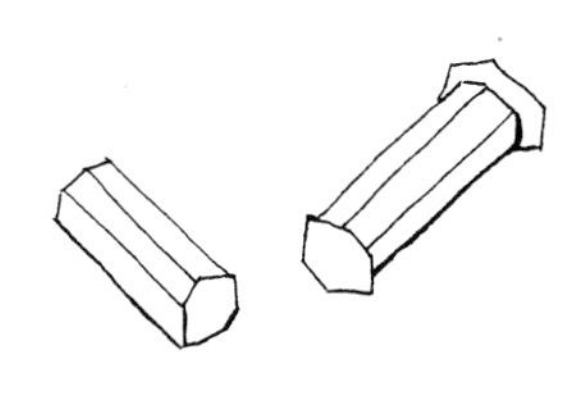

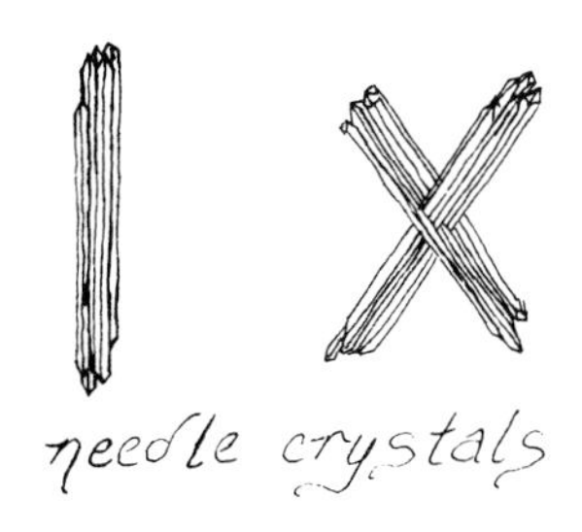

Snow Crystals

with the unaided eye. While I didn't see two identical snowflakes, I did manage to see the following kinds: hexagonal plates, stellar crystals, capped columns and powder crystals, which together added one more inch to our blanket of snow.

Clouds form whenever air cannot hold water vapor in invisible form due to the amount of vapor and the relative temperature of the air. Clouds, which are made up of water droplets so microscopic that thousands could fit on the head of a pin, are seen only because large numbers of droplets are concentrated in one area. Along with the droplets, there are minute particles of dust and salt from the surface of the earth and sea that have been carried miles up into the sky by prevailing winds. Droplets of water begin to accumulate around a nucleus of dust or salt, and when the accumulation becomes sufficiently heavy, it falls to earth as a raindrop.

If the temperature in the cloud is below freezing, however, water vapor changes directly to ice crystals, and the union of hundreds of ice crystals around a nucleus makes one snowflake. Snowmaking is partly a chain reaction within a cloud. When many flakes have been formed, they tumble about while falling, breaking off chips of ice that then become the nuclei for still more flakes.

The shape a snowflake will take is determined by the temperature and humidity of the air in which the crystal is formed. Stellar crystals form in low clouds where the temperature is not too cold and where there is plenty of moisture. Because of their intricate designs, these six-pointed stars often interlock while falling, and end as large conglomerate flakes occasionally as large as two inches in diameter.

Hexagonal plates make up only a small percentage of all the snowflakes in a storm and often appear along with stellar crystals. These six-sided flat crystals have varying degrees of design on their surfaces and may be up to three-sixteenths of an inch in diameter.

Column crystals, up to one-fourth of an inch, form in very high cold clouds where there is little moisture. Since it is common for a crystal to pass through a number of atmospheric conditions before it lands, the column crystals may pass through conditions that will produce hexagonal plates on both ends.

Needle crystals are extremely common and may account for much of a storm's accumulation. These long, slender, six-sided columns with fine points projecting from the ends, range in length from one-fourth to three-eighths of an inch and often freeze together.

Powder crystals are the best for skiing since they do not pack. Although the crystals seem like small grains of snow, they are really minute columns and plates connected to each other in irregular formations too small to be distinguished by the naked eye.

Once snow crystals land on the ground, they start to lose their fine detail through a process called sublimation. In sublimation the fine outer parts of the crystal evaporate and condense on the larger central part of the crystal, which makes almost all fallen crystals change soon into small granules of ice.

December 19, 1973 A Creeper on the Basswood

I have been watching a brown creeper hunting for food. Its characteristic foraging behavior is to alight at the base of a tree and spiral around the tree as it travels up. The bird worked over a large basswood trunk as it picked up bits of beef suet that the nuthatches had taken from our feeder and stored in cracks up and down the tree. Upon reaching a high point in the tree, the creeper flew to the base of an American elm and once again started working its way up. It climbed as woodpeckers do, holding on with its toes and leaning back on its stiff tail feathers. This one was alone, which is usual at this time of the year.

The brown creeper is about the size of a black-capped chickadee. It is a slender, inconspicuous brown bird with a long, thin, curved bill that is unsuited for pecking but is perfect for gleaning insects and their eggs and larvae from the crannies of the tree bark. Its roost is either in tree holes or clinging to bark on a protected area of a tree trunk.

December 20, 1974 Woodpecker Drumming

Our landscape is even more picturesque today with the addition of white frost. While out on a trail observing animal tracks in the snow, I heard a woodpecker, either a hairy or a downy, hammering, but I was unable to tell which one it was from a distance. Hairy woodpeckers can be identified by the size of their bills that are at least as long as their heads from front to back while the bills of the downy woodpecker are much shorter.

Although I have often heard the drumming sound in February and March, it was a pleasant surprise to hear it this early. Later I checked other naturalists' observations and found that drumming may begin as early as November and continue until summer. Both species use resonant trees on which they hammer for several reasons: to announce their territory, to attract a mate or to establish pair bonds. This drumming serves many of the functions that song does in other birds. Usually both male and female have separate posts on which to drum, each post strategically located within the territory.

December 21, 1978 First Day of Winter

Today, on the shortest day of the year, a pair of cardinals stayed at the feeding station until eighteen minutes after sunset. By astronomical calculation, winter arrived at 11:21 p.m. Astronomers can tell us the exact moment in each year when the earth will reach the point in its revolution about the sun so that the North Pole is inclined 23½° away from the sun. We then have the winter solstice and our longest night and shortest day, which is eight hours and forty-six minutes in the Twin Cities area. For meteorologists, winter runs from December 1 to February 29. As a phenologist, however, I would say that this year winter started on November 17 because on that day we received eight inches of snow that is still here.

After the first day of winter, the daylight, which was eroding away, will reverse, but with shorter nights we can expect colder temperatures. In the interiors of middle-latitude northern hemisphere continents, January is the coldest month. Usually there is a temperature lag of thirty to forty days after the period of minimum solar radiation, which allows the air and ground to cool down as much as possible. The summer hemisphere actually receives two to three times the amount of solar radiation received by the winter hemisphere.

States like Florida, Texas, Arizona, California and Hawaii sell sunshine, but for those who have to, or want to live with winter, it is a remarkable season in Minnesota. Every year our winters come with snowflakes, icicles, juncos at the feeders, cottontail tracks, skiing and outdoor skating and last year's down jackets and wool overcoats.

December 22, 1978 Christmas Cactus

A Christmas cactus in the Waconia post office is nearing bloom peak, and although I didn't note the opening date of its first flower this year, last year it was on November 14.

There is only one Christmas cactus (*Schlumbergera bridgesii*), and it blooms in response to short days in December and January and often continues blooming into March. Its cherry-red flowers vary in color intensity depending upon various growing conditions.

Thanksgiving cacti are similar in appearance, and because they are frequently found blooming in plant stores from Thanksgiving to Christmas, they are often incorrectly called Christmas cacti. The two types of holiday plants have different leaf characteristics. The leaf margins of Thanksgiving cactus have two to four sawtooth projections on each side while leaf margins of a Christmas cactus are rounded with scallops along the edges.

Holiday cacti are native to tropical parts of Brazil and grow nonparasitically on other plants in the wild, receiving their water and nutrients from rain, dust, air and organic material from decaying plants. Christmas and Thanksgiving cacti adapt well to windows and greenhouses and can be set outside in the summer. They should receive bright light but not direct sunlight, which will burn them severely.

December 23, 1978 Starlings and House Sparrows

Several area birders gathered today for the annual National Audubon Society's Christmas Bird Count in the Excelsior area. The number of species counted this year was fifty-two and the number of birds, 7,293. Three species, the mallard duck, house sparrow and starling, accounted for more than half the total, and each of these three had more than 1,000 counted individuals. If such a count had been made in this area a hundred years ago, the house sparrow and starling would have been missing from the list.

The house sparrow, also called English sparrow, is not a native of North America nor a relative of our native sparrows, but it belongs to a family of birds called weaver finches. They are found throughout Europe and in much of Africa and Asia and were first introduced into this country in 1850. The birds were released in Brooklyn, New York, by European settlers to remind them of home and to control insect pests. They are now widespread in North America inhabiting all areas but deserts and high mountains. This species was introduced in the Twin Cities area in 1875 and became established as a breeding bird two years later. Many of the early house sparrows perished when weather conditions were especially severe as it took some years to develop a breed hardy enough to endure the long, cold winter. House sparrows first reached the Duluth area in 1887.

When living in parks and around shopping centers in cities, house sparrows seldom move more than a mile from their birthplace, but those in small towns and suburbs often flock to outlying small grain and hay fields in summer. Shelter in winter is essential to them as a sparrow without a roost and food will die after fifteen hours at 32°F. They often roost together on ivy-covered walls, but in cold weather I sometimes find them roosting singly in niches and corners of buildings. They are little birds, weighing only one and one-fourth ounces each, but are very aggressive and many people believe they drive native birds away. They are, however, one of the few links that some people in cities have with the outdoor world. Although house sparrows are noisy and insolent and monopolize the feeders, still no other wild creatures may do so much to cheer us up. Out of the whole living world, we are the ones they have chosen to be their friends.

The starling was introduced from Europe into Central Park, New York City, in 1890 when sixty birds were released. I have read that the person responsible for the introduction of the starling wanted all of the birds mentioned by Shakespeare to be found in North America. Starlings quickly took over New York City and rapidly spread across the country making their first Minnesota appearance in 1929 in Fillmore County. Now they are found as a breeding species everywhere in the state including wilderness areas like the Boundary Waters Canoe Area, but they are most numerous in farming areas.

Starlings are aggressive birds that deprive many native birds of their nesting and roosting sites. Their feeding and roosting habits in cities and airports cause many problems, but they are beneficial, too, as they are among the most efficient predators of ground insects. At this time of the year they will gather for roosting about one to two hours before sunset. Then small groups join other small groups that are circling around, and as one large mass they fly over their roost, suddenly diving into its center.

December 24, 1969 A Robin in the Crabapple Tree

Fifteen inches of snow covered everything, and more was still coming down as I took a quick walk at noon and watched the wind blowing the new snow flakes into drifts. We're going to have a white Christmas.

On December 6 my father, brother and I had spotted a robin in a crabapple tree that was still loaded with red fruit. As I approached the crabapple collection in the Arboretum today, I wondered if the robin would still be there or if it had finally left for the winter. But not only was the robin still around, it was busy eating from the same tree we had observed it in two and one-half weeks earlier! I'm sure it's the same robin, which, for some reason, did not have the flocking and migrating instinct, or perhaps at the time when most of the other robins migrated, was physically unable to join them. This lone robin was now busy devouring the small red apples and collecting snowflakes on its back. It will probably be spending Christmas Eve in a sheltered roost somewhere near the woodland garden.

December 25, 1978 Merry Christmas

The cardinals looked like true Christmas Birds as they were busy at area feeders today along with several other winter species. The bright red males with black faces are unmistakable while the females with the same conical beak and crest are only tinged with red. Although they prefer to feed on the ground, a snowcover of twelve inches made sheltered, raised feeders good feeding spots.

The cardinals are usually the earliest birds at the feeders in the morning and the last to leave at dusk, sometimes feeding so late during winter days that we have trouble seeing them. They never tire of sunflower seeds, but they will also eat cracked corn, wheat, suet mixtures, sorghum, barley, millet, peanuts, melon seeds, raisins, corn bread and even white bread. This bird, more than any other, has come to symbolize bird feeding. The availability of feeding stations has made their northward expansion possible. In the nineteenth century the cardinal was only a visitant entering Minnesota from the southeast along the Mississippi River, and it was not until the mid-1930s that it was established as a permanent resident in the Twin Cities. Planted and native evergreens help provide shelter and may encourage range expansion, along with plentiful food supplies from feeders.

The cardinals are generally nonmigratory, and banding records have shown that adults rarely go more than a few miles from their birthplace. In the wild they feed on the seeds of ash and pine trees and seeds in the fruits of wild grape, sumac and dogwood, to name just a few. Actually they will eat weed seeds and wild fruits from nearly every kind of tree, shrub or vine that is available to them. It's interesting to note that in summer the cardinals are highly insectivorous.

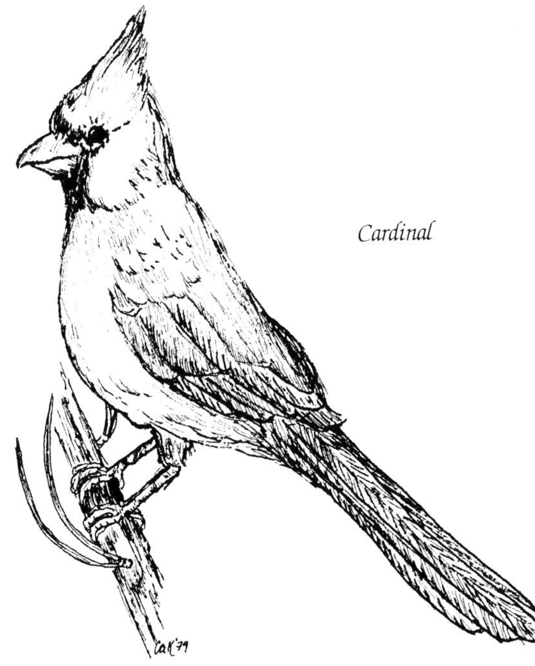

Cardinal

December 26, 1970 Snow Rollers

The air temperature had been close to 0°F around midnight, but by 7:30 a.m. as I drove to Carver Park Reserve, it was 35°F, and a west chinook was strong. We had about one-half an inch of new snow on the ground, and Jack Mauritz, Carver Park naturalist, and I observed "nature's snowballs" on the lakes and flat meadow areas. These rolls of snow get started somehow by the wind, and as the wind continues to blow them along the ground, they grow to a foot or more in diameter.

Although they are shaped like a wheel, I learned later that they are officially called snow rollers. They are a rare natural phenomenon, that need specific wind, temperature and snow conditions to form. The snow rollers I saw were probably formed in a ten-to-thirty-minute period early this morning.

December 27, 1969 Seventieth Audubon Christmas Bird Count

The annual National Audubon Society's Christmas Bird Count was held in the Excelsior area today despite the snowy conditions. Twenty-five dedicated birders counted forty-seven species or approximately 7,400 birds. The census was taken within a fifteen mile diameter circle centered at Chanhassen. Kathy Heidel and Jack Mauritz, naturalists at Carver Park Reserve, and I covered one section of this large circle, counting nearly 1,800 birds including twenty-nine different species in the area of Carver Park, Victoria, the Horticultural Research Center, the Arboretum and Excelsior.

Listed below are the birds we counted:

Canada goose 100
mallard 196
black duck 5
wood duck 2
ring-necked duck 1
ruddy duck 1
American coot 1
red-tailed hawk 1
ring-necked pheasant 19
rock dove 11
starling 57
house sparrow 961
red-winged blackbird 1
cardinal 4
yellow-shafted flicker 1
red-bellied woodpecker 2
hairy woodpecker 9
downy woodpecker 11
blue jay 30
common crow 16
black-capped chickadee 41
white-breasted nuthatch 21
red-breasted nuthatch 1
robin 1
cedar waxwing 77
common redpoll 150
American goldfinch 3
slate-colored junco 37
tree sparrow 8

This was the nineteenth annual Christmas bird count in this area and was begun in 1951 by Mrs. M. E. Herz and Mrs. Phillip Tyron, both of Christmas Lake. A local count must take place late in December or early in January during a single twenty-four hour period. Our Excelsior Christmas count is one of over 900 bird counts from the entire country that will be reported to the National Audubon Society this year.

Dr. Frank Chapman, an ornithological pioneer, began the count in Englewood, New Jersey, in 1900 as a substitute for heavy Christmas bird-shooting. The Audubon Society regards the counts as very successful, and they steadily grow in popularity and importance. At the first count, twenty-five reports were filed by twenty-seven participants. In 1964 more than 12,000 people from over 700 local counts in fifty states and several provinces of Canada took part. They sighted 532 different species and tens of millions of individual birds including more than 40 million red-winged blackbirds. The count is unquestionably the world's greatest cooperative survey of wildlife.

Scientists use the mass of data accumulated over the years to keep track of the increase or decline of various species, to learn more about life cycles, to add to their knowledge of birds' migratory habits and to aid in animal population studies.

December 28, 1977 A Junco's Return

I found that a junco, which had joined several other winter birds at the feeding station for some cracked corn and millet seeds, was wearing an aluminum leg band with the numbers 1290-15-417. This is significant to me because the bird was banded here at the same feeding station last year, one of four juncos I banded December 1, 1976, the first day of my bird-banding career.

Other banders have shown that many individual, dark-eyed (formerly called slate-colored) juncos return to the same winter area each year demonstrating their ability to return to winter areas as well as to summer breeding grounds. Juncos nest in the northern coniferous forests, but they migrate south in fall spending the winter anywhere between southern Canada and the Gulf of Mexico.

December 29, 1978 Pheasant Tracks

Today I spent several hours working in the Andersen Horticultural Library with its seemingly unlimited resources. During my months of writing in the library, I have used several hundred volumes devoted to horticulture and natural history, together with current periodicals. Librarian June Rogier and assistant librarian Jenna Stickler are a part of the fine resources, and they have helped me find materials many times.

Needing a break, I headed out on the Arboretum grounds where freezing rain last evening and early this morning had left a thin coat of ice on everything. The fir and pine needles, the branches and twigs of trees and shrubs, and the top of the snow sparkled in the sunlight. The wind blowing through the still-attached brown leaves of the white oak sounded like a hard rainfall on a warm summer night. In five months irises will be blooming, but now a foot of snow covers the dormant rhizomes where a pheasant has left tracks. I could see where the pheasant had landed, tail dragging before the feet hit, footprints heading off in the distance.

The ring-necked pheasant is not a native bird but was introduced into the state in 1905, and many thousands were released between 1915 and the early 1920s. They have become established and are locally common in the southern part of Minnesota. Pheasants are numerous in the Twin Cities suburban areas where they can find sufficient cover and artificial feeding by local residents. The common name, Chinese ring-necked pheasant, tells us where they originated. Our pheasant is a hybrid whose original strain came from China. Pheasants are native to the older-inhabited parts of the world, chiefly Asia where more than one hundred species and many hybrids are found. The domesticated chickens are all descended from pheasant ancestors.

Because of its terrestrial habits and ability to run and hide, we are more likely to see pheasant tracks than the bird itself. If a person gets too close, it will flush into flight and climb steeply for a short distance, then spread its wings and glide slowly down. Pheasants join together in the fall and winter in flocks from three to over one hundred birds that will feed and roost together. The size of the flocks is dependent on the abundance of food and suitable roosting cover. Roosts are usually in lowland swamps and marshes where cattails and other vegetation provide cover while a few birds will roost in trees.

The pheasant, like a domesticated chicken, is omniverous, eating anything digestible. Insects make up a considerable part of its summer diet, but in the winter weed seeds and grain, tree buds and small fruits left hanging on branches make up most of its diet. The grain that it eats is largely waste grain picked up in stubble-fields or along railroad tracks. Pheasant flocks feed in the morning and early evening, but they are known to stay in their roosts if the weather is severe.

December 30, 1972 Seventy-third Audubon Christmas Bird Count

It was raining at 8 a.m., and the temperature was 36°F as I looked out at the birdfeeders where I saw blue jays, black-capped chickadees, white-breasted nuthatches, cardinals, tree sparrows, downy and hairy woodpeckers and a pileated woodpecker having breakfast at the feeders. We had started looking and listening for owls in the Carver Park Research area two hours earlier, and I was fortunate enough to find one screech owl, the only one seen, in an old barn.

Six of us recorded twenty-two species of birds in the Audubon Christmas Bird Count in our area, which was only a small section of the Excelsior count. A total of 8,700 birds representing fifty species was counted by twenty-six birders within a circle with a fifteen-mile diameter centered at Chanhassen. Notable species and numbers that were recorded include: mallard, 5,209; pileated woodpecker, 4; downy woodpecker, 58; black-capped chickadee, 312; brown creeper, 2; starling, 121; house sparrow, 673; red-winged blackbird, 1; cardinal, 123; American goldfinch, 293; slated-colored junco, 102.

December 31, 1976 Cold Morning Birds

With a minus 30°F temperature this morning, the old saying, "As the days get longer, the cold gets stronger," is true. Soon after sunrise our feeding station became extremely active as tree sparrows, black-capped chickadees, blue jays and other birds were joined by red squirrels and a gray squirrel.

Since the behavior of the birdfeeder birds on cold winter mornings has always interested me, I have kept a record of what I saw and heard on five days. This is a summary, in sequence, of the birds and their activities:

40 minutes before sunrise
  Quiet, with no birds heard or seen
35 minutes before sunrise
  Heard the musical, metallic twittering of tree sparrows
  The first tree sparrows at the feeders
30 minutes before sunrise
  Four cardinals feeding on the ground below a feeder
  Ten tree sparrows feeding on the ground below a feeder
25 minutes before sunrise
  Heard the first white-breasted nuthatch and American goldfinch
  Saw twenty-five tree sparrows at the feeders

20 minutes before sunrise
First black-capped chickadee appeared at a feeder
First juncos arrive
15 minutes before sunrise
Heard the first chickadee and a downy woodpecker
10 minutes before sunrise
First downy woodpecker on suet feeder
5 minutes before sunrise
The first blue jay at a feeder
1 minute before sunrise
Heard common crows
The red-bellied woodpecker and pileated woodpecker at the suet feeders
Sunrise
Ten species of birds active in large numbers at the feeding station

SELECTED REFERENCES

The list is not meant to be comprehensive. Rather, these are the books which the author found useful and recommends for reference and reading pleasure.

NATURE STUDY IN GENERAL

Blacklock, Les. *Ain't Nature Grand!* Bloomington, MN: Voyageur Press, 1980

Carson, Rachel. *The Sense of Wonder.* New York: Harper & Row, 1956.

Costello, David F. *The Prairie World.* New York: Thomas Y. Crowell, 1969.

Daniel, Glenda. *The North Woods of Michigan, Wisconsin, and Minnesota.* San Francisco: Sierra Club Books, 1981.

Davids, Richard C. *How to Talk to Birds.* New York: Alfred A. Knopf, 1972.

Gray, Dick. *Passwords for All Seasons.* Minneapolis: Dillon Press for the Freshwater Biological Research Foundation, 1973.

Hill, Hibbert. *Reflections on Water.* Minneapolis, 1967.

Leopold, Aldo. *A Sand County Almanac.* London: Oxford University Press, 1949.

Lukes, Roy. *Once Around the Sun*, a Door County Journal. Baileys Harbor, WI: Pine Street Press, 1976.

Olson, Sigurd F. *Listening Point.* New York: Alfred A. Knopf, 1958.

Palmer, E. Laurence. *Fieldbook of Natural History.* 2nd Edition. New York: McGraw Hill, 1975.

Rood, Ronald. *Who Wakes the Ground Hog?* New York: W.W. Norton, 1973.

Stokes, Donald W. *A Guide to Nature in Winter.* Boston: Little, Brown, 1976.

Teale, Edwin Way. *North With the Spring.* New York: Dodd, Mead, 1957.

Thoreau, Henry David. *Walden.* New York: Bramhall House, 1951.

ANIMAL LIFE

Barker, Will. *Winter-Sleeping Wildlife.* New York: Harper & Row, 1958.

Buck, Margaret Waring. *Where They Go in Winter.* New York: Abingdon Press, 1968.

Martin, Alexander C. *American Wildlife & Plants.* New York: Dover, 1961. (reprint of 1951 ed.)

Murie, Olaus J. *A Field Guide to Animal Tracks.* Boston: Houghton Mifflin, 1954.

BIRDS

Arbib, Robert. *The Hungry Bird Book.* New York: Taplinger, 1971.

Bent, Arthur Cleveland. *Life Histories of North American Birds.* New York: Dover. 21 volumes (reprints from earlier eds.)

Bull, John. *The Audubon Society Field Guide to North American Birds, Eastern Region.* New York: Alfred A. Knopf: distributed by Random House, 1977.

Commons, Marie Andrews. *The Log of Tanager Hill.* Baltimore: Waverly Press, 1938.

Cruickshank, Allan D. *1001 Questions Answered About Birds.* New York: Dodd, Mead, 1958.

Dennis, John V. *A Complete Guide to Bird Feeding.* New York: Alfred A. Knopf, 1977.

Eiserer, Len. *The American Robin.* Chicago: Nelson-Hall, 1976.

Flugum, Charles T. *Birding from a Tractor Seat.* St. Paul, MN: Charles Truman Flugum, 1973.

Grant, Karen A. *Hummingbirds and Their Flowers.* New York: Columbia University Press, 1968.

Green, Janet C. *Minnesota Birds.* Minneapolis: University of Minnesota Press for the James Ford Bell Museum of Natural History, 1975.

Greenwalt, Crawford H. *Hummingbirds.* Garden City, NY: Published for the American Museum of Natural History by Doubleday, 1960.

Harrison, Hal H. *A Field Guide to Birds' Nests.* Boston: Houghton Mifflin, 1975.

Hickman, Mae. *Care of the Wild Feathered & Furred.* Santa Cruz: Unity Press, 1973.

Kortright, Francis H. *The Ducks, Geese and Swans of North America.* Washington, DC: American Wildlife Institute, 1943.

McKenny, Margaret. *Birds in the Garden.* New York: Grosset & Dunlap, 1939.

Peterson, Roger Tory. *A Field Guide to the Birds.* 4th Edition. Boston: Houghton Mifflin, 1980.

Robbins, Chandler S. *Birds of North America.* New York: Golden Press, 1966.

Roberts, Thomas S. *The Birds of Minnesota.* Minneapolis: University of Minnesota Press, 1932. 2 volumes.

Russell, Franklin. *Corvus the Crow.* New York: Four Winds Press, 1972.

Sparks, John. *Owls.* New York: Taplinger, 1970.

Terres, John K. *The Audubon Society Encyclopedia of North American Birds.* New York: Alfred A. Knopf, 1980.

INSECTS AND OTHER INVERTEBRATES

Borror, Donald J. *A Field Guide to the Insects.* Boston: Houghton Mifflin, 1970.

Ebner, James A. *The Butterflies of Wisconsin.* Milwaukee: Board of Trustees, Milwaukee Public Museum, 1970.

Evans, Howard Ensign. *Life on a Little-Known Planet.* New York: E.P. Dutton, 1968.

The Hive and the Honey Bee. Hamilton, IL: Dadant & Sons, 1975.

Holland, W.J. *The Moth Book.* New York: Dover, 1968. (reprint of 1903 ed.)

Klots, Alexander B. *A Field Guide to the Butterflies*. Boston: Houghton Mifflin, 1951.
Lutz, Frank E. *A Lot of Insects*. New York: G. P. Putnam's Sons, 1941.
Mitchell, Robert T. *Butterflies and Moths*. New York: Golden Press, 1964.
Morse, Roger A. *Bees and Beekeeping*. Ithaca, NY: Cornell University Press, 1975.
Naylor, Penelope. *The Spider World*. New York: Franklin Watts, 1973.
Pellett, Frank C. *American Honey Plants*. Hamilton, IL: American Bee Journal, 1923.
Pyle, Robert Michael. *The Audubon Society Field Guide to North American Butterflies*. New York: Alfred A. Knopf, 1981.
Root, A. I. *The ABC and XYZ of Bee Culture*. Medina, OH: A.I. Root Company, 1972.
Teale, Edwin Way. *The Junior Book of Insects*. New York: Dutton, 1953.
Zim, Herbert S. *Insects*. New York: Golden Press, 1956.

MAMMALS

Barkalow, Frederick S. *The World of the Gray Squirrel*. Philadelphia: J.B. Lippincott, 1973.
Burt, William Henry. *A Field Guide to the Mammals*. Boston: Houghton Mifflin, 1964.
MacClintock, Dorcas. *Squirrels of North America*. New York: Van Nostrand Reinhold, 1970.
Orr, Robert T. *Mammals of North America*. New York: Doubleday, 1971.
Rue, Leonard Lee. *The World of the White-tailed Deer*. Philadelphia: J.B. Lippincott, 1962.

REPTILES, AMPHIBIANS, FISH

Breckenridge, W. J. *Reptiles and Amphibians of Minnesota*. Minneapolis: University of Minnesota Press, 1944.
Eddy, Samuel. *Northern Fishes*. Minneapolis: University of Minnesota Press, 1974.
Phillips, Gary L. *Fishes of the Minnesota Region*. Minneapolis: University of Minnesota Press, 1982.
Wright, Albert Hazen. *Handbook of Frogs and Toads*. Ithaca, NY: Cornell University Press, 1949.

PLANT LIFE

Alexander, Taylor R. *Botany*. New York: Golden Press, 1970.
Durant, Mary. *Who Named the Daisy? Who Named the Rose?* New York: Dodd, Mead, 1976.
Haughton, Claire Shaver. *Green Immigrants*. New York: Harcourt Brace Joanovich, 1978.
Lawrence, George H. M. *An Introduction to Plant Taxonomy*. New York: Macmillan, 1955.
Morley, Thomas. *Spring Flora of Minnesota*. Minneapolis: University of Minnesota Press, 1969.

EDIBLE WILD PLANTS

Fernald, Merritt Lyndon. *Edible Wild Plants.* New York: Harper & Row, 1958.

Gibbons, Euell. *Stalking the Wild Asparagus.* New York: David McKay, 1962.

Harrington, H. D. *Edible Native Plants of the Rocky Mountains.* Albuquerque: University of New Mexico Press, 1967.

Nearing, Helen. *The Maple Sugar Book.* New York: Schocken Books, 1970.

Peterson, Lee. *A Field Guide to Edible Wild Plants.* Boston: Houghton Mifflin, 1978.

GARDENING, REFERENCE

Snyder, Leon C. *Gardening in the Upper Midwest.* Minneapolis: University of Minnesota Press, 1978.

Wyman, Donald. *Wyman's Gardening Encyclopedia.* New York: Macmillan, 1971.

GARDEN FLOWERS

Crockett, James Underwood. *Perennials.* New York: Time-Life Books, 1972.

———. *Roses.* New York: Time-Life Books, 1971.

Luxton, George E. *Flower Growing in the North.* Minneapolis: University of Minnesota Press, 1956.

Nehrling, Arno. *Peonies, Outdoors and In.* New York: Hearthside Press, 1960.

North American Lily Society. *Let's Grow Lilies.* North American Lily Society, 1964.

Price, Molly. *The Iris Book.* Princeton, NJ: D. Van Nostrand, 1966.

Taylor, Norman. *1001 Questions Answered About Flowers.* New York: Dodd, Mead, 1963.

CULTIVATED CROP PLANTS

Aldrich, Samuel R. *Modern Corn Production.* Champaign, IL: A & L Publications, 1975.

Heiser, Charles B. *The Sunflower.* Norman: University of Oklahoma Press, 1976.

Hill, Lewis. *Fruits and Berries for the Home Garden.* New York: Alfred A. Knopf, 1977.

Limburg, Peter. *What's in the Names of Fruit.* New York: Coward, McCann, 1972.

Martin, Alice. *All About Apples.* Boston: Houghton Mifflin, 1976.

Swenson, Allan A. *Landscape You Can Eat.* New York: David McKay, 1977.

Wilhelm, Stephen. *A History of the Strawberry.* Berkeley: University of California, Division of Agricultural Sciences, 1974.

Wilkinson, Albert E. *The Encyclopedia of Fruits, Berries, & Nuts.* Philadelphia: Blakiston, 1945.

MUSHROOMS, FERNS, MOSSES, ETC.

Bigelow, Howard E. *Mushroom Pocket Field Guide.* New York: Macmillan, 1974.

Bland, John H. *Forests of Lilliput.* Englewood Cliffs, NJ: Prentice-Hall, 1971.

Christensen, Clyde M. *Common Edible Mushrooms.* Minneapolis: University of Minnesota Press, 1943.

Crum, Howard. *Mosses of the Great Lakes Forest.* Ann Arbor, MI: University Herbarium, University of Michigan, 1973.

Miller, Orson K. *Mushrooms of North America.* New York: E.P. Dutton, 1972.

Prescott, G. W. *How to Know the Fresh-Water Algae.* Dubuque, IA: Wm. C. Brown, 1954.

Schlichting, Harold E. *Algae.* Austin, TX: Steck-Vaughn, 1971.

Smith, Alexander H. *The Mushroom Hunter's Field Guide.* Ann Arbor, MI: University of Michigan Press, 1963.

Tryon, Rolla Milton. *Ferns of Minnesota.* Minneapolis: University of Minnesota Press, 1980.

POISONOUS PLANTS

Hardin, James W. *Human Poisoning from Native and Cultivated Plants.* Durham, NC: Duke University Press, 1974.

Kingsbury, John M. *Poisonous Plants of the United States and Canada.* Englewood Cliffs, NJ: Prentice-Hall, 1964.

Wodehouse, Roger P. *Hayfever Plants.* New York: Hafner, 1971.

TREES, SHRUBS, WOODY VINES

Hoag, Donald. *Trees and Shrubs for the Northern Plains.* Fargo: North Dakota Institute for Regional Studies, 1965.

Keeler, Harriet L. *Our Northern Shrubs.* New York: Charles Scribner's, 1928.

______. *Our Native Trees.* New York: Charles Scribner's, 1927.

Rosendahl, Carl Otto. *Trees and Shrubs of the Upper Midwest.* Minneapolis: University of Minnesota Press, 1955.

Snyder, Leon C. *Trees and Shrubs for Northern Gardens.* Minneapolis: University of Minnesota Press, 1980.

Wyman, Donald. *Trees for American Gardens.* New York: Macmillan, 1951.

WILD FLOWERS

Klimas, John E. *Wildflowers of Eastern America.* New York: Alfred A. Knopf, 1974.

Monserud, Wilma. *Common Wild Flowers of Minnesota.* Minneapolis: University of Minnesota Press, 1971.

Moyle, John B. *Northland Wild Flowers.* Minneapolis: University of Minnesota Press, 1977.

Niering, William A. *The Audubon Society Field Guide to North American Wildflowers.* Eastern Region. New York: Alfred A. Knopf, 1979.

Peterson, Roger Tory. *A Field Guide to Wildflowers*. Boston: Houghton Mifflin, 1968.
Rickett, Harold William. *Wild Flowers of the United States*. New York: McGraw-Hill, 1966–1971. 6 volumes in 14 parts.

EARTH SCIENCE

Edson, Lee. *Worlds Around the Sun*. New York: American Heritage, 1969.
Kirk, Ruth. *Snow*. New York: William Morrow, 1978.
Leet, L. Don. *Physical Geology*. Englewood Cliffs, NJ: Prentice-Hall, 1965.
Schaeffer, Vincent J. *A Field Guide to the Atmosphere*. Boston: Houghton Mifflin, 1981.
Schwartz, George M. *Minnesota Rocks and Waters*. Minneapolis: University of Minnesota Press, 1954.
Watson, Bruce F. *Minnesota and Environs Weather Almanac, 1976*. Minneapolis: Bolger, 1975.

OUTDOOR EDUCATION

Allison, Linda. *The Sierra Club Summer Book*. San Francisco: Sierra Club Books/Charles Scribner's, 1977.
Brown, Vinson. *Knowing the Outdoors in the Dark*. Harrisburg, PA: Stackpole Books, 1972.
Caldwell, John. *The New Cross-Country Ski Books*. Brattleboro, VT: S. Greene Press, 1971.
Comstock, Anna Botsford. *Handbook of Nature-Study*. Ithaca, NY: Comstock Publishing, 1939.
Headstrom, Richard. *Nature in Miniature*. New York: Alfred A. Knopf, 1968.
Joy of Nature. Pleasantville, NY: Reader's Digest, 1977.
Link, Michael. *Outdoor Education*. Englewood Cliffs, NJ: Prentice-Hall, 1981.
Mitchell, John. *The Curious Naturalist*. Englewood Cliffs, NJ: Prentice-Hall, 1980.

INDEX